PLOUGHSHARES
SOLOS

VOLUME 5

OMNIBUS

EDITED BY LADETTE RANDOLPH

Ploughshares Solos are published several times a year as e-books. The series, which features longer stories and essays, is edited by Ladette Randolph, *Ploughshares'* Editor-in-chief. Please see our website, pshares.org, for submission information.

Ploughshares, a journal of new writing, is guest-edited serially by prominent writers who explore different personal visions, aesthetics, and literary circles. *Ploughshares* is published in January, April, and July at Emerson College: 120 Boylston Street, Boston, MA 02116-4624. Telephone: (617) 824-3757. Web address: pshares.org. E-mail: pshares@pshares.org

ISBN 978-1-62608-071-3
ISSN 0048-4474

Series design by Endpaper Studio
Text set in Minion.

Printed in the U.S.A. by The Journeyman Press.
10 9 8 7 6 5 4 3 2 1

Emerson
COLLEGE

massculturalcouncil.org

ART WORKS.

National Endowment for the Arts
arts.gov

MIX
Paper from responsible sources
FSC® C002965

PLOUGHSHARES
SOLOS

VOLUME 5

OMNIBUS

Introduction

LADETTE RANDOLPH

Writer and literary critic Sergio Pitol makes the claim that "[w]orks of art express . . . the best energy humans are capable of producing." For Flannery O'Connor, literature is a particular human achievement: " . . . in the long run, a people is known, not by its statements or its statistics, but by the stories it tells. Fiction is the most impure and the most modest and the most human of the arts. It is closest to man in his sin and his suffering and his hope."

It's little surprise that as the ground beneath our feet has shifted this past year, the serious readers I know have all turned to literature. Where else would we go when everything we've taken for granted is now in doubt, and our very sense of reality is challenged by circumstance?

Our reasons for reading in a time of disruption vary, just as our reasons for reading at any time vary, but one thing doesn't vary: literature remains the single most significant means of connecting with another individual consciousness across time and space. On the page, we encounter our most thoughtful, insightful contemporary writers as well as the vast intelligence of writers from the past, the best of whom remain not only relevant but essential to our understanding of what it means to be human. When we meet the other on the page, we find, among many things, much needed perspective about our own time and place.

Though efficiency experts might belittle the idea, literature makes an argument for the messy, the irrational, the unexplainable, the deviant. Literature goes beyond history to unearth the odd, the particular, the outlier, and the non-conforming. It enacts philosophy; it expresses those experiences and feelings most real and meaningful to us that cannot be shared anywhere else; literature lays bare the soul of a character as a means to expose what matters most. Or, as John Williams says, it "allows you to know someone other than yourself."

It seems stories are very often about characters being tested in a time of crisis. Perhaps those of us who are habitual readers of literature have been practicing how to face our own crises. By reading stories about how others have reacted, often imperfectly, to change, we feel less alone in our private struggles. Scholar Edith Hamilton says of the ancient Greek tragedian Æschylus that he grasped "'the antagonism at the heart of the world.' . . Mankind . . . fast bound to calamity by the working of unknown powers, committed to a strange venture, companioned by disaster . . . The fullness of life is in the hazards of life." We read alone, as we live alone, but in the solitude of the page we find solace in one another.

In the world of literature, there are no pre-fab answers to the riddles of life. On the contrary, literature makes explicit the complexity and nuance of our brief existence. Literature does not comfort so much as it confronts. It does not give us a roadmap or serve as a guide; rather, by foiling our desire for easy answers and quick formulas for success, maybe it teaches us to be tolerant of ambiguity. Mostly, though, if we are readers, we are never truly lonely. Literature, like a great banquet, is a space of bountiful abundance. We are invited to join a feast of wide-ranging, wildly diverse conversation, full of wit, gaiety, wisdom, and sorrow. We take our fill. There is more available. Everything is in a continual process of regeneration and renewal. We may lose heart in the moment, but around that table stories remind us we're part of something ongoing.

I'm sure that my reading this past year for the Solos series was influenced in subtle ways by the prevailing mood of the country; I was guided mostly, however, by my sense of an individual writer's commitment to delving deep, to facing with honesty and courage the demands made by the story he or she is telling. I was not looking for a particular kind of story, and I have no prescription for what makes a given story endure in my mind; instead, I approached each manuscript with openness, willing to follow the writer who persuaded me with his or her mastery. Once there, I was often surprised; at times, I put my emotional comfort at risk; I encountered people and places I hadn't thought I cared about; I discovered exquisite details, scenes that touched me; and all for what I'll call the truth of the story.

Like Kaat Mertens, the titular narrator of Edward Hamlin's Solo "Kaat," says, "with the smallest of gestures the fabric of life can be torn." After being confronted by a new reality, neither Kaat's discipline as a scholar nor her repeated attempts to create a blissful domesticity are sufficient sources to help her navigate new emotional territory.

Hugh Coyle's excerpt "Koppargruva," taken from his novel-in-progress *Peace at Last*, about the life and work of Alfred Nobel, begins as Nobel is traveling incognito on the steamship Favorite. It's the first leg of a round-trip journey across Lake Superior, where he is promoting his invention of nitroglycerin to the owners and managers of the mines in Marquette, Hancock, and Houghton. Nobel is a wanted man when we meet him, since word has reached the U. S. about the blasting accident in Stockholm that killed his brother and four others. Hounded by the need for secrecy, he resents the system of justice that holds him accountable for the unintended ill effects of his invention, but he will soon learn that is not the only thing holding him accountable.

In his essay "Face the Music," Michael Lowenthal—along with other talented, ambitious young musicians in the elite Dartmouth jazz band—is forced to question everything he's previously understood about music when Sun Ra arrives on campus to lead a week-long master class. Sun Ra doesn't try to ease their confusion, and instead tells them, "Ya'll seem so worried . . . about playing the notes. But you can play more than just notes on a page, you know. You can play the wind or the river. You can play the sun rays."

Eli Mandel's essay "Footing it Slow: A Walk with Keats" is a young writer's attempt to understand Keats' work by retracing his legendary walk through England and Scotland. As Mandel says, "Poetry and walking have a shared and rich history—all the more so, it seems, when the walking is hard. The march of marshaled syllables aligns with the footfall, the poet's line with the walker's. We do not escape from a long walk or a long poem unbruised." Keats once referred to the earth as "this vale of soul-making" and unsurprisingly, Mandel, like Keats before him, is altered by the arduous journey.

Ebo, the protagonist of Rachel Kondo's story "A Girl of Few Seasons," who lives on the island of Maui in Hawai'i, enlists in the military during the Vietnam conflict, not to escape poverty, but instead for the free trip to the basic training camp on the island of O'ahu.

Ebo, who was party to a tragedy in his childhood that irrevocably marred the life of his family, seeks atonement in O'ahu from the only person who can give it. But before he leaves home, he must first dispose of his pet pigeons, not only because there will be no one to care for them once he leaves, but also because he believes "if the business of the pigeons had never happened, that day wouldn't have happened."

Gabe Markowitz, audiophile and narrator of Tim Parrish's story "The Critic," leverages his acute listening skills into a career as a music critic, but he only rises to national prominence after he writes a shocking review in which he "reduced the voice of a generation"—a singer/songwriter whom he refers to only as "the Twerp"—"to a pile of steaming dog poo." Markowitz admits that this vicious early review had "given him an edge. People loved the insolence of it. After getting away with that, he could say anything, no matter how outrageous, and the public perception of his brilliance grew." Now, though, as he reaches the end of his career, he's beginning to doubt himself: "What if everything he'd written had covered the sound, not revealed it." In an act that either tests or is a testament to his sensibility, Markowitz forces himself to listen again to the album that made his reputation but may have cost him his soul.

Carolyn Ferrell's ingenious "A History of China" tells the story of a family through their dishware. As the story begins, the narrator, Sasha Jean, has returned for the annual family reunion on her father's side. A messy, dysfunctional, lively, fully human lot, Sasha Jean's extended family may be best characterized by the seemingly indestructible Corelle; whereas, her parents' history is better illustrated by the fate of her mother's delicate Melitta during her misguided flight from Germany to New York to marry the man she'd just met. It's unclear what sort of dishware best characterizes Sasha Jean. One thing is sure, though: she has a lot of secrets, and one of those secrets will change everything for her father's family.

Uche Okonkwo's story "The Girl Who Lied" opens with its young narrator, Tola, observing, "The first time I saw Kemi she was causing a scene." After Kemi and Tola become friends at the Lagos State Girls' Secondary School in Badagry, Tola will have many occasions to wonder about the motives of Kemi's mysterious actions. Tola remains loyal to Kemi as the other girls "came and went as they pleased, taking the bits of her that they liked. There was an unspoken consensus among them. Kemi was fun, in small, carefully selected doses." After an event so troubling that no one, not even Tola, can quite understand it, Tola will take a stand, risking her friendship to tell the truth in the hope that it will bring Kemi the help she needs.

"These days I like the edge . . . I need the edge," says Kyle Waller, the newly retired and at-loose-ends "efficiency czar" in Lisa Horiuchi's story "Bones." Waller's belief that "seeing what's possible and committing to what's practical" is "the key to being successful in everything you do" will be severely tested when he recklessly sets out on a mission to find the bones of a fabled skeleton near the unexcavated Mayan city of El Pilar on the border of Guatemala and Belize.

I hope these collected Solos will give you a few hours entertainment, and perhaps a little deeper insight into our common humanity. Amidst the relentless fearmongering and finger-pointing of this past year, I experienced each of these Solos as a little reprieve, not from reality—quite the opposite—but from the clamor of undigested information. In their own ways, each has given me a more complete understanding of the world and the many ways of being in it, including a portrait of the great Sun Ra at the end of his career, who once told the members of the Dartmouth College jazz band, "People need to be tuned up. They're out of tune with the universe. That's why they have to hear my songs: cosmos songs." Like Sun Ra's "cosmos songs," may these stories help you get in tune.

Face the Music:
My Improbable Trip to Saturn
(Or Close Enough) with Sun Ra

MICHAEL LOWENTHAL

Sun Ra claimed to hail from Saturn, but he and his Intergalactic Arkestra still had to suffer the trials of earthly travel. When his agent phoned us to say they'd be driving up early, a day before their hotel was expecting them, we had to scramble to find beds.

Adam, our piano player, lived in Panarchy, a frat that had bucked its Greek identity and become a refuge for students too queer, in a range of senses, to fit in at tight-assed Dartmouth. He asked his pals if they'd host one of the world's most offbeat jazz bands, and the Panarchists, always game, agreed. Mattresses and questionably clean bedding were dredged up, dusty couches cleared of detritus. Adam's girlfriend, Angela, commandeered the kitchen, churning out hundreds of dumplings for dinner.

I must've come late, because I found my bandmates already gathered on the floor, Indian-style, gazing up at a cockeyed armchair in which, as if enthroned, sat Sun Ra. He looked like no creature I'd ever run across. Said to be seventy-five, he seemed a hundred, till I peered closer: a toddler's puffy cheeks, eyes aglint with childish restlessness. His goatee was dyed an uncanny shade of orange, the hue of a Dinka tribesman's hair, or maybe a Mohawked punk's. His bulk, shrouded in a floor-length poncho, appeared almost weightless, ectoplasmic.

"…get the planet ready for space beings," he was saying. "People need to be *tuned up*. They're out of tune with the universe. That's why they have to hear my songs: *cosmos* songs."

His voice came in lispy, whispered bursts; we all leaned in.

"My music's *power*-ful," he said. "Few months back, we played behind the Iron Curtain. What happened? Y'all saw: the Wall came down!"

On and on he speechified, his brown skin blushing plummy as his vehemence increased: *history versus mystery*—his *story*, my *story*—*knowledge of the ancient unknowns*…Part lecture, part homily, part string of schoolyard brags, his spiel was equally baffling and bewitching. It might've been the murmured self-talk of a homeless man. The other Arkestra members (he'd come with eight or nine) hovered at the room's margin, gobbling dumplings, chiming in occasionally with the "Mm-hmm" or "That's right!" you'd hear at a Baptist church.

And the students at Sun Ra's feet? Some were nodding, brows furrowed, as if in a foreign-language class; others were trying their best not to laugh.

Our group, the Barbary Coast, was the Dartmouth College jazz band—like Panarchy, an oasis at our otherwise WASPy, old-guard school. Don, our director, did what he could to shake things up, to expose us to worlds beyond our blinders. Every winter, he invited in a guest artist, who'd teach us for a week, then guide us in a Saturday-night performance. In recent years, we'd had a string of hall-of-famers: Max Roach,

Slide Hampton, Lester Bowie; each, in late career, had mastered the master-class circuit.

But Sun Ra had never done a college stint like this, let alone at a place as reactionary as Dartmouth. Even at Panarchy, you could sense the culture clash, see how squeamish Sun Ra was at being a college mascot. He looked as comfortable as a parrot in the Arctic.

Or maybe I was projecting my own discomfort.

At twenty, I'd played the trumpet for fully half my life: thousands of hours of embouchure training and finger drills and scales. I was good, and loved to play, but what I truly excelled at was excelling; musical discipline was part of my whole strive-for-straight-A's M.O. But now, four months from graduation, soon to be spun out from the academic gravitational field, I was wondering (among a welter of discomposing questions) how the trumpet would fit in my new life. I wasn't nearly good enough to make a living from it. Without the structure of school, without the earning of brownie points, would trumpet playing lose its meaning? Or would it, conversely, give me a tether to cling to?

All of which was a way of asking: What had my years of follow-the-track striving finally won me? Was this how I wanted to live?

The overachieving me had, increasingly, been warring with another self who yearned to shed his "best little boy in the world" duds. For one thing, I'd lost some faith in the world I wanted praise from. Two years back I'd come out as gay, then banded with campus leftists, hot to undermine the old-boy system. While classmates suited up for investment banker interviews, I was deciding to try my hand at writing. I'd recently found out I'd be our class valedictorian, but that achievement induced almost as much unease as pride: that I could so succeed within the very system I questioned seemed to cast doubt on my integrity. Addled and angsty, I couldn't tell which version of me was true, which would serve me in the world and which might soon grow hollow.

Enter Sun Ra, brimming with eccentric insurrection, claiming his mercurial music's power to topple walls. He kindled in me a combination of skepticism and envy: I didn't think I wanted to believe what he believed, but he sure made me long to believe *something*.

*

Sun Ra was one of the great jazz visionaries, according to Don, who gave us a crash course on the man. In the 1940s, still named Herman Blount, he'd played in Chicago with the famed Fletcher Henderson (whose rowdy big-band numbers I adored). Then, in the '50s, he'd become Le Sony'r Ra, proclaiming he'd arrived from outer space, and started making his "music of the spheres." He'd been a pioneer in using synthesizers, said Don, in treating all manner of sounds as jazz. He'd toured the world for decades, his "Arkestra" always performing in flamboyantly weird regalia: sequined robes, floppy wizard's caps. They'd put out maybe two hundred albums.

"He's built a kind of cosmological cult," Don explained. "Science fiction, Egyptology, a bunch of black pride. But hey, if it's not your thing, don't get stuck on the spiritual stuff. The *music* is what's really out of this world." It wasn't the shapeless muck, he said, that often gets a pass as "experimental." They played Monk and Ellington and wacked-out Disney tunes, deploying nervy intervals and harmonics. They'd influenced everyone from Herbie Hancock to Sonic Youth. "Just try the music, OK?" said Don. "Keep an open mind."

Normally, in advance of the visit, our guest artist would ship us his charts: full-scale arrangements, pages long, with multiple parts each for trumpets, saxophones, and so on. But Sun Ra demurred; first he wanted to see what our band looked like.

Don mailed him a photograph. We waited.

A packet of music finally came, but the envelope was thin. He'd sent ten or so single sheets; on each was scrawled

a title and an unadorned melody—without chords or tempo
marks or any other accompaniment, like jingles from a kindergarten songbook.

What, if anything, we wondered, did this have to do with
the photo? Had Sun Ra seen our buttoned-up, upper-crust
looks (and the fact that all but one of us were white) and
decided this was as much as we could handle? Don phoned
and asked what we should do.

The pages turned out to be the alto sax parts. Sun Ra said
to transpose them for every other instrument. "Then play 'em
all together. *Real slow*."

Dutifully we rehearsed the songs in death-march unison. But the tunes were confoundingly simple. The more we
played them, the less sense they made, like words repeated
so often they crumble into nonsense. Was the music a kind
of avant-garde joke?

Or were we, in our cluelessness, the joke?

*

My doubts about Sun Ra weren't so different from lingering
qualms I had about the very nature of jazz. Its open-ended-
ness flummoxed me. I'd learned classical music first: right
notes vs. wrong notes, success measured as easily as in math.
Later, in high school, when I first attempted jazz, I found
I had a terror of ad-libbing: If all the notes were mine to
choose, how could I ever know I got them right?

So I fashioned an escape hatch: whenever my part called
for an open trumpet solo, I'd go home, compose some lines,
learn them by heart, then perform this faux improvisation
at the concert. Eventually, following the music's letter if not
its spirit, I rose to the rank of first trumpet. I even made the
all-state jazz ensemble.

At college, my perseverance continued to pay off; I landed
a coveted spot in the Barbary Coast. The music was intim-
idating—funk and bebop, Afro-Caribbean—but Don was a

man of endless patience, whose slouch and scraggly beard belied a scrupulous passion for the music. When he urged me to embrace improvisation, I took the task head-on: boning up on blues scales in any number of keys, rehearsing licks and chords and rhythm changes. What I lacked in feel, I tried to replace with effort; by senior year, most of the time, I could ad-lib adequately, without usually leaving a song in ruins.

Adequately. Does any word in the language have less jazz?

I continued to worry I wasn't hearing the music right. Or maybe the trouble was that I still believed there *was* a right. I could solo, but always with a clammy fear of failure. Exactly when I should've felt most free, I shrank with self-conscious inhibition.

*

Tuesday evening, arriving for our first rehearsal with him, I saw Sun Ra sitting by himself at the piano, staring down glumly at his hands. He wore the baggy poncho again, as well as a woolen skullcap. He looked more subdued, even lonely. It turned out he'd stayed at the hotel after all (Don had located an open room), while the other players partied at Panarchy, shooting pool and jamming at all hours. In fact, they'd decided to camp out there all week. Three of them had crashed on the floor in Adam's room, he told me—he'd woken at six and found them passing around a bottle of wine, saying, "Hey, give me some of that mouthwash!" But now, at rehearsal, the players appeared no worse for the wear, gamely volunteering to act as coaches.

Sun Ra remained in a kind of exile at the piano, seemingly oblivious to us all. Someone should be tending to him, I thought…but not me. I feared getting closer, nervous that he'd sniff my doubts—about him, and about myself. He started plinking around on the keyboard, growing jaunty, then smiled arcanely, as though his string of notes had told a punch line. He looked at the ceiling, and told us to get started.

Or that's what I *guessed* he'd said. His voice was wispy, barely audible. He seemed to ask for a song with "space" in the title. Of course, in his repertoire, that hardly narrowed it down—just among the tunes he'd sent were "Island in Space," "Sons of the Space Age," and "Spacelore." I was flipping wildly through my stack of loose pages, when he mumbled, with no particular rhythm, "Onetwothreefourfivesixsevenand—"

I whipped my trumpet up to my lips in time to flub a note. The saxes squawked, followed, a beat late, by a trombone blurt.

Sun Ra said nothing, simply stilled his hands on the piano, and we all figured out to stop playing. He gazed up and away, as if to a distant nebula, and then, in a voice as thin as tracing paper, went, "Onetwothreefourfivesixsevenand—"

Now we all came in on the same downbeat, but that was the extent of our achievement. Each of us played at a slightly different speed, none of which seemed to be Sun Ra's.

Beside me stood Laura, our trumpet virtuoso. A freshman, she played with disarming sophistication, technique as sharp as her gem-cut jawline. "Excuse me, um…sir?" she said. (She and I had discussed the tricky problem of address—should we call him Mr. Ra? Mr. Sun?) "Excuse me," she said again. "Can I ask something?"

Sun Ra trained his glance more or less in her direction.

"When we rehearsed," she said, "we did this four times slower."

Sun Ra seemed to consider this. Unflappably, he nodded.

"Right," said Laura. "But now you're counting it off super-fast? I don't get it. Which way should we play?"

A gleam livened his eyes. He was a jester playing a bodhisattva, or vice versa. "Depends," he said, "on what you want to hear."

The rest of the rehearsal was only more unnerving. Pronouncements blazed forth from him but seemed to evanesce before they reached us, leaving only contrails. The Arkestra members tried their best to guide us: Marshall Allen hunkering with the saxes, counting rhythms, Michael

Ray kibitzing with the horns. When I complained that I didn't get what Sun Ra meant, Michael told me, "Watch his face. Always just keep watching. Anything else, I'll be here to translate."

Translate seemed too tame a word. We kept trying to speak in English, but out of Sun Ra's mouth came spaghetti. I set down my horn, and slumped onto a stool.

"Listen!"

It was Sun Ra, his voice aimed straight at me. I looked into his dark, expansive gaze.

"Your ear's a harp," he said. "A harp made of strings. My music vibrates strings in there that never moved before. It's gonna make your head hurt. Don't worry." With that, he stood and shuffled to the door.

I should've stayed to hear my fellow band members' reactions—there'd be strength in bellyaching together. But I was so wrung out from untying tangled thoughts I just packed up and took off.

As soon as I emerged into the cold New Hampshire night, my skull's plates shifted with a tight, tectonic pressure. *Depends on what you want to hear*, he'd said—an empty riddle. As if wanting were all success required. I stomped home, mad at him and madder at myself (why should I let a quack like Sun Ra tip me off my hinges?). Beneath my boots, the snow crunched a steady, stringent beat.

*

The second rehearsal went not much better.

Sun Ra had decided against playing the tunes he'd sent, the ones we'd sweated through for weeks. Instead, he'd spent the day composing new material.

Jothan Callins, another Arkestra trumpeter, told us not to fret: Sun Ra's switcheroo was standard practice. The man conjured up new pieces nearly every day. He often used the date as a title; mid-concert, he might abruptly announce

"April 6," and the band would paw through their sheaves of music for that date's tune.

Jothan seemed agreeably nerdy—less astro jazz than small-town postal clerk—but his attempt at reassurance backfired. If at first I'd felt the rug was being pulled from under me, now I doubted there'd ever been a rug.

Section by section, Sun Ra tried to show us what he wanted: playing a custom-tailored part, asking each group to play it back by ear. Without a page in front of me, though, I felt ashamedly lost, a chartless sailor trying to get to port by just the stars. Laura, whose ear was excellent, managed to pin the new licks down, jotting them on a blank sheet, but by the time Sun Ra modeled the riffs again, they'd changed, and Laura's notes were moot.

Finally, after an hour of wearying tug-of-war, it was time to try our parts together. Sun Ra counted off in his helter-skelter way—"Onetwothree now go"—and we came in. The racket was awful, eyeball-rattling: the clatter of a multicar pileup.

What Sun Ra hadn't explained—or we'd not understood—was that he'd written the parts in conflicting time signatures: saxes and trumpets in 4/4 time, drums and bass in 3/4, piano in 7/4, 'bones in 5/4. He seemed peeved we hadn't figured it out. "Not just that you're *playing* wrong," he said, "it's that you're *thinking* wrong. Exercise the muscles of your brain!"

We tried again, but it was worse. Bedlam. We gave up.

Walking home, I battled a headache twice as sharp as the previous day's.

*

The next rehearsal was Friday, the day before the show. Surprise, surprise: Sun Ra opened more musical cans of worms. Songs he'd written hours before—or made up on the spot.

Don surely sensed our collective nervous anger, and his anxiety must've dwarfed ours. Ticket sales were beyond any previous concert (by show time, the hall would be sold out), and we had virtually no charts prepared. Diplomatically, Don suggested we work on tunes we'd tried before, and Sun Ra, without much fuss, agreed. But even when we summoned forth the riffs as we remembered them, something inevitably wasn't to his liking. The closer we came to repeating what we'd learned in previous sessions, the faster Sun Ra switched what he was doing.

"Y'all seem so worried," he said, "about playing the *notes*. But you can play more than just notes on a page, you know. You can play the wind or the river. You can play the sun rays."

A cop-out, I thought. If anything goes, nothing needs perfecting.

But fine. He was the visionary.

And so when, with a toss of his hand, as if scattering bird-seed, he signaled for the next song to start, I decided to play precisely nothing the way we'd learned it. I'd find a novel way to mutate every note: coming in a millisecond ahead of or behind the beat, tonguing hard or slurring through a half-valve. I'd like to say I did this out of open-minded virtue, but cussedness was closer to the truth. If he was hell-bent on undermining our book-learned perseverance, it seemed only fair to try to beat him at his game.

But, strangely, my mischief-making failed to wreck the music. Sun Ra was accompanying us, as usual, on piano, and for every note I sabotaged, he seemed to change his playing, widening the song's sidelines so I always stayed in bounds. Could it be? I tried again—a purposely sharpened note— and Sun Ra's fingers danced into a new configuration, his chord seemingly built on my suggestion. Back and forth we went in our loony musical leapfrog, till I was convoluted with amusement.

Sun Ra flashed a smile at me—not gloating but in grati-tude—and now I saw this kind of sport was the goal. *You're right, it's a game,* I imagined him saying, *but all of us are on the same team.* I couldn't say we sounded great, or that I fully "got" it; I still searched for handholds in the din. But now I was attuned to, not tuning out, his whimsies.

We moved on to a stumper of a song called "Friendly Galaxy." Previously I'd been thrown by its herky-jerky melody, but Sun Ra's grateful playfulness had loosened my resistance; now I let my knees and shoulders act as shock absorbers, and brightly bodysurfed the song's swells. Looking around at the band, I started to sense a split: who was in on the music's fun, who wasn't. It felt a bit like showing up at a party stoned, then scanning the crowd and thinking, *He is too. And her. Not him.*

Sun Ra wrote a vamp the saxes couldn't seem to learn: they played with stricken fingers, sour mouths. "The problem," he declared, "is you don't *want* to know it. The 'bones look like they do. Let them try." Matt, an Asian studies major, led the trombone section. Pale and blond, as placidly compassionate as a chaplain, he huddled with Pete, a toothy, earnest grad student in chemistry. It was hard to picture two less probable avant-gardists, but after some hasty transposition, they nailed the vamp with gusto.

Adam, too, on piano, was playing with abandon, sporting a winky shine within his eyes. "See?" said Sun Ra. "He used his *ears*. Just like Jesus Christ did. Used his ears and listened to the people."

Sun Ra's patter was only growing deeper in its weirdness, but now its very weirdness was what helped me find its sense. The less I took him seriously, the more seriously I could take him…which seemed, to my delight, like a riddle he might spout.

It was still unclear how we'd throw a show together, but as we finished rehearsing I felt buoyant. I walked out with my head full of imagined Sun Ra–isms: *The less you grasp for something, the more you'll come to grasp it. The less you think you know, the more you know.* I wasn't sure I could quite make myself believe them, but I was so intent on their mazy kind of logic that I was halfway home before I noticed I didn't have a headache.

*

Sound checks were normally swift affairs—formalities, re-ally. An hour at most on stage, the afternoon of a concert, just to test the mikes, the acoustics. But when Sun Ra, on Saturday, took his place among us (he wore a comically big, Russian-style, round fur hat), he launched another full-scale rehearsal. Again: new songs, new riffs, new ways to play old riffs. Now that he'd begun, he said, to get a better sense of us, he was matching the music to our "vibrations."

Discontent began to percolate among the band, a low-sim-mering claustrophobic panic, but Sun Ra didn't notice—or, if he did, didn't care. The sound check stretched to two hours, two and a half, three…

The first to leave was Laura, gathering her music in her fists. She muttered something, maybe an excuse about home-work, and quietly slipped off stage.

When Jothan asked what the trouble was, I said we hadn't expected so long a session. "Three hours?" he said. "Three hours is *nothing*." The Arkestra sometimes practiced for *fif-teen*. They lived all together in a Philadelphia row house: slept together, ate together, everything'd together. "Night or day," said Jothan, "Sonny can call rehearsal. You just have to be there, you know? Always be there. Be ready."

Maybe that worked for the Arkestra, but not the Barbary Coast: minutes later, another defection, and soon a steady stream, till more than a third of the band had bolted. Sun Ra couldn't help but notice; his deep eyes dimmed. He looked like a Santa Claus, tired from hauling gifts, who'd learned none of the children liked his toys.

I found myself, for the first time, feeling bad for the guy. The week here must've been as hard for him as it was for us—harder, maybe, since he was on our turf. I thought about his claim to have come from another planet. *Hadn't* he, when he set foot on this campus?

I, too, had felt like an alien at Dartmouth: proudly gay, and political, and—maybe worse—a bookworm. Sheepishly, though, I harbored an affinity for the school, its woodsy, insular, L. L. Bean allure; I didn't want to break its mold so much as carve out niches that would fit me. To that end, I'd found my kin, not least among the jazz band. But here we were, the Barbary Coast, purported nonconformists, failing to embrace Sun Ra's quirks.

Matt and Pete had stuck around to rat-a-tat their two-note vamp—which Sun Ra now requested on *every* song—bobbing with the fervency of converts. Were they just being charitable, or did they dig the style? Maybe they were wondering the same of me.

I resolved to compensate for our fellow students' rudeness: by being doubly attentive, by beaming good vibrations. This wasn't tough, because I'd actually begun to like the music—or, at least, begun to like the notion that I could like it.

*

For guest-artist concerts, we split the night in two: a first set by the Barbary Coast together with our guest, a second by the guest and his own group. I wish my recollections from our set were sharper, but the shock of what happened next has skewed those memories, like paintings shaken crooked by an earthquake.

Feeling encased in a body cast of nerves: that I remember. Nerves about my own performance, and also about the band's. After the sound check's walkouts, I feared there'd be bad blood. But once we took our places and faced the sold-out house, my bandmates immediately found their manners. (Laura had even bought a special multicolored cap, and donned it now in a show of good sportsmanship.) If anything, we all behaved too well—Sun Ra included.

I can conjure the image of him strutting onto the stage in a gold lamé cape and a wide, bejeweled velvet hat that looked nicked from a Renaissance Faire. The eager crowd, nine hundred strong, clamored with applause, and Sun Ra gave a big, grand poobah bow. But then, when he turned around and sat at the piano, he sent us what I read as a modest, yielding grin. Was he, in his own way, as stiff with nerves as I was? At the time, I think I guessed he balked at working with amateurs, worried we might make him look the fool. Now, knowing a bit of what it means to be a mentor, I wonder: Did he maybe worry *he'd* make *us* look bad? He started playing, it seemed, more timidly than in practice, and so we inched out after him onto the music's tightrope, everyone scared of knocking the others off.

It was Michael Ray who finally cut the tension. Along with Marshall and Jothan and a couple other players, Michael was sitting in with us, maybe as a fail-safe. Now he sprang into action, with jack-in-the-box pizzazz. On "Love in Outer Space," he pranced about the stage, crooning with evangelical (or was it self-mocking?) charm: "Sunrise! Love for the world to see. Sunrise in outer space. Love for every face!" When he soloed, he screeched a streak of higher and higher notes, pretending to tug one leg up on a long invisible string, as if his leg's increasing rise were what controlled the music's.

Everyone laughed, and the laughter gave permission to our playing.

Oh, right, I thought. This should be *fun*. And so it was, for the rest of the set: a tickle fight turned into sound. I don't recall the songs so much as the force of their happy whiplash, drowning out the previous noisy strife of our rehearsals. The audience couldn't hear that weeklong clang; they heard music.

We finished, and basked in the ovation. Sun Ra was as hard as ever to read, but he seemed pleased. Or not displeased. Maybe just relieved.

I was too: for having performed capably, and for letting myself enjoy it. Also I was glad for Don, who'd gone out on such a trembly limb. We followed him downstairs to our practice room, high-fiving. If the show hadn't been transcendent, neither had it been a train wreck; there was a lesson in there somewhere.

I'd already buffed my trumpet and was packing it in its case—antsy to go upstairs again and claim a seat for the Arkestra's set—when Michael Ray materialized at the door and beckoned to Don. After a brief consultation, Don called me over, along with Matt and Pete and a couple of our peers.

Michael was now in costume: orange tunic, satin dunce cap studded with ruby sequins. "Quick, grab your horns," he said. "Sonny wants to see you."

No time to glance around and gauge the band's reaction. (Envy, I'd guess, in equal measure with pity.) We five students scrambled after Michael up the stairs and burst into Sun Ra's dressing room. Surrounding him were acolytes tinkering with his outfit. Piles of composition paper spilled from old suitcases. On the table: a battered Disney songbook.

He said nothing, but somehow used his silence to confirm that we were meant to join him for his set.

If I'd been taut with nerves before, now I was limp-limbed, unstrung. But the shock had its own irreversible momentum, like the rush of drugs finally kicking in. And so, despite my wobbly legs, I was soon stepping back on stage.

The Arkestra's ranks had doubled with a spate of late arrivals: June Tyson, vocalist and dancing violinist; John Gilmore, so inventive a tenor saxophonist that John Coltrane had asked him for lessons. But even the guys who'd been with us all week appeared new: they wore shimmering robes, natty hats and chains—transformed by their garments, like priests.

At last Sun Ra sashayed on stage, emitting antic energy. He raised his arms (but wait, I thought, what *music* are we playing?), then *whap!*—whipped his hand at the air, as if swatting an insect; the band, at the instant of the fancied insect's doom, pounded out a massive, motley chord. Without quite having known it, I was playing too. How had I chosen my note? No idea.

When Sun Ra hurled his hand again, we struck another chord, a cluster of entirely different tones. Every player had chosen anew, and no one had consulted, and yet the sound was ringingly coherent.

Sun Ra twirled, his arms and wrists as fluid as a geisha's. *Pa!*—he flung his fingers out, like someone shooting craps— *pa! pa!*—with each fling, we forged a different chord. Even the notes that shouldn't have fit within the cluster did. Dissonance and harmony, consonance and clash: the sound kept swallowing its own tail.

I felt attached to the band, like one foot of a centipede: as it moved, so I must move; as I moved, so must it. Was I playing or being played, or both?

The song—if that was what it was—tumbled toward a climax, Sun Ra's rowdy guiding jabs arriving ever faster, till *shh!* His arms shot down; the Arkestra cut to hush; the hall throbbed with complicated silence.

I would've liked to pause there, to parse my exhilaration, but Sun Ra, at the piano now, was banging something new, and Jothan whispered, "Watch. Follow me." Sun Ra's intro wandered, appealingly arrhythmic. Then, a frenzy: Jothan and the other players scrambling (had they all caught a signal I'd missed?), rifling through their piles of sheet music. Just in time, Jothan nabbed the page he'd been pursuing and slapped it on the music stand we shared.

I was a skillful sight-reader, and aced the written part. My legs were solid under me again.

Soon the song evolved to a daisy chain of solos. Gilmore's tenor gushed a tone I'd never heard before: divine, demonic, gracefully disconcerting. Next went Marshall Allen, with feral, spastic hands like mad rodents scrabbling along his sax. The squabble of it had me hypnotized.

It took me a second to notice something on my arm. A finger. Jothan's. Jabbing at my elbow.

Crap, I thought, I've missed another cue. (They came so fast!) I looked around, only to sense the Arkestra looking back. I dared a glance at Sun Ra, whose brows seemed to waggle ever so slightly in my direction.

"C'mon," said Jothan. "It's you. It's your solo."

His calm smile brought to mind his statement yesterday: *You just have to be there. Be ready.* How often, playing jazz, had I tried and failed to do that? A hoarder of self-consciousness, unable to clear my brain of clutter.

Terror trampled through me. What key were we in? But there was no more time to fret: Sun Ra had shoved me off the ledge, I fell and fell and—whoa...

I floated!

A fresh feeling: pregnant with pure space. Nothing for me to do now but fill that space with notes. Or with noise. Was there so big a difference? Instead of trying to live up to a sound I'd heard before, I tried to...just *play*, and discovered that I could. I played and played, deliciously dazed, then somehow knew to stop. The song swept on, and now I swam within it.

Soon we were on to another tune I'd never heard before: it swung with the brio of an intricate big-band number, but also had the candor of a rhyme from *Sesame Street*. The band started dancing in a kind of conga line—around the stage, up into the crowd—singing the admonitory lyrics:

What do you do when you know that you know
that you know that you're wrong?
You've got to face the music!
You've got to listen to the Cosmos Song!

As we sang, Sun Ra chanted a descant from the piano: "You in the Space Age now...ain't no place you can run... you can't run away...Space Age is here to stay..."

The band paraded on, daffily proselytizing, over and over again: *Face the music!* The words came from my mouth, but I felt they were addressed to me, even if I didn't fully understand the message—which must, I sensed, go way beyond jazz.

At some point—after another enigmatic sign—Jothan and the others gently told us we were done. We walked off stage to warm applause, as Sun Ra started another stomping tune. Our urge to whoop and jump around was squelched by the backstage techie, and so we settled for hugs, ardent handshakes.

I was giddy with disbelief, with pride at my ad-libbed breakthrough. How could I express my gratitude? I grabbed a pencil, an unmarked sheet of composition paper. "I'm not sure," I wrote, "I could say I've been to Saturn. But tonight, playing with you, was pretty close. Thank you. Your music has changed my life."

I slipped the note into the middle of Sun Ra's Disney song-book, then buried the book in a thick stack of music.

*

I was eager to carry something of Sun Ra forward with me, but college has a way of gumming up your every synapse, and it was hard in the following days to keep hold of my bliss. The all-involving week with him had left me so behind—with friendships and work and, most of all, my thesis—I could only focus on catching up.

I'd been awarded what Dartmouth called a Senior Fellow-ship, which let me abstain from taking courses, in order to pursue my own project. I'd applied in a tantrum of frustra-tion, claiming to be disgusted by the academic treadmill, but maybe—though I couldn't quite admit this to myself—just as sick at how adept I was at sprinting on it. I'd told the ap-plication jury I wanted to write a novel, and needed a year's liberty to do it.

Why had it come as such a surprise that writing a novel depended on its own kind of drudgery? In fact, as the year progressed, my thesis had often seemed the quintessential office job. Every morning, I trudged up to my humdrum li-brary room, sat at my desk, and poked some words around: less like bolts of inspiration, more like nuts and bolts. Was this a disappointment or a relief? I wasn't sure.

For now, I had to knuckle down and grind out the novel's ending—a big task on a bigger list in the dash to graduation: produce another issue of a newspaper I'd helped start; plan protests with my activist-minded friends; get ready for a final concert, when I would bow out of the Barbary Coast.

That's what I expected when I headed, a month later, to one of the band's regular rehearsals. The Coast had settled back to our usual routine, which, in spring, meant picking songs for the Senior Feature show. But that night, before we got going on our run-through, Don pulled me and Matt and Pete aside. Sun Ra's agent had called, he said. Something about a secret note, stuffed inside a book? The Arkestra would be headed out on tour in May, to Europe, and Sonny wanted the three of us to join him.

"Wait," I said. "Us, as in the three of us, specifically?" (I hadn't signed my hidden note.)

"Yeah," said Don. "He knew the ones he wanted. He described you."

"Oh, my gosh," said Matt.

Pete said, "That's insane!"

The whoops we'd suppressed backstage after our performance now erupted wildly from our throats. Dorkily, we danced around the room.

After we'd calmed down, Don divulged more details. We'd miss the last two weeks of the term, returning only days before commencement. It was crazy. We'd be passing up not only this term's end, but the glorified, party-filled last weeks of our college lives. Dartmouth students simply didn't do that.

One of us said, "But we *have* to, don't we? I mean, don't we have to?"

Of course we did. It was in our stars.

One last thing: the agent had mentioned a show, soon, in Boston. To prep for the tour, we should come and play the gig, he'd said.

Yes, we told Don. Yes to it all.

*

The day of the concert, I wore what passed for wild within my closet: a faded purple button-down, a brightly patchworked Guatemalan vest. Matt picked me up for the two-hour drive to Boston, where Pete, going separately, would meet us.

The ride to Boston always involved a bit of culture shock—speeding from our sheltered, rural postcard of a campus to a city I saw, then, as so chaotic—but this day's trip launched us toward an inconceivable distance. By journey's end, I wondered, what worlds might I have seen? More than that, I wondered who I'd be.

It was hard to find the words to bring this up with Matt. Instead, I expressed my fears in terms of the concert's details: Would there be written parts? Would we be asked to solo?

We headed to an address at Northeastern University. A group of students were waiting for a promised preshow workshop, but the Arkestra, they told us, was nowhere to be found. Uncertainly, we joined them in their vigil.

We waited, and waited, as evening fast approached. It struck me we all might unwittingly be complicit in a cutting-edge conceptual performance. Maybe to one-up John Cage and his four minutes, thirty-three seconds of silence, Sun Ra had composed a piece for a band that doesn't show.

Half an hour before the concert's scheduled start, a bus pulled up, and out straggled the bleary-looking Arkestra. Jothan saw us and shook our hands, as did Michael Ray, but no one else seemed to note our presence. Sun Ra scuffled by with an air of depthless blankness, and disappeared into a dressing room.

While band members busied themselves backstage, Matt and I stood silently, shrinking against a wall. Could Sun Ra have forgotten he'd asked us here to play? Worse, had he had a change of heart? Panicking, I worried I had breached a rule of etiquette. Had I done something (my purple shirt?) that proved I was unworthy?

Pete arrived, and wanted to know the deal. What could we say? We could only huddle together, hoping we'd not come so far for nothing.

The show was already twenty minutes past curtain time when we were ushered over to Sun Ra, who sat pasha-like atop a pillowy chair, a great heap of garments before him. He made a gesture that June Tyson, the vocalist, understood. From the mishmash of costumes, June picked out a robe, then held it up speculatively before me. Sun Ra shook his head: too short. "No 'earth clothes' showing," he insisted. June tried another, then another, till Sun Ra consented to a kind of saffron toga and flaccid purple hat that made me look like one of the Seven Dwarfs.

Naturally, I felt silly, but the aura of solemnity kept me from cracking up. In truth, I wanted *not* to laugh; I wanted to be transformed.

Suddenly it was show time. Sun Ra was helped up, and we all crowded onto the stage. The hall was rife, I knew, with jazz cognoscenti: students from nearby Berklee College and the New England Conservatory, who'd mastered more music theory than I'd ever heard of, and surely could outplay me on a bad day. But I was the one up here. I tried to look convinced.

The show was a volcano, urgently erupting; creating itself out of itself, all flow. A smash of drums, a piling-on of horns. Meanwhile, an oldish guy (Art Jenkins, I later learned) skulked around the stage performing a cryptic melodrama. He space-sang in the spookiest, most sublime voice I'd ever heard, a goblin with a tracheostomy tube.

Sun Ra was both impish and imperious, bossing us with wiggles of his hands. He played behind his back, with his elbows, his knuckles—he was having furious fun.

At last came the moment I'd both hoped for and dreaded. Sun Ra gave me the scantest wink, or I thought he did. Iffily, I lifted my horn to solo. Michael Ray elbowed me. "Naw, not here," he said. "Go up front."

Alive with fear, my skin throbbing, I threaded my way forward, and teetered at the edge of what seemed a vast black void. Could the crowd see past my costume to the floundering impostor inside? Behind me, the drummers beat an ominous jungle soundtrack. I answered with some anxiously honest notes. My tone was blunt, and modest, and more or less unmuddled. I pictured the shifting colors of a sunset.

Soon I heard another horn, and spun to find Jothan, his trumpet thrust toward me like a lance. I batted notes back at him, and we jousted, trading riffs. A spotlight hit us, or maybe I imagined that toasty glow. We finished to a bracing cheer, the biggest I'd ever earned. The audience had no way of knowing I was just a student, and so they weren't grading on a curve; they'd cheered purely for the performance.

The rest of the show, I rode a stream of jittery joyful verve, amped up by the inch-close risk of failure. We played "Love in Outer Space," which I had down cold, but other tunes were unfamiliar: Sun Ra's take on a Chopin prelude, a Wes Montgomery cover, some slantwise blues, a bunch of cosmic jazz. Mostly, miraculously, I managed to keep pace.

The show ended with a great gust of applause, strong enough to blow us out into the chilly Boston night. I chummed along with the Arkestra, groupies tailing to see where the party would be. Just past Symphony Hall, we swarmed into Café Amalfi, whose name rang with all the panache and cosmopolitan glamour of the world I now guessed I might be part of.

*

I scoured the next day's *Boston Globe*: nothing about the show. The keenness of my letdown was dismaying.

But the following morning, there it was: "Sun Ra and his Arkestra play some imaginative originals and a few surprises."

I skimmed past "the riffs were really clicking," past praise for Marshall Allen's flute work, and zeroed in on a sentence

I immediately learned by heart: "Aside from one sideman dancing with a black ventriloquist's dummy, the most surprising visual aspect was the presence of three Caucasians in what has heretofore been a resolutely nonwhite ensemble."

I loved the grandiloquence, the heady whiff of consequence: confirmation that what we'd done was as momentous as I wanted to believe.

*

Don would later say Sun Ra's visit changed his life. When Michael Ray assembled an Arkestra offshoot, the Cosmic Krewe, he asked Don (who'd mostly been teaching, and not performing, for years) to play "jazz funk of the future" on valve trombone. The world took note, and soon Don played with such big acts as Phish.

Adam, on whose bedroom floor the Arkestra had crashed, was also asked to join the Cosmic Krewe. That gig led to others, which led to even more; two decades later, Adam's a prolific professional player, who's toured as a State Department "Jazz Ambassador."

Even for those who didn't pursue jazz careers, the pull of Sun Ra's gravity remains potent. Matt, the trombone player, recently emailed me from China, where he works on information technology but also, sometimes, performs music, for fun. "Played a trio gig last night that had definite tones of Saturn," he wrote.

As for me, I don't play Sun Ra's music anymore—not even in an amateur group, or by myself at home. In fact, I haven't played my horn for more than twenty years. Its dusty case is buried in my closet.

*

Three weeks after our Boston gig, Don pulled me and Matt and Pete aside before rehearsal, but this time he had distressing news: Sun Ra was in the hospital; his agent thought he might've had a stroke. The Arkestra had already canceled shows. The tour was off.

And that, as it turned out, was that.

Life went on. I finished the draft of my novel, turned it in. The Barbary Coast put on our Senior show, and I was back to being nothing more than what I truly was: a decent dabbler in a solid college band.

*

Almost right away, my trumpet playing dwindled. Without the Coast, my motivation flagged; it was hard to practice when I didn't know what for. Eventually, I moved into a Boston apartment, where neighbors would've carped about the racket, I told myself.

True, I could've found a group to join, rented a practice space. Hell, I could've simply used a mute. Maybe the trumpet was something I just outgrew.

But all this time it's irked me that I lost my drive to play the horn so soon after my near miss with Sun Ra, that my almost-break led only to…well, my fervor dying.

Led to.

Why am I so tempted to draw a link?

The tour's cancellation took the wind from our sails, sure, but for me it was secretly a relief. As much as I'd longed for adventure in the abstract, I feared how the actual trip might fly: the foreignness of where I'd play and whom I'd play with. Easier just to stay at school, enjoying the hard-earned graduation season.

Maybe I already knew it would make a better story: the whopper that got away. I've told it over the decades to dozens of my friends who knew nothing of my trumpet-playing past. Especially these days, in my hopelessly square middle age, I love dropping Sun Ra's name: I rub it like gold leaf along my weathered, wooden life. And yet, though the facts are true, the story's always rung a little false. I've billed it as a tale about coming *this close* to something, when really, I can see now, it's more about learning how far away I'd always be. And the story, as I told it, let me dodge some harder questions: Could I really play well enough? Would the Arkestra have embraced me?

*

Recently, through the unaccountable wizardry of the Web, I found a bootleg recording of the Boston show; in no time, a group of mp3s arrived in my Dropbox. (Imagine Sun Ra's joy—his music beamed through space at the speed of light!)

For days, I couldn't bring myself to click the files open. What if I'd actually bungled my solo? What if my playing spoiled the performance? But when I finally summoned the guts to listen, what I heard was, in its way, even more disturbing.

There are licks that sound like mine, and then another horn: Jothan, I figured, coming downstage to joust. But no—the second horn sounds more like me. Did Jothan actually solo first, and did *I* join *him*? Have I had it backwards for twenty-four years? I've listened a dozen times, and still can't tell. Maybe that seems a good thing: when it counted, my playing passed muster. But Jothan was a pro. Shouldn't I be able to tell his solo from my own? Shouldn't *any* listener? That I can't goes to the heart of why I pulled away from jazz.

Not that Sun Ra and his music weren't exacting. His style, often mislabeled "free," in fact took great control: a methodical open-mindedness, a rigorous relaxation. And yet the music's power—like that of all true jazz—depended on heart-not-head abandon. Which is how a passable amateur, clad in hat and robe, could seem—perhaps could even *be*—as key to a performance as a veteran who knew his stuff cold.

But I see now that my unlikely moment of success offended me—offended my sense of effort and reward. If I was going to do well at something, I wanted it to demand skills impossible to sidestep. As sorely as I chafed against the grind of meritocracy, I found out that I needed it to thrive. And what had seemed the awakening of my footloose cosmic spirit was really an expression of my same old striving self, who craved to be the teacher's pet. My full-bore plunge into Sun Ra's jazz showed I'd gotten his message exactly wrong. Conforming to someone else's style: that's what Sun Ra scorned. His gospel centered instead on perceiving each person's spark, and finding the means to set it aflame.

But playing with him did help me discover my own nature: I wanted to be spontaneous, but not *that* spontaneous; wanted a calling where ad-libbing didn't count for quite so much. Better for me the dogged, fussy climb toward expertise. Jazz had been an outlet when my life was full of strictures and I liked to think of myself as offbeat; now that I was starting the open solo of adulthood, I had to face the truth of my own music.

*

I saw Sun Ra one last time, two years after our Boston show, a bit more than a year before he died. He'd booked a gig at Johnson State, a small school in the far north of Vermont.

I knew Sun Ra was sick—he'd had another stroke or two— but still, when he emerged on stage, the sight was shocking. He'd been stuffed into a wheelchair an aide was slowly pushing; his face was distant, at once stiff and listless. He was positioned at the keyboard facing away from us, and never turned around during the concert. Only his two pudgy hands moved.

Much of the Arkestra, as if in morbid tribute to their leader, also seemed uncommonly decrepit. June Tyson's crooning came out bitterly off-key; John Gilmore's solos emerged in emphysemic spurts. And yet, as ever, the music was ineffably magnetic. Controlled chaos, centrifugally absorbing the crowd's energy, then blazing it back at us tenfold.

After the show, I somehow got backstage. Sun Ra looked wrung out, empty behind the eyes. I muscled through some well-wishers and knelt beside his wheelchair. "I played with you at Dartmouth, and in Boston," I reminded him. "I just wanted, again, to say thanks."

Sun Ra gazed off beyond me.

His aide said, "Enough. He needs to rest."

But then: a word. And another. I strained to understand.

"Go on, now, move closer," someone said, nudging me.

I leaned in, my ear almost touching Sun Ra's mouth.

At last, in the tracing-paper voice I well remembered—noble but surprisingly demure—he whispered, "Give me your number."

People around me were going, "What'd he say? What'd he say?"

I told them, and they said, "Go on, do it!"

I scribbled on the concert program my full name, number, and address. His aide took it and folded it and tucked it into Sun Ra's pocket. The old man smiled. I never heard from him.

Koppargruva

(novel excerpt from Peace at Last*)*

HUGH COYLE

*"M. Nobel, the reputed inventor of nitroglycerine,
has been visiting this and the other copper mines for
the purpose of introducing this powerful explosive
agent. M. Nobel assured Captain Stevens that by
this compound the great masses of copper, upon
which gunpowder has no effect, can be sundered."*
—Travel article *in The New York Times,* August 16, 1866

Each day, the steamship *Favorite* made the round trip between the iron-mining town of Marquette and the twin
copper-mining towns of Hancock and Houghton on Michigan's upper peninsula, an area collectively known as "The
Portage." On this midsummer morning, a fast-moving

line of squalls had delayed the *Favorite*'s departure from Marquette and agitated the waters of Lake Superior into dark gray chop and whitecaps. Passengers huddled beneath umbrellas and wind-snapped awnings along the docks and flinched whenever lightning struck the tall masts of anchored schooners. Along with the subsequent cooler, drier air came a slight yet discernible tang of metal and ozone that led Alfred to wonder if, startled, he had bitten his tongue or lip. He raised his white-gloved hand and, selecting an inconspicuous spot near the knuckle of the index finger, lightly touched his tongue to the silk.

No trace of red in his saliva.

Proof enough, then: the rain-soaked pallets and barrels of iron crowding the docks had sent the suggestion of blood into the air, not his own anxious reflexes.

When the boarding bell sounded, the *Favorite*'s passengers filed up the wet gangway. Alfred jostled among them, a bag in each hand representing nearly everything he had brought overseas from Germany. Since his departure in April, Prussia and Austria had taken up arms against one another. American newspapers now reported that Italy had entered the conflict as well. Would this slow down or speed up the sales of explosives from Krümmel, his factory near Hamburg? Unlike his father, Alfred distrusted forecasts linked to military ventures. One may as well base one's business decisions on the weather. In addition to that, his factory manager's last telegram had reported outbreaks of cholera in nearby cities and towns. With so many variables influencing European economies, the recent settlement of legal disputes over the American patents for blasting oil came at a most opportune time. Here was a nation focused on unification and reconstruction rather than conquest and division. Here was a more reliable, more lucrative source of potential profit.

Alfred settled into a small cabin just aft of the starboard paddle wheel. He would have preferred a forward cabin, ahead of the repetitive plash and shoosh of the turning wheel, but wealthy vacationers had reserved the best accommodations months in advance. The ticketing agent thought Alfred lucky enough to book a private cabin on a day's notice—a cancellation resulting from cholera in the States, perhaps—especially during the height of the summer tourist season, when city dwellers fled north to escape the heat and stench of urban life. Newspaper and magazine advertisements urged readers to "embark on a 'Superior' adventure in a rugged and picturesque wilderness!" Some featured drawings that reminded Alfred of the Swedish archipelago and its sublime landscapes. A man could vanish quite easily in such a wilderness, he thought. And, if the need arose, a wanted man could make a run for his life across the northern border and into Canada.

"*Je cherche asile,*" Alfred said aloud, testing his French. "I seek asylum," he said, testing his English. Unfortunately, this far from home, both Swedish and German would likely be useless.

Back in New York City, editorials continued to call for Alfred's arrest or, at the very least, his immediate deportation. The more bloodthirsty legislators in the nation's capital had sponsored legislation to convict him retroactively for the hundreds of deaths caused by the recent nitroglycerin blasts in Panama and San Francisco. He had memorized the proposed law: "Every death, directly or indirectly caused by transport of his blasting oil on ships or conveyances of any kind, is to be considered murder of the first degree and is to be punished by death."

If the bill passed, Alfred would become a fugitive, an instant renegade.

Such misinformed legislation reminded him of the atmosphere in Stockholm after the so-called "Nobel Blast," which, as before and forevermore, reminded him of his brother Emil's death. Emil had dreamed of visiting America after completing his university degree and would have made a fine traveling companion. If he were there with Alfred at that very moment, just as the *Favorite* pulled away from the dock, he would have raced to the uppermost deck to wave goodbye to each and every person on the Marquette shoreline. Such a kind and caring soul, Emil. A brother to all.

"Plash, shoosh, plash, shoosh," Alfred whispered, mimicking the paddle wheel. He had expected the noise to be irritating, and yet the words sounded playful, soothing even. Were they even real words? What language? And how long had he been standing there with his bags still in his hands, fixated on some unseeable object, some ghost or spirit in the cabin, as if some magician had taken him for a stooge and placed him under hypnosis? *Struntprat*, all of it. Or, as the more decent Americans liked to say, *hornswoggle*.

Beneath the floorboards, the roar of the coal-stoked boilers rose along with the whine of the screw propeller. This sound, too, should have annoyed him, but instead the engine's thrum recalled John Ericsson. How fitting that Alfred was traveling under his fellow Swede's name. John Ericsson, who had redesigned the screw propeller for use in American steamships and revolutionized the travel industry. John Ericsson, who had redeemed himself after the deadly explosion of his "Peacemaker" cannon by building the USS *Monitor*, the Union's armored warship that helped change the course of the Civil War. Yes, here in this second-class cabin stood J. Ericsson, not A. Nobel, not the man who might have been sentenced to hang if only the authorities had thought to inspect his baggage before boarding.

Alfred opened up his leather traveling kit. Inside, a bottle of light purple oil stood securely beside three taller vials of nitroglycerin, enough for a dozen or so demonstrations, and certainly more than enough to sink a midsized steamship. No need to alert the porter or captain, however; the boiler room below decks posed a far greater risk to passenger safety. In fact, Alfred considered his blasting oil no more dangerous than maple syrup, and so, if pressed, he would claim that these bottles were souvenirs from New

England intended as gifts for his business contacts ⸻
Upper Peninsula. If pressed further, he'd take a sip ⸻
sweet-tasting liquid to prove it. It wasn't as though he ha⸻
engaged in such reckless experimentation in his youth, a⸻
he knew well enough to brace for the resulting headache.

Alfred removed his coat, vest, and shirt, all damp from both rain and perspiration, and laid them out on the narrow bed. He sprinkled the purple oil along the spine and underarms of each, the scent transforming the room into a florist's shop. According to an apothecary back in New York City, lavender oil not only served to mask unwanted body odor but would also keep the countryside's mosquitoes and biting flies at bay. The dual-purpose nature of the liquid appealed to Alfred, and yet in such close quarters, the stuff reeked like a prostitute's cheap perfume. He thought to open the porthole and clear the air, but tatters of gray from the ship's central smokestack fluttered past the window like ashen swallows. Surrendering, he lay on the floor and closed his eyes, a mistaken corpse smelling the flowers heaped upon his own grave.

No; that was unlikely. No one would bring flowers to Alfred Nobel's grave. Of that he was sure. And the very idea of lying awake in his own casket, about to be buried alive, jolted him upright.

Alfred opened the porthole despite the inrushing smoke. Truth be told, he preferred the smell of carbon to lavender. It was more elemental, more intrinsic to his love of chemistry.

The *Favorite* churned past the harbor's new breakwater and the recently rebuilt Marquette Harbor Light. These represented better omens of Alfred's upcoming business prospects, prime symbols of the North's booming economy. As the rest of the United States rebuilt itself after the Civil War, Michigan's iron and copper mines stood ready to provide the necessary resources and flourish. There was money to be made here along the Great Lakes, and Alfred had every intention of securing great sums of it for himself.

*

By mid-afternoon the *Favorite* turned west to cross Keweenaw Bay, targeting the passage known as Portage Entry along the far shore. With the heat and glare of the noonday sun passed, a number of passengers, a freshly dressed Alfred among them, left the confines of the lower decks to stretch their legs up top and take in the scenery.

The steamship, which had felt so small and insignificant on the open waters of Lake Superior, now towered above lily-strewn bogs and beaver-dammed marshlands as it maneuvered through narrow, winding channels. Bullfrogs along the shore leapt into and under the water at its passing; dragonflies that had been skimming the surface flitted off into the surrounding woodlands. Every half mile or so, ramshackle docks jutted out from the sedge-choked riverbanks. There, the children of trappers and lumberjacks paused in their afternoon swims, dripping and waving like the members of some newly discovered primitive tribe. But no, Alfred thought, the passage of sailboats and steamers had become quite routine by now, and the faces of individual, well-dressed travelers had probably blurred long ago into sameness in the locals' eyes. Even so, he lifted his hand and waved back, a gesture more like patting a sleeping dog's head than offering a hearty hello to friends.

Alfred flinched when the ship's horn blew. On a nearby dock, a cluster of boys hopped about in spastic delight. Perhaps that had been the goal of all that waving all along— something to break the monotony of a hot summer day, something to set all their hairs on end, something to startle the most stubborn crows from the pines along the riverbank.

Hard upon the blast, the engines of the *Favorite* slowed and the paddle wheels came to a stop. Fearful that pirates might have blocked the ship's passage or, worse yet, that a local sheriff had halted the vessel for a surprise inspection,

Alfred moved from the stern toward the bow. Nearly half a mile ahead, another steamer, somewhat smaller than the *Favorite*, had run aground and listed at a slight angle amidst cattails close to shore.

As the *Favorite* drew closer, Alfred scanned the other ship's decks for passengers. Apparently, most had already been evacuated and transferred to other vessels. Only the captain and four uniformed crewmen, two white and two black, remained on board, and these five had set up a picnic lunch of sorts near the bow. Each man held a bottle in hand with breads, cheeses, peaches, and pears spread between them, no doubt raided from the galley.

"Ahoy!" the *Favorite*'s captain called out from the bow. "Any trouble?"

"Been here since morning," the other captain shouted back. "Storm blew us aground. Waiting on a tug from Torch Bay. Reckoned you might be it."

"Not from this direction."

The other captain looked up and down the channel as if the day's heat had rendered east and west indistinguishable. "Carry on, then," he said, tilting his bottle in a toast toward the *Favorite*'s passengers. "Me and the boys'll just enjoy the sights here a while longer." His fellow crewmembers raised their own bottles and smiled broadly like drunkards on a holiday. Meanwhile, men such as Alfred, who had, without so much as a moment's notice, abandoned his own responsibilities in New York City to embark on this unscheduled trip, left behind a mystery, a gap in the narrative that his New York associates would struggle to explain. "Mr. Nobel has not been seen today," his colleague Deveau would tell potential investors and tradesmen as he penciled in each postponement on the calendar. Maybe the news would hold off the police with their ludicrous warrants or deter the endless stream of lawyers with their most recent challenges to his explosives patents. Deveau might have felt compelled to check Alfred's hotel room and, finding it empty, notified the authorities or checked local hospitals. Yes, the often over-looked Alfred Nobel would now be looked for, searched for, hunted down.

Or not.

Perhaps his business partners were celebrating his dis-appearance, relieved to think that he had returned to Ham-burg at last. If Ericsson chanced by the office, he'd shrug off any alarm. "Nobel does this from time to time," he'd tell them. "He was my apprentice years ago, and even then, he'd vanish for days on end. Never did find out where to or why. And frankly, gentlemen, we shouldn't give a good goddam where the devil's run off to."

The *Favorite*'s paddle wheels jerked into motion. No doubt the stokers and rakers in the boiler room were hard at work again after a too brief a respite, toiling in heat nearly twice the temperature of the open air, heat that had led some of the male passengers to slip off topcoats and loosen collars. Many of the women, meanwhile, suffered in silence under parasols. A few lifted gloved hands to wave farewell to the crewmen of the stranded ship.

Not wanting to witness any of their lewd replies, Alfred ducked below decks, out of the sunshine. He reasoned that a nap might restore his good mood before the *Favorite*'s arrival in Houghton. Instead, the quick shift from bright light to darkness triggered a migraine that forced him to bed and made sleep impossible. To distract himself, Alfred placed faces like masks on the pain: first and foremost Tal Shaffner, the would-be colonel to whom he had grudgingly granted the American rights to his blasting oil patent, though solely for military purposes. No need for Alfred to dirty his own conscience with such malevolence. For the more civil mining and railroad applications, the patent for blasting oil remained his and his alone. Warfare had the unfortunate habit of alienating, bankrupting, or killing off repeat customers. "Losers and dead men don't pay debts," his father had cautioned him during the Crimean War. Al-fred took the lesson to heart, even though his father's con-

tinued loyalty to the Russian military after their defeat on
the Malakhov had ruined his munitions business and left
the Nobel family bankrupt.

The shared patent with Shaffner now made him a de
facto partner in Alfred's new corporate entity, the United
States Blasting Oil Company. Partner? Alfred considered
Shaffner to be more like a leech, a huckster sucking away
at the lifeblood of others. Years ago, the man had tried to
steal credit for Samuel Morse's dreams of girdling the globe
in telegraph cable. That said, Shaffner's characteristic slip-
periness might grease the wheels of industry, which could,
in turn, free Alfred from the loathsome tasks of breaking
bread amongst the lawyers, kissing the ring fingers of poli-
ticians, and sipping whiskey with the warmongers.

At the risk of stoking his rancor—or perhaps, he realized,
to justify and thereby tame it—Alfred removed a large envelope from his traveling bag and shook several sheets of
paper out onto the bed. Here was Shaffner's proposed text
for their joint company's stock certificates, as hyperbolic and
bloviated as any press release the man had ever concocted
about himself: "For more than four centuries, the common
gunpowder, invented by the somewhat mysterious monk
Berthold the Black, was the only explosive chemical compound used for the purpose of hunting, warfare, and blasting. Now, a modern Berthold Schwarz has been born, who,
not as his grandsire in the dark cell and alchemical kitchen
of a convent, but in a sun-beamed laboratory of chemical
science, has invented a compound, the explosive power of
which surpasses the power of gunpowder quite as much as
the ball of a gun surpasses in swiftness and destructive power
the dart of an Indian…This man is Alfred Nobel."

Alfred might just as well have shoved the pages down
his throat to induce a fit of vomiting and thereby settle his
soured stomach.

From the same envelope he shook out several recent clip-
pings, mostly letters and editorials from various New York
newspapers. In one after the other, the writers depicted him

as an evil and unwelcome foreigner deserving the uniquely American humiliations of being stripped naked, tarred and feathered, and run out of town on a rail.

Such hospitality for the man whose explosives were allowing the country to extend its rail system from one coast to the other.

Alfred picked up one last clipping, an article he had torn from one of the old magazines that littered the lobby of his decrepit New York hotel. "The Horrors of Travel" the title read, and beneath that, a "graphic but by no means extravagant illustration" that showed skull-headed Death astride a hurtling locomotive, his gleaming scythe raised as the train's cowcatcher swept aside broken corpses along the tracks. Elsewhere in the drawing, a blazing schooner sank into the sea while a steamship exploded, hurling blackened bodies into smoke-filled skies. Alfred reread the text: "During the present year, Death appears to have set his mark upon the traveler, whether by railway or by the steamboat. It is a fact that more lives have been lost by accident this year than in some of the severest battles of the war. In most every case, the disaster has been needless; it has arisen in carelessness in conductors, employees, and directors, who should in every such case be responsible for the murders committed."

How true, Alfred thought. Let every man who has ever mishandled an otherwise benign and helpful scientific invention join him in the defendant's box before the judge and jury. If the inventor must hang, then let all mankind hang along with him and swing together in peaceful inferiority. If one feels compelled to blame the rope for the noose, then one should be prepared to feel the cinch of it around one's own neck.

There. Just like that, Alfred's headache was gone, burned off like fog by the blazing sun of his anger, and just in time. Through the porthole, the town of Houghton spread out along the hillside, aglow with promise in the golden light of late afternoon. In the surrounding cabins, passengers shifted their baggage about, eager to be among the first to disembark. Perhaps they, too, had studied such pictures and read such articles. Perhaps, throughout the entire voyage, they had been imagining the boiler beneath them exploding, the ship being ripped apart, their own fragile bodies being torn asunder. Maybe some had even glimpsed his face on deck or in the passageways and recognized Death itself, Alfred the Black, come to this reunited country not only to tear apart hillsides but to lay waste to all of humanity.

*

The following morning, ravens and jays quarreled in the terraced gardens beneath the south-facing balconies of Douglass House, billed as the region's finest hotel. Across the Keweenaw Waterway, the streets of Houghton's sister town Hancock scaled the opposite hillside. Steam-powered hoisthouses along the ridgeline screeched as engineers hauled up buckets of copper ore from the depths of the Quincy Mine, Alfred's destination for the day. A jaundiced sun glowed behind smoke rising up from the kiln-houses, where the heat-intensive process of calcination broke down the ore to release the trapped copper. Off to one side, a wide stretch of burnt slag, the cast-off waste rock, defaced the hillside like a frozen black cascade. To the uneducated eye, it must have looked like so much filthy chaos, but to Alfred, this represented the glorious marriage of chemistry and industry, mankind's inevitable triumph over nature. To think that the days and weeks spent holed up in his own laboratories could speed progress along even more dramatically—Well, that was a sermon best delivered later in the day to anyone lacking his own great conviction.

In the dining room downstairs, Alfred selected a table in a quiet corner away from direct sunlight. As was his habit and preference, he ate his breakfast while scanning the local newspaper, in this instance Houghton's *Mining Journal*. He was pleased to find some poetry among its pages, limericks mostly, along with a digest of news from around the country. One story in particular caught his attention, a follow-up to reports of a fire that had ravaged half of Portland, Maine. Investigators had linked the conflagration to a schoolboy who had been tossing firecrackers about during the city's Independence Day celebration. Would this child, too, now be stalked and sentenced to swing from the gallows, even though he had detonated only a pinch or two of explosive powder? What good was justice if it couldn't be meted out fairly and evenly?

Alfred shook and folded the paper as if in response to his own rhetorical question. Glancing at his pocket watch, he calculated the time remaining before the next ferry crossed over to Hancock. He hoped to arrive at the Quincy Mine between shifts, when the superintendent, Captain Stevens, would be most easily met and a brief demonstration of nitroglycerin arranged.

As it turned out, the captain was expecting Alfred. Word had reached him that "Professor Nobel" had been visiting iron mines in the Marquette area and had been spotted aboard the *Favorite* the day before. Alfred only half-believed the captain and wondered if someone back in New York, most likely Shaffner or Deveau, had telegraphed queries to both new and prospective buyers in an effort to locate their missing colleague. It wouldn't have surprised him to learn that his rival Otto Bürstenbinder, in yet another bold deceit, had been impersonating him across the countryside in an effort to drum up sales for his own explosives company.

Stevens invited Alfred to help himself to a cup of coffee in the miners' canteen while he supervised the shift change. "The coffee's probably not as strong as your blasting oil," Stevens said, tapping his stomach, "but it'll leave a good-enough hole if you drink too much."

An obliging guest for the sake of business, Alfred selected one of the less-stained tin mugs and stood on line with several miners. As the morning was warm and no women were present, the workers shambled about the canteen in various stages of undress, free for the moment of the heavy, protective clothing required deep underground. One miner, freshly surfaced from the previous shift, stood shirtless just outside the canteen and squinted in delight as the sun's rays warmed his pale shoulders. In stark contrast, Alfred felt conspicuous in his tailored suit coat, his relative cleanliness, his eagerness about the day ahead.

A man broke into the line behind Alfred and leaned over his shoulder. "*God morgon,*" he said in smooth and effortless Swedish. Alfred turned to wish him good morning as well, mindful to conceal his sudden quiver of homesickness.

The man introduced himself as Nils Forsberg, formerly of Falun, where he had worked in Sweden's largest *kopparg-ruva,* or copper mine. His hair, cut uniformly short in typical miners' style, showed flecks of gray, as did his well-trimmed mustache. The expression on his round face hinted at a life filled with more sadness than satisfaction, but his squared shoulders boasted of strong perseverance.

"The great scientist Carl Linnaeus once visited the *Stora Kopparberg* in Falun," Alfred said. "He compared it to hell on earth, as did the poet and philosopher Swedenborg."

"I can't recall meeting either man there," Forsberg replied, "but we'd have had that in common. We use gunpowder in the mines here, but you of all people know that. In Falun, we'd light huge bonfires deep in the mines, let them burn all night. They'd go out, the rocks would cool and crack, then down we'd go the next morning to break them apart, all the tunnels still hot as ovens. We had a saying: 'A man gains in smoke what he loses in sweat.' Some days it felt like I could cough up kibbles of charcoal. Here, it stays cool down below. Much more comfortable for an old man like me, easier to breathe, though some of the younger ones still find cause to complain."

Alfred let the man talk without interruption. The sound of his native tongue bolstered his spirits more than any cup of coffee ever could.

Forsberg had arrived at the Portage with a quartet of miners recruited from Cornwall, England. He had met the men in steerage during their transatlantic crossing, and they quickly became drinking and card-playing buddies. Forsberg's knowledge of English was poor enough to begin with; being drunk didn't help him any. And so, when the Cornish men told him about the bounty of mining jobs out west, he thought they were heading for gold country in California. It wasn't until he has stepped off the steamship and sobered up in Houghton that he realized the error, along with the fact that he had no money left to correct it. "I haven't had a drink since," Forsberg said, "much as any man in my place would surely love to drown his sorrows."

The Quincy mine employed mostly immigrants from England, Ireland, France, and Germany. This left Forsberg, like Alfred, an outsider of sorts. He said that recruiters had begun placing "help wanted" notices in Scandinavian newspapers and passing out handbills to Swedes arriving in New York and Boston. Alfred recalled seeing several such posters while waiting at the customs office, which led him to wonder if this fleeting observation, stored somewhere deep in his mind, had served as the catalyst for his impromptu trip to Michigan.

At the sound of the shift-change whistle, the miners swigged the last of their coffees, grabbed up their gear, and headed outside. "Time to go down," Forsberg said. He picked up his lunch pail and gestured with it toward Alfred's traveling bag. "I see you brought your own."

"Lunch?" Alfred laughed. "No. Work, I'm afraid."

Forsberg raised his eyebrows, anticipating an explanation, but Alfred said no more. Behind them, a pair of young boys dashed about the canteen and gathered up the miners' tin cups in metal buckets.

"Well then," Forsberg said. "It's been a pleasure and an honor to meet a fellow countryman, and a famous one at that."

"I'm not sure I agree with fame, or that fame agrees with me," Alfred replied, "but the good feelings are mutual."

Alfred followed Forsberg outside, where his fellow miners lined up outside a windowless structure that resembled a large latrine. What happened next held all the novelty

of a magic act. Though the building could fit only two or
three men standing, a dozen or more disappeared inside. No
stranger to mines, Alfred didn't fall for the trick. The enclosure prevented the shaft inside from flooding and kept its
ladder clean and dry for safe and easy passage. A short distance away, dozens of men waited outside another structure
that protected the skip, the large iron cart that could drop six
or so at a time down hundreds of feet of nearly vertical track,
their quick descent controlled by a thick steel cable tethered
to one of the hoist engines.

Toward the back of the canteen, Captain Stevens emerged
from what Alfred guessed to be a private dining room. He
came up and slapped a broad hand on Alfred's shoulder as if
they could tally their friendship in years, not minutes. "We'll
let the day shift get settled in down below," Stevens said. "In the
meantime, let me give you a tour of the works above ground."

For the next hour or so, the captain guided Alfred into
and through a variety of buildings named after whatever
one could find inside: rock-house, hoist-house, boiler-house,
shaft-house. With his box-shaped head and broad shoulders,
Stevens fit the image Alfred had conjured of Paul Bunyan, the
gigantic hero of American folklore. He also proved to be a
talkative man, proud to the point of hyperbole when discussing the mine's plans for development: its recent decision to
replace horses with steam-powered hoists, its plans to install
mechanical ladders in several main shafts, and the owners'
hopes for expanding copper extraction along the shores of
nearby Torch Lake. Additional rail lines and trestles would
connect all of the mines to a central processing facility to
save time and money in the long run. In this context, Alfred thought, nitroglycerin purchased from the United States
Blasting Oil Company seemed a logical if not inevitable decision. When he said as much, Stevens looked down at Alfred's traveling bag with a childlike hint of curiosity. "I don't
suppose you've traveled all this way just to show me facts and
figures," he said.

"Then you've guessed what's inside."

"I had my suspicions. You see, I do my research, too, Mr. Nobel. I even took the liberty of sending a man down into the mine this morning to drill a blast hole—following your published specifications, of course."

"So this grand tour was a ruse."

Stevens seemed taken aback by Alfred's outspokenness. "I hope you don't consider it a waste of your time," he said. "I thought it wise to demonstrate our commitment to advancements first, to establish our interest in your product."

"Yes, yes," Alfred replied. "All well and good, I suppose, but unnecessary. Let's go down and have a look at the drill hole and see if we can't use it for a small demonstration."

The captain led Alfred into a changing hut and looked him up and down to determine approximate sizes before handing him his new outfit for the day: ill-fitting, hob-nailed cowhide boots; a coarse white sack coat and matching duck pants; too-big black kid gloves; a plain white linen cap; and a dirt-crusted, malformed hardhat fashioned out of felt soaked in resin. Alfred surrendered his own clothes into the captain's safekeeping and regarded himself in a dust-streaked, full-length mirror. Such a small creature masquerading in grown men's clothes, a pitiful homunculus.

"Here's your dip," the captain said. He affixed a candle to the front of Alfred's hat with a wad of red clay. He looped the wick of a second candle, "just in case," around the top-most button of Alfred's jacket. Stevens fashioned a strap of sorts from a cast-off pair of suspenders to secure Alfred's bag against his back. "Wouldn't want that to tumble down into the mine ahead of us now, would we?"

"If it did fall, the bag itself would be the only casualty, I assure you," Alfred said. "The blasting oil is perfectly safe. I've brought only a small amount with me, hardly enough for concern. Even so, as you will see, a small amount is just as powerful as five times its weight in gunpowder, which you no doubt have stored in abundance down below. And never an accident with that, I'm sure." Alfred couldn't hold back

his sarcasm. He considered it a professional courtesy not to
mention that, on his way to the mine that morning, he had
seen several men with missing limbs and burnt faces wandering jobless and probably drunk about both Houghton and
Hancock.

"Just in case," Stevens said, still eyeing Alfred's traveling
bag with concern, "might I suggest we go down by ladder
rather than the skip?"

"Of course. You'll find me to be a firm believer in precau-
tions, even those proven to be unnecessary."

In truth, Alfred strongly preferred the skip to climbing, if
only to lessen the amount of physical labor and time spent
underground. The skip would have also provided a jolt of
energy far greater than the canteen's weak coffee—another
example of the captain's overstated claims. Alfred was well
aware that skip accidents didn't always involve snapped ca-
bles and runaway carts, however. According to the hotel's
desk clerk, a trammer had been nearly decapitated just days
earlier while engaging in some horseplay in the cart. "Shaved
half his face right off," the clerk said, pressing one hand up
against the side of his head for emphasis. An unnecessary
gesture, Alfred thought at the time, and yet, here on the
threshold of the mine itself, where blood and sweat would
be indistinguishable from the dampness along the dark shaft
walls, effective.

Captain Stevens closed the door to the shaft-house, struck
a match, and lit the candle on Alfred's helmet. Alfred returned the favor. "I'll let you determine the pace," the captain
said by way of invitation.

Alfred lowered himself as if into a lake or a pool, simultaneously startled and relieved by the sudden drop in
temperature. He imagined the cold winds of Niflheim, the
frozen Norse underworld, rising and swirling around his
feet, stinging his toes despite his oversized boots. To keep
any inkling of panic at bay, Alfred counted the iron rungs as
he descended: over the next few minutes, eighty bars that his
gloved hands struggled to grasp.

Their initial descent accomplished, the two men paused on a small wooden platform. Adits, horizontal tunnels that led to adjacent shafts, branched off to each side. From every direction, the echoes of miners' striking pickaxes, chisels, and hammers created an off-kilter counterpoint.

"Farther down?" Alfred asked.

Stevens nodded as if unwilling to disturb the darkness with speech.

Alfred shuffled over to another square hole just a few steps away from the bottom of the first ladder. Worried that he was proceeding too slowly, he quickened his pace on descending and lost count of the rungs, a small enough lapse in focus, yet one that rankled him all the same.

Down to the next platform, then down again, to where the air grew thick with gunpowder smoke and a smell that might easily be mistaken for brimstone. Alfred prepared himself for sudden blasts. The first rumble, however, originated from far above, a quick-moving thunderclap that turned out to be the skip barreling down the adjacent wood-beamed tramway. The cart had been emptied of ore up above and sent back down with a ghostly trio of miners, their wide-open eyes reflecting the flicker of Alfred and Stevens's candles as they sped by and below.

Soon Alfred lost track not only of rungs but of levels. He paused to take out his pocket watch in an attempt to calculate their downward pace; by his estimation, they were now nearly five hundred feet below the surface, maybe approaching one of the lower levels of Dante's Inferno— perhaps the ninth and final circle, Treachery. If that were true—and it seemed as likely a destination as any for a man such as him—the ladder might end abruptly and drop him into Caina, the frozen lake in which traitors to kin were stripped naked and imprisoned in ice, their ever-upturned faces white as hoar-frosted glass.

Perhaps sensing his guest's hesitation, the captain motioned for Alfred to stop at the next platform. From there they proceeded horizontally along the adit, with Alfred taking care not to stumble over the rails laid down for the trammers' carts, one of which had been left near the opening of a winze, one of the shorter perpendicular shafts that connected two levels. Shaft, adit, winze: Alfred prided himself on having learned the miners' terminology and hoped to add his three patented synonyms—glonoin oil, blasting oil, nitroglycerin—to their lexicon.

Captain Stevens leaned against the cart and waited in silence, occasionally glancing at his own watch. At last, the winze-hole began to glow and a miner emerged, followed closely by four others. The men helped one another up into the adit, each only slightly surprised to find Alfred and Stevens already waiting. The last man up was Forsberg, leading Alfred to wonder if the other four were his Cornish friends.

"We brung him along in case we needed to translate," the first man explained to Stevens. "I heard them speaking Swedish over coffee this morning."

"A wise decision," Stevens replied.

"We drilled down here a ways, away from the winze and number four," the man said, his voice receding into the darkness along with his candlelight. Alfred followed the sounds of their footsteps and the rustling fabric of their trouser legs, occasionally glimpsing a backwards-turned face or the faint gleam of metallic ore along the tunnel walls. As they moved, he explained to the men his reasons for coming to the mine and for traveling with explosive substances in clear violation of the law, "a point upon which," he stressed, "I must demand your complete cooperation and discretion so that no one else hears of our little demonstration here today."

A few grunts came from up ahead, sounds that, in Alfred's opinion, signified neither agreement nor refusal. "Gentlemen," he said, stopping for the moment. "If you cannot agree to this, then there's no reason for us to proceed any farther."

"Of course they agree," Stevens said. "I wouldn't have asked them along if they couldn't be trusted."

"Good enough, then," Alfred replied.

They followed the twisting adit until Alfred could no longer determine direction. What felt like north could just as easily be south; noon may as well have been midnight; summer, winter. Only up and down remained distinct. As if to amplify the sense of disorientation, the walls of the adit narrowed and receded at irregular intervals; at times the men could walk two abreast comfortably while at others they filed through gaps only as wide as the ties between the rails. In these tighter quarters, exposed nuggets of metal in the rock walls glinted and reflected Alfred's candlelight more frequently, proof that they had rediscovered the rich Pewabic copper lode after wayward sections of worthless trap rock.

"Here's the spot," the man up front shouted. "Right down here, along the vein."

Just a few steps away from where the tram rails stopped, the walls of the tunnel closed in. Previous blasts had carved out niches and hollows, but the finishing work of chisels and pickaxes had yet to form a recognizable arch. Likewise, no beams or bracing supported the surrounding rock, increasing the risk of collapse.

The men stood against the rough sidewall to let Alfred pass and inspect the drill hole. Textbook perfect, as he had hoped. "This will do fine," he said with an exaggerated nod. He fumbled with gloved hands at the clasp of his traveling bag. Worried that his actions might be perceived as comical or, worse, inexperienced, he removed the gloves, took out a vial of nitroglycerin, and held it up in front of his candle so that the men could admire its honeylike glow.

Two of the miners stepped back, no doubt frightened to see an explosive held so close to an open flame.

"No need to worry," Alfred said in a calming voice. "Nothing to fear. Heat alone is an insufficient catalyst for any explosive reaction."

He opened the vial, half expecting that the men might retreat even farther. Instead, Forsberg leaned closer as if curious about the blasting oil's scent. The others followed his lead. One of the men, the captain perhaps, brushed against Alfred's shoulder and caused a drop of oil to spill onto the back of his hand. He dabbed at it immediately with the glove but to little avail. The contact had been made, liquid to skin, and as a result, a minute or so into his explanation of the properties of nitroglycerin and its numerous benefits over gunpowder, a pulsing headache intensified from dull to disorienting as if someone, somehow, had constructed a looping tramway inside his skull and sent not one but several ramshackle skips careening along its track.

Before his fingers became too unsteady, Alfred poured a small amount of the blasting oil into the drill hole. He recapped the bottle and set it on a nearby rock, hopeful that the miners hadn't noticed his now-trembling hands.

Alfred crouched down. "A moment, please," he said, as if the gesture were part of the demonstration, perhaps a silent prayer for safety and successful outcomes, perhaps his own personal plea to whatever gods or goddesses commanded human anatomy that the migraine wouldn't escalate into nausea or, worse yet, diarrhea—an unwelcome occurrence in any location, let alone deep in the darkest bowels of the earth itself. By way of prevention, then, he lay down on his back, struggling with all his mental fortitude to ignore the rough and jagged rocks beneath his shoulders, the rail pressing into the small of his back, the dust and rock smut settling on his face. "Just a touch of dizziness," he said. "The cool air…a bit of claustrophobia… I imagine many visitors to the mines are likewise overcome by the unfamiliar environs. Nothing to worry about. I'm sure it will pass in no time at all."

Forsberg leaned over and blew out Alfred's candle, which had begun to drip hot wax along the side of the helmet and perhaps threatened to set the whole thing on fire.

Alfred shut his eyes to search for a moment of peace in the darkness. At first the silence seemed absolute, but soon enough he could hear the expectant breaths of the men around him, and beyond that, the echoing inhales and exhales of all the men down in the mines, their stalwart lungs sucking in smoke, dust, and oxygen and expelling noxious carbon dioxide as if they were all mere constituent parts of the underworld's respiratory system. As the pain in his head ebbed and flowed, Alfred imagined some guardian spirit lifting his head to place a pillow underneath. Ebb and flow, ebb and flow…let the stabbing pain fade to waves, deep to shallow, the rhythm of tumult relaxing to lullaby.

At last he felt sure that the tide had fully receded and that he might stand without cause for concern. How many minutes had passed? One? Ten? No matter; the men seemed patient enough, maybe thankful for the added respite from manual labor. "A minor drawback, for which I apologize," Alfred said. "Travel, I'm afraid, doesn't always agree with me." He brushed himself off as if the clinging dust was the physical residue of the headache itself. As he did, Forsberg bent down to retrieve his folded-up coat.

"You had us worried there for a moment," Stevens said. "It's a long way up to fetch the doctor. Just as far to get him down."

"There's no need. None," Alfred said. "I'm fine, as good as ever." He reached into his traveling bag, startled to find a vial missing—but no, there it was on the rock, exactly where he had set it down. His fingers touched upon a smaller bottle of medication for headaches, some useless quackery foisted upon him by a back-alley doctor in New York. No; better to tough out this onset in front of the men rather than amplify concerns with a swig of some unlabeled elixir. Instead, Alfred withdrew a corklike object and turned his attention to the drill hole. "And now we insert the blasting cap, another of my inventions." Once he had placed the cap and set the fuse to an appropriate length, he struck a match and held it out to the captain. "Would you do me the honors?" he asked.

Stevens lowered the match toward the end of the fuse. Before he could light it, Alfred tapped him on the shoulder and pointed to his helmet. "I meant my candle, so I can find my

way out," he said. The men laughed, relieved at the touch of
humor, however slight. "I worry that you faster men might
leave me behind in the dark."

Stevens obliged and relit the dip.

Alfred struck a second match and handed it to the captain
as well. "Now you may proceed with the main attraction."

Stevens lit the fuse, and the men dashed back the way
they had come, stepping high so as not to trip over the tram
rails. When Alfred assured them that they had retreated to
a safe enough distance, they huddled together and turned
back toward the terminus. "Any moment now," Alfred said,
focused on the countdown in his head. He took in a deep
breath and, before he could exhale, the end of the tunnel
blossomed with light. A shock wave pummeled past, blowing out all the men's candles at once. Though such demonstrations had become mundane, Alfred's heart still raced at
the thrill of the climactic blast.

Forsberg was the first to react; Alfred could recognize a
Swedish accent even in the man's laughter. The others joined
in, the surge in adrenaline prompting both amazement and
relief. Alfred knew the explosion had surpassed their experiences with gunpowder; he had used enough nitroglycerin
to ensure it. As all their eyes readjusted to the darkness, the
men struck matches and relit each other's candles.

Alfred gestured for the men to go have a look. They
needn't wait for the smoke to clear, as very little hung in the
air. Even the dust seemed to settle out more quickly than
after a gunpowder blast.

In the dim candlelight, Alfred could see that the men were
impressed by what they found at the blast site. Eyes open
wide and jaws gone slack, they stretched out ungloved fingers
to touch and test the blasted rock face. The wall hadn't simply
cleaved and tumbled down, as it would have with gunpowder; it had shattered into dozens of fist-sized pieces, with
specks of reddish-orange copper clearly visible amidst the
surrounding green and gray rock.

"Several things worth noting," Alfred said as if addressing a classroom. "First and foremost: a welcome lack of heat and smoke. Second: the size of the resulting rock pieces. You'll notice it requires less breaking down and is therefore much easier to carry and load in the skip. Quicker transit, higher productivity. Third: no blackening as you'd have with gunpowder." He pointed to a dull yellow sheen on the wall near where the hole had been drilled. "The oil leaves no residue, leaving the copper vein clearly visible for subsequent blasting."

"Shall we drill another hole, then?" asked one of the Cornishmen.

"No, no," Captain Stevens replied. "I think we've seen enough for one day. And I'm sure Mr. Nobel doesn't want to use up his precious supply of blasting oil all in one place."

In actuality, Alfred had two more vials back in his hotel room, plenty for visits to several more mines. He would have welcomed an opportunity to use it all up before returning to New York or, if circumstances demanded, before traveling back to the coast across Canada. Even so, Stevens was both captain and Alfred's host at the Quincy mine. He shouldn't risk any disrespect by overstaying his welcome, especially after such a successful demonstration.

"I'll ring for the skip to take us back up," Stevens said, perhaps suggesting that the luxury of riding rather than climbing topside was, in itself, more than adequate reward for the demonstration.

On that account, Alfred would kindly have to disagree. He hadn't come this far north for an underground joyride. No; there was profit to be had here, and he wouldn't settle for less than his own hard-won share.

*

Back in his private dining room, Captain Stevens served up a lunch of reheated stew, and though the chunks of meat floating among the root vegetables were rather flavorless and unidentifiable, Alfred finished off the bowl and followed the captain's lead in sopping up the remaining broth with a wedge of otherwise dried-out bread. As they ate, Stevens inquired about Alfred's experiences and observations at other mines, both in the US and abroad, in an obvious attempt to gain some competitive edge on the market. "In all instances," Alfred answered, "their advantage was nitroglycerin." He wouldn't elaborate on any engineering improvements he had seen nor would he share, on returning to Europe, news of any improvements that Stevens had discussed earlier in the day. "My business is chemistry," he said, somewhat exasperated. "Not mining, not railroad construction, not artillery manufacturing. I am happy to leave the final judgment in those areas to experts such as yourself, each to his own endeavor." It was only a half-truth, but in Alfred's experience, successful flattery often depended on the suspension, however temporary, of one's own superiority.

Later that afternoon, as the two men finished reviewing numbers in the main office, the tops of miners' heads bobbed past the windows during the shift change, some returning to their homes in company-built neighborhoods, others headed into town for drinks or down to the lake for a rinse and a swim. According to the captain, some men would go without washing for days and instead wait for one of the region's strong summer storms to blow in. "They'll stand out there in the rain like fools," he said, "and I'm thinking maybe they're praying for God to send down a thunderbolt and strike them dead on the spot."

"Mining's not an easy life," Alfred said.

"No one ever promised them it would be," the captain replied without pity.

When the time came for goodbyes, the sun still blazed above sparse stands of trees to the west. Outside the superintendent's office, Forsberg ran up to meet Alfred. Freshly washed and dressed in simple Sunday church clothes, he seemed hesitant, almost ashamed, as if what he were about to say might ruin whatever small friendship had developed between them. After a few minutes of empty chitchat in Swedish about the lingering heat and the convincing power of the day's demonstration, Alfred grew impatient. "Come, man," he said in English. "There's obviously something you mean to tell me. Don't make me dig for it."

"Well, sir, I know it's short notice, and without a doubt you're a very busy man, but if you can spare some time, there are some other folks over in Swedetown who I'm sure would be honored to meet you. I've even managed a buckboard here to take us over." He motioned toward the waiting vehicle, a far cruder carriage than any Alfred had ridden since leaving Europe. The single horse in front looked pale and exhausted, perhaps having been spared death and sold off to some miners after the company installed steam-powered hoists.

"Swedetown?" Alfred asked.

"Oh, sure," Forsberg said. "Just like Frenchtown for the French and Limerick for the Irish. Swedetown's not as nice maybe, at least not yet, but once more of us come over, it will be a grand place to live."

Something in Forsberg's humble aspirations reminded Alfred of the many promises his mother had made in Stockholm while his father chased after contracts in Russia. Though she struggled to feed him and his brothers on a grocer's wages, she often described how wondrous their lives would be when the entire family moved to St. Petersburg, with draft-free bedrooms for each of them and a deep pantry fully stocked year-round. She would have enjoyed a trip to Swedetown, he imagined, and by the end of the visit, she'd have made dozens of new lifelong friends. Alfred certainly didn't hope for as much, and yet he felt he owed his mother the effort, if only to describe the neighborhood and its residents to her on his next trip back to Stockholm.

The buckboard crawled along the dirt road, veering right and left as if trying to avoid every stone, stick, and pothole. Several other miners jumped into the back, thankful for a free ride home, but two younger men leapt off when they realized they'd get home sooner on foot. Alfred held tight to his traveling bag, fearful that the miners might mistake him for a wealthy investor and wonder how much money he'd brought along with him. Only Forsberg knew the actual contents, and, judging from how he'd stiffen after every bump in the road, he seemed to be working hard to keep from thinking about it.

As they approached the new neighborhood, Alfred made mental notes to include in a letter home to his mother: *Rocky roads, rocky yards. Drafty log houses set atop posts, two-story wooden death traps. Lacking in modern amenities, but clean and well-kept enough. A prevalent fishy odor outside, despite being a mile or so from the lake.*

Forsberg shared his home with Patrik and Ilga Larsson, a younger couple that had been among the first to respond to the mining company's Scandinavian recruitment efforts. Alfred instantly understood why a handbill distributor on the docks might have singled out Patrik Larsson: Blond and blue-eyed, his muscular build made him a fine candidate for breaking and hauling rock, and his animated facial expressions spoke to an underlying curiosity not common in most manual laborers. When Forsberg introduced him, for example, Larsson scanned Alfred up and down as if examining some unclassified specimen, his raised left eyebrow suggesting attempts to match his observations to the proper Linnaean taxonomy. So, at least, it seemed to Alfred.

Alfred had hoped that any gathering might be small and that those assembled might converse in Swedish with an agreeable mix of intimacy and informality. As it turned out, Forsberg had boasted rather prematurely to his fellow workers that Mr. Alfred Nobel, the famous Swedish inventor, would be a guest in his home that evening. In anticipation, neighbors had brought over a variety of chairs from their own houses and an outside grill had been heaped with freshly caught walleye. Two of Forsberg's Cornish friends soon knocked at the door, followed by another Swedish couple, an older Welsh gentleman, and a trio of Irish brothers. Alfred rose and shook hands with each new arrival, flattered when guests referred to him as Doctor Nobel or Professor Nobel, of which he was neither. Many brought a flask or bottle of some traditional liquor from their native land, but Alfred limited himself to a simple tea that Ilga Larsson had brewed at his request. There was no need to risk any sickness or drunken behavior in the company of these people, he thought, much as they insisted he join them in one toast after another: *To England! To Wales! To the Emerald Isle! Till Sverige, mitt hjärta, mitt hem!*

Alfred raised his cup for each but took a sip for only the last.

Luckily, the workmen were hungry, and so dinner followed without much fuss or delay. In addition to the grilled fish, Ilga had roasted some corn and boiled some summer squash, the latter picked that afternoon from a small garden she and another woman tended between houses. Though she expressed slight embarrassment for the simple offerings, Alfred felt grateful for the overall blandness and lightness of the meal. The afternoon discussions with Captain Stevens, accompanied by the questionable stew and yet more canteen coffee, had left him quite conscious of his stomach's rising acidity.

As Ilga passed by with a water pitcher, Alfred reached up to get her attention. He wished to thank her for the meal, but she sidestepped his touch before disappearing into the kitchen.

Forsberg must have noticed the confused look on Alfred's face and, sensing an opportunity to engage him in private, invited him to step outside in front of the house and away from potential eavesdroppers. "Mr. Nobel," he said, "I know you're a very smart and important man. You've little time for the likes of me, and I'm honored more than I can say that we've been able to share even this small meal together. That said, I was wondering... You see, whenever I can, I send money back home to Sweden to help my wife and my little boy, Soren. He's eight years old, nearly nine by now. Only I don't know if the money reaches them, and my wife makes no mention of it in her letters. She can't read or write, and maybe she doesn't want to mention the money when her brother stops by to help with the letters. Maybe it makes her sad to think how much more they need before they can join me here in America. And so, I was wondering..."

Forsberg removed a small folded envelope from his front pocket and held it out between them. Alfred could see that it wasn't an actual envelope; Forsberg had merely fashioned a crude mail pouch from an old safety poster.

"Could you use your connections to deliver this to my family when you return home? It's all I've got, and as I know you to be a decent and honorable man, I don't fear you'd steal it, not that you'd be tempted to keep such a small sum for yourself anyway. But please, if you could, get it to my Alva and Soren? The address is there, on the envelope." Forsberg tapped the front, where he had written his wife's name and a barely legible address in blunt pencil. There was little doubt in Alfred's mind that any previous packet in such condition would have been deemed undeliverable by the postal service and tossed into the dead letter bin.

"I shall give it my best effort," Alfred said. He carefully refolded the envelope and tucked it in his breast pocket. "And I'd be happy to include a short note of my own telling them what a pleasure it was to have met you."

Despite a thin layer of grime on Forsberg's cheeks, Alfred could see the man blush. "It's much appreciated," Forsberg said. "And one day I hope I will have the opportunity to do right by you as well."

"Just tell Captain Stevens that you're in favor of using my blasting oil," Alfred said. He meant it half-jokingly but instantly regretted the mention of business so soon after Forsberg had bared his soul. "Truly, there's no recompense needed, not between one Swede and another. Not between friends." The last word was wholly for Forsberg's benefit, and yet Alfred felt rather glad to have said it.

The miner reached out to shake Alfred's hand but then, just as quickly, drew him in for a heartfelt embrace.

The two men returned inside. In their absence, the conversation had grown louder and taken a darker, more caustic turn. Alfred hung back just outside the room as one of the Irishmen finished speaking. "...in the papers all the time, death after death from the stuff."

"You Irish are just worried it'll mean less work for you and your blasters, and less money because of it," the Welshman countered.

"I'll say this," Ilga said as she gathered empty plates from the men. "I wouldn't want my husband going near it. It killed that man's brother and my cousin's son besides, and he comes around here saying it's safe as houses. Let me tell you; back in Stockholm, none of us will be forgetting the Nobel Blast any time soon, nor the devil that caused it."

Alfred didn't need to see Ilga to know that she was gesturing toward the front door, calling everyone's attention to him without realizing that he stood there listening. He wondered which of the accident's victims had been her cousin's son: his brother Emil's classmate and colleague, Carl Hertzman? The handyman, Johan Nyman, coughing up blood and struggling to breathe with a steel rod wrenching his jaw open? Or the young boy, Herman Nord, his once-cherubic face caved in and blistered beyond recognition from the explosion? Images of each appeared before him, vivid as though two years were two minutes earlier. He clenched his fists at his sides to stave off the urge to vomit.

Ilga broke the silence. "I don't regret what I've said," she stated calmly. "And now, there. It's done and behind us and there's no way to call it back, so all of you men can just get on with it." She hustled into the kitchen with the plates and dropped them with a clatter into an empty metal basin. A moment later, the back door thwacked shut behind her.

"Maybe it's best if I take my leave," Alfred said.

Several men, Forsberg among them, looked away, perhaps

apology or consolation.

Alfred went to retrieve his traveling bag, which he had tucked it safely beneath his chair at the start of the meal. Now it was gone. He looked under nearby chairs as inconspicuously as possible. Had someone inadvertently kicked the bag beneath another chair? Had he been seated somewhere else at the start of the evening? Were all of the guests accounted for, or had someone snatched the bag up and run off with it?

"I seem to have misplaced my traveling case," he said at last in a calculated blend of confession and accusation.

"My wife took it out back," Patrik Larsson said. "She thought it might be safer there. That we might be safer." There was no mistaking the coolness in his voice.

Alfred excused himself and sidled through the dining area, through the empty kitchen, and out the back door. Ilga sat on the short wooden stoop, bent forward like a child mapping the passage of ants along the ground. "Your husband mentioned that you had taken my bag out back," Alfred said from behind, his voice soft so as not to startle or upset her further.

Ilga lifted one hand in the direction of the latrine a hundred feet or so away. "It's over there."

For a moment Alfred worried that she might have tossed the bag down the shithole in anger, but as his eyes adjusted to the dim evening light, he could make out its shape near the door. "There's something I wish to place inside," he offered by way of explanation—an excuse, really. He took out Forsberg's envelope and held it up as proof, but Ilga continued to stare at the ground, disinterested.

Alfred stepped around her and made his way toward the outhouse, careful to avoid an errant squash vine that had forked across the path. He bent over the bag and tucked Forsberg's money inside, next to the bottle of lavender oil. Behind him, the door to the house slammed once more as Ilga returned inside.

If the thought of cholera hadn't terrified him so much, Alfred might have made quick use of the latrine before leaving. Instead, he stepped as quietly as possible around the outside of the house. Glancing in through the windows, he saw Ilga seated and crying in the center of the dining room, her husband crouched beside her. Alfred searched for Forsberg's face among the other men, but he was gone, vanished inside his own home.

Alfred started back toward the mine. His feet ached, his ankles rubbed raw by the ill-fitting mining boots. From the road along the ridgeline, he could look across the Keweenaw Waterway to where the hillside above Houghton caught the old-blood glow of the fading sunset. Below, the water spread out stilled and indigo in the deepening shadow of the Quincy ridge. Gaslights on the ferry glowed as it skimmed the lake toward Hancock. If Alfred hurried, he could be on board for the return trip and arrive back at the hotel without further delay. Otherwise, he'd have an hour or more to pass among the off-shift miners crowded inside Hancock's pubs and saloons.

Just outside the center of town, he could hear the rowdier drunks and their raucous mix of quarrels and songs. On opposite sides of the town's central street, small groups had stumbled outside of their respective drinking establishments. The still-warm air did little to sober them up. Some shouted half-hearted insults across the street at one another, British accents on the left, hints of Irish brogue on the right, fists brandished as they spoiled for some made-up excuse to fight.

Luckily, both groups ignored Alfred as he scuttled past, just another mousy bloke from some city back east, nobody of any interest or consequence to real men like them.

*

Back in the welcome privacy of his hotel room, Alfred used a pocketknife to slit open Forsberg's envelope. He shook the contents out onto a small table near the washbasin. In dirt-

stained bills and coins, the Swede had gathered less than five
dollars to send back home: $4.83 to be exact. Such a paltry
sum would hardly cover travel to the nearest port, much less
secure overseas passage for a woman and child.

With that in mind, Alfred left the bills on the table as a
gratuity for the hotel housekeeper. He rinsed and dried the
coins with his handkerchief before dropping them into his
pants pocket. From a hidden pouch sewn into his waistcoat
lining, he withdrew his wallet and lifted a leather flap toward the back. There he had concealed a substantial sum of
Swedish *kronor,* likely more money than Forsberg or any of
his superiors made in a year, enough for any man, a fugitive
from the law perhaps, to begin life anew in a foreign country.

Alfred tucked the bills inside the makeshift envelope and
placed it back in his traveling bag. It might not be enough to
bring the entire Forsberg family together again, at least not yet.
Even so, Alfred knew, it was a start, and a good one at that.

Footing Slow: A Walk with Keats

ELI PAYNE MANDEL

We read fine things but never feel them to the full
until we have gone the same steps as the Author.
—John Keats, letter to John Reynolds, May 3, 1818

PROLOGUE

"I purpose...to make a sort of Prologue to the Life I intend
to pursue....I will clamber through the Clouds and exist."
—Keats, letter to Benjamin Haydon, April 8, 1818

I t might have been a dream. I cannot convince myself of some of the most basic facts. Constant movement north. Deepest sleep. Two watery poached eggs for breakfast, Tesco sandwiches for lunch and dinner. State of mind like a stalagmite—subterranean, agglutinative, crystalline. Repeat and repeat. I wake up and doubt it. But of course it happened. My iPhone has the photos to prove it. I can still tie those muddy boots with closed eyes. Cross the nylon cords, pull tight, snag behind the metal hooks. Repeat and repeat. Tie at the top. Then the backpack, with the top compartment (passport, Swiss army knife) that throws its weight and unsettles the whole apparatus. Widen the stance to keep balanced. Lean forward, bend knees just a bit. Align the shoulder straps, cinch the waist strap, the chest strap, realign the shoulder straps. Walk. Repeat and repeat. If I doubt the totality, I trust in the rote details. And I trust in the poet who haunted me and the paths I took. He was a ghost, and he was a solid presence. He was my quicksilver companion.

I

There is a joy in footing slow across a silent plain...
Yet be the Anchor e'er so fast, room is there for a prayer
That man may never loose his Mind on Mountains bleak and bare;
That he may stray league after League some great Berthplace to find
And keep his vision clear from speck, his inward sight unblind—
—Keats, untitled poem enclosed in a letter to Benjamin
  Bailey, July 18, 1818

In the summer of 1818, John Keats took a very long walk. He had spent the winter and spring holed up in Devonshire, caring for his tubercular brother, Tom. As a physician trained at one of London's most prestigious hospitals, John must have known that his younger brother's condition was almost certainly terminal. Meanwhile, his other younger brother, George, was planning to

set sail for the American West with his newly wedded wife.
The Keats brothers were orphans. Their one sister, fifteen-year-old Fanny, was difficult for them to visit, thanks to a rather sinister guardian who strictly limited access. Their inheritance was similarly sequestered. In short, John Keats was separated or about to be separated from his entire, close-knit family. If that wasn't bad enough, he had just published a book of poems, *Endymion*, to virtually no notice, let alone acclaim. So he went for a walk. He was four months shy of twenty-three. Three years later he would be dead of tuberculosis.

The idea for the walk belonged less to Keats than to his friend Charles Brown. Brown was also trying to make a name for himself as a writer, but without a medical degree to fall back on. At the time, he lived a ten-minute stroll from Keats in the London village of Hampstead. Brown was a hardy traveler on foot. Together Brown and Keats planned to walk through the Lake District, into and around southwestern Scotland, across the Irish sea into Ireland, back to Scotland and north to Glasgow, through the Inner Hebrides, and then straight through the Highlands to John o' Groats—a village widely, though incorrectly, believed to be the northernmost settlement in mainland Britain. The pair at least contemplated a return route as well, cutting east across Scotland through Perthshire to Edinburgh and then south into northeastern England. If they had taken this route, they would have walked well over a thousand miles.

With money scarce and his brother's situation fragile, Keats hesitated to start such a long journey. But at heart he seems to have wanted it deeply. To his friend the painter Benjamin Haydon he wrote: "I purpose...to make a sort of Prologue to the Life I intend to pursue...I will clamber through the Clouds and exist. I will get such an accumulation of stupendous recollections that as I walk through the suburbs of London I may not see them." On the surface, the letter is exuberant, but I take its buoyant tone with a grain of salt. After all, Keats is suggesting that, as things were, he felt as if he hardly existed. He would prefer, it seems, to paint over his London life with memories of something else. I hear the same desperate wanderlust in a letter from around the same time to his medical-school friend John Reynolds, where Keats hints at this bleaker motive, this need to purge his spirit in the hope of its renewal: "I have many reasons for going wonder-ways: to make my winter chair free from spleen—to enlarge my vision—to escape disquisitions on Poetry and…Criticism….if Brown holds his mind, over the Hills we go."

So over the hills they went. The two Londoners had allotted themselves four months. The actual walk lasted just forty-four days, as compounding misfortunes shaved days and then weeks off the trip. Keats and Brown abandoned the Irish leg of their journey almost immediately after arriving. Everything in Ireland cost three times as much as in Scotland, and the Irish mile turned out to be one and a half times as long as its Anglo-Scottish equivalent. Then, on July 22, Keats contracted a fever and a miserable sore throat while walking in the bogs of the Isle of Mull. The farther north they went, the worse Keats felt. Upon arrival in Inverness on August 6, Brown summoned a local physician who deemed Keats "too thin and fevered to proceed on the journey." Brown continued on to John o' Groats, but Keats boarded a packet boat bound for London two days later. According to Brown, Keats had walked 642 miles.

On Monday, June 24, 2013, I laced up my Vasque Breeze GTX 2.0 Size 11 medium hiking boots and strapped on my Osprey Atmos 65 backpack. Then I walked out the front door of the Royal Kings Arms Hotel in Lancaster and into the cold sunlight. Keats and Brown had been here, or hereabouts, on Thursday, June 25, 1818. The night before, after bidding George farewell at the port of Liverpool, they had taken a coach to Lancaster, where, on account of a heated local election, they were unable to find a hotel. After a night in a pri-

vate house, they set out walking. One-hundred ninety-five
years later (minus one day, to take advantage of a Sunday
hotel-room discount), so did I.

My plan was to hound Keats—day for day and, when possible, step for step—until he arrived, sick and tired, at Inverness six weeks later. Perhaps I should have been concerned
that only two people (to my knowledge) had published accounts of retracing this walk. One of them did it in a car. The
other was an American professor named Nelson S. Bushnell,
who wrote a remarkably thick tome called *A Walk After John
Keats*. Bushnell, who seems to have possessed superhuman
vigor, cheerily tacked on side trips when he felt that Keats
and Brown's average pace of 14.59 miles per day wasn't sufficient. (On July 11, 1931, Bushnell walked twenty-eight miles,
rowed an additional five miles in the Ross of Mull, and then,
to top it off, did another six miles on foot.) As a rule I do not
exercise. I am six feet tall and roughly 140 pounds, which
means my fully loaded Atmos 65 weighed nearly 20 percent
as much as I do. I have no outdoors skills, little sense of direction, and a predilection toward crippling anxiety, to say
nothing of an overpowering fear of food poisoning. I am
not, in brief, an ideal candidate for a physically strenuous,
psychologically demanding, and gastronomically perilous
expedition to the hinterlands.

Then again, I was not trying to keep up with Bushnell. I
was trying to keep up with Keats. Keats was only five feet tall.
Six hundred forty-two miles at five feet works out to about
1.6 million steps. At my height, I could get away with 300,000
fewer, give or take. Also in my favor was that Keats was two
years older than I was at the time of his walk, which in my
mind made him positively middle-aged. I had another major
edge on him. Whereas Keats would have tested positive on
the Mendel-Mantoux tuberculin sensitivity test, had it been
invented, I did not have a latent case of tuberculosis (at least,
not the last time I had a checkup). Best of all, I did not have
to walk for days at a time eating only oatcakes. ("I was once

in despair about them," Brown wrote.) I mulled it over. On balance, despite my shortcomings, I decided I should easily be able to keep pace with my ghostly companion.

I had a vague sense that 642 miles was still a very long way and that it would take a toll on my body. I did not consider adequately what it would do to my mind. I have obsessive-compulsive disorder. OCD is not, as is often thought, about dusting bookshelves twice a day or sequencing socks according to their Pantone Color Matching System identification numbers. OCD is not really about having to wash your hands a lot either—though that can be one outward manifestation of the disorder, and at times, I have washed my hands an awful, awful lot. Hand-washing is only the tip of the neurotic iceberg. More often than not, OCD is about guilt and doubt taken to pathological extremes.

In the psychiatric literature, I have read repeatedly about people with OCD who develop a very specific, crippling anxiety about driving their cars. The afflicted driver, who is perfectly competent behind the wheel and possesses a clean driving record, hits a small bump or pothole and becomes convinced that she has just run somebody over. She hasn't run a red light or driven on the sidewalk, and there isn't a person to be seen in the rearview mirror. There is no reason to believe she has struck so much as an ant. But despite the preponderance of evidence to the contrary, she can't shake the sense that she's just mowed someone down. Shattered a spine into half a dozen pieces. Crushed a head. She calls the police to check for local accidents, considers turning herself in. Nothing helps. In her mind she is constantly on trial in a felony manslaughter case that never adjourns, in which Not Guilty is an impossible verdict.

I do not know how to drive. I do not even know how to ride a bike. There is no viable avenue open to me for running someone over. But the underlying obsessive themes—the crushing sense of guilt, the highly particular instruments of self-inflicted psychic torture—are as familiar to me as my own palm lines. At the age of seven, when I started perusing crime stories in the Metro section of *The New York Times*, I became convinced that I was a psychopath. Throughout my childhood I feared that I exhibited telltale signs of becoming a serial killer and that at any moment I might snap. I refused to handle kitchen knives (what if I decided to disembowel my family?), skirted subway platforms (what if I decided to shove off innocent bystanders?), and sometimes sat on my hands (what if I decided to kill people in a way I hadn't yet conceived?). In adolescence, sexual predation replaced cold-blooded murder. At age thirteen I feared I might be a pedophile because—lo and behold—I was turned on by other thirteen-year-olds. And so on. The massively prolifer-ating labyrinth overtook and repurposed every corridor of thought that it could find.

Today, with talk therapy and medication, I don't punish myself like this much—at least not most—of the time. But I still can find myself gripped by the anxiety that I might somehow hurt someone very badly. The (im)possibility that I am sexually deviant still sometimes grabs me by the throat, although I do not feel attracted to children and am happy with my own girlfriend. OCD comes and goes in cycles. A surge in obsessive-compulsive anxiety sometimes takes a while to reach the shores of consciousness. When I set out walking that morning in Lancaster, I did not appreciate fully the size of the cresting wave. And I certainly did not consider how forty days in the wilderness would stretch its amplitude to tsunami proportions. "Then glut thy sorrow on a morning rose / Or on the rainbow of the salt sand-wave," Keats wrote. He had his famous melancholy. I had my OCD.

In retrospect, I am glad none of that struck me before I boarded a flight to Heathrow. I might not have walked at all. And I did want to walk, deeply. I have no idea when I first learned of Keats' trip. I don't even remember where I would have discovered it. But I do remember reading "Ode on a Grecian Urn" (written less than a year after Keats' walk) for the first time, one rainy afternoon in the spring of my senior year of high school. Like one of its well-wrought lovers, "for ever panting, for ever young," I still feel arrested in that moment, frozen in the thrill of the urn. A poem could do that? And what was that exactly? The poem was a bottomless basin filled with perfectly clear water. Keats became a guide that afternoon. I looked to him for initiation into the mysteries of his art.

Later, I also looked for initiation in the bowels of Sterling Memorial Library. I looked for it in Cleanth Brooks and Paul de Man. The urn was accruing a veneer of dust worthy of some of the books I was pulling off the shelves. The depthless water was getting cloudy. I feared that academe had reintroduced Keats' poetry to the ravages of time, that I would watch his poems wither and die on the vine. I was beginning to fear that I would never write anything halfway decent if I continued to stay in the British Literature section of the stacks until closing time. Like Keats, I wanted to escape. I wanted out, temporarily, from all the "disquisitions on Poetry and Criticism." I wanted to be in the world and to be more of the world. At the same time, paradoxically, I thought that being out and about in the world would get me deeper into the poetry and the criticism that I care so much about. I hoped that by following Keats I would worm my way inside his brain and plant myself there, like a virus inside a cell. I would be there as he walked, watch as the rich harvest of poems that he would write after his return took nascent shape. I would see the poet's tree bloom to ripeness, and just maybe I could harvest the fruit.

SEDATION (FOR NERVOUS PATIENTS)
—*sign in a dentist's window, Kendal*

The first thing I saw on exiting the Royal Kings Arms in Lancaster was a large sign for the Brooklyn Brewery. I grew up in Brooklyn, and here was its eponymous beer advertised in the window of a Lancashire pub. It was comforting, if a little confusing, to see a trace of home at the outset of this walk. I took my first steps and left Brooklyn behind.

I've never met a sign, even a classic American stop sign, that I didn't think had a deeper meaning. Thanks to an overdose of comp lit semiotics courses and an OCD-addled mind, I find it hard to believe that, as in the Keats ode that had first seized me, beauty is truth, truth beauty, and that was all I needed to know on earth. I walked through the Lancaster morning toward the banks of the River Lune. A few hundred yards from the river, I passed a schoolgirl, maybe age fifteen, waiting on the sidewalk. Could I possibly feel some sort of inappropriate sexual attraction to her? (I didn't.) What if my glance at her was itself a form of violation, and I had caused irreparable trauma? (I hadn't done that either.) That is the legalistic language favored by my OCD in its cross-examinations. I walked on. My thoughts stayed stuck.

My goal for the day was Kendal, a town approximately twenty miles north of Lancaster and just outside the boundaries of the Lake District National Park. A bicycle path along the old Lancaster Canal would take me most of the way there. Technically, I was already straying from Keats' path. He had walked to Endmoor instead, a tiny hamlet five miles southeast of Kendal. Despite increasingly desultory hours of Googling (where was the monomania of OCD when I needed it?), I had found nowhere to spend the night in Endmoor. I could not, as Keats had in Lancaster and elsewhere, simply knock on a stranger's door and expect to be taken in. (Keats spent the nights of his walk in a mixture of inns and private homes. I spent the nights of mine in a mixture of inns and B&Bs that hadn't had a guest for the past thirty years.) It frustrated me to be this unfaithful to my companion from the start, but the 195-year interval between us made this kind of deviation unavoidable. All else equal—which it hardly was—Keats and I were walking in different Englands.

I crossed the Lune Aqueduct, and from then on my path ran parallel to and only a few inches above the Lancaster Canal. The once-important commercial waterway was now the demesne of pleasure barges. Backyards opened directly onto the water. I could see directly into kitchens, dining rooms, bedrooms. I felt I was trespassing. Did I like peering into people's homes? Was I a peeping Tom, a voyeur? Was I sure? OCD cherishes the empty frame in which it can inscribe its lurid anxieties. It tells you not to think of a pink elephant—because nothing could be worse than a pink elephant—and then, lo and behold, you think of a pink elephant. I made myself imagine seeing naked people of all shapes, sizes, sexes, and ages inside the houses along the canal, just to make sure I didn't feel anything out of the ordinary. What was the ordinary, anyway? I cursed those suburban windows, each and every one.

Keats' letter to his brother Tom, in which he mentions the start of their walk, says nothing about the route he and Brown took to Endmoor or what they did along the way. The letter does add—rather smugly, I began to feel as the day wore on—that "we have not been incommoded by our knapsacks; they serve us capitally, and we shall go on very well." My knapsack felt as if I had loaded it with bricks that were now engaged in some kind of violent migratory shuffle. Each time I got the load equitably apportioned between my shoulders and torso, the pack's contents would rearrange themselves. Meanwhile, the tongue of my left boot began to dig into my ankle at a tender angle. My sister, an experienced backpacker, had warned me repeatedly to break in my boots before I walked any farther than the Korean grocer around the corner. Naturally, I never had. Now I had to stop every ten minutes or so to retie the laces in what, I hoped, would be a less painful configuration. By early afternoon, I could barely think anymore. My feet needed all my energy.

In the village of Carnforth, I found myself briefly, although hopelessly, lost. The canal had begun to run parallel to the M6, the main motorway in the North, and the bike path had diverged shortly thereafter. One wrong turn, or more accurately one right turn neglected, and I had wound up standing on a corner in English suburbia. There were little redbrick walls everywhere. Laundry was out to dry. The plumber was paying somebody a visit. I had trudged less than ten miles, and it was still at least that far to Kendal. I found my way again. Then I found a bus stop. And so I cheated on Keats for the second time in my first day of walking. I didn't really care. He was just a ghost, wasn't he? He didn't get hungry or tired or anxious. I wanted to know where I'd sleep, what I'd eat for dinner, and whether I could walk the next day without my cranium wedged in the obsessive-compulsive vise.

Kendal, when the bus dropped me off there, did not live up to its nickname of "Auld Grey Town." It was actually a pretty town, set amid rolling and uncommonly green hills. The transition from suburb to countryside had happened sometime on the bus. The air was distinctly cleaner here, and the River Kent, which ran through part of the town, rushed along more happily than the River Lune. When I walked up and down the main street, I noticed several storefronts devoted to the fitting and adjustment of dentures. (The bus, I remembered, had had an exceptionally senescent ridership.) One of these geriatric dentists prominently advertised, in blue block letters, SEDATION (FOR NERVOUS PATIENTS). I could get used to Kendal, I thought.

But the next morning, after a night in a surgically clean bed-and-breakfast—less clean after I inhaled an entire loaf of bread and hunk of cheese while sitting in bed—I was on the move again. I planned to walk to Ambleside by way of Windermere, both iconic Lake District villages. Ambleside was Keats' destination from Endmoor. After an interminable twenty-four hours, our routes were finally aligned. I suspect, although I cannot know for sure, that the route I took to Ambleside was very close to Keats', since I found myself walking much of the day beside the roaring A591. Highway planners tend to favor direct routes, as, I wager, did the old carriage roads and walking paths they supplanted. If Keats stuck to the obvious trails, he and I were likely walking in step with each other.

My ghostly companion could get himself very excited while ambulating. His prose erupts into poetry when he describes seeing the famous Cumbrian lake of Windermere—Winander in his spelling—for the first time:

> [T]here is no such thing as time and space, which by the way came forcibly upon me on seeing for the first hour the Lake and Mountains of Winander—I cannot describe them—they surpass my expectation—shores and islands green to the marge—mountains all round up to the clouds....[T]he two views we have had of [Windermere] are of the most noble tenderness—they can never fade away—they make one forget the divisions of life...and refine one's sensual vision into a sort of north star which can never cease to be open-lidded and steadfast over the wonders of the great Power.

That night, reading in the comfort of my B&B bed, I was thrilled to find traces of the "north star" and much of the rest of this material in one of Keats' celebrated sonnets, "Bright Star," in which the star watches "The morning-waters at their priestlike task / Of pure ablution round earth's human shores." Keats had turned a moment from his walk into enduring art. But when I first glimpsed Lake Windermere, I was shambling along a narrow path beside the A591. The lake was indeed stunning, and I could see why it had seared itself in Keats' memory so. For me, 195 years minus a day later, the air was filled with automobile exhaust. I jumped every time a Renault or Rover hurtled past at arm's length from me. I couldn't work myself up to a suitably Keatsian level of new-age nirvana. Besides, I could hear something large about to overtake me. I stubbornly refused to look behind, but the something soon walked right past me. It was a blind man and his dog. "All right?" the blind man asked me. I gave him a good long stare. The dog glanced back at me. Then they were gone.

I thought I saw an out. Shortly after the blind man passed beyond my sight, on the crest of another hill, I spotted a promising escape into Keats' world—a wooden arrow directing me away from the A591, over a series of stone walls, through green and golden fields, toward Windermere. I heaved myself over a stile, broke into an amble—the most exuberant form of propulsion I could manage—and found myself immobilized in a swathe of nettles. Every direction I turned, they detonated, like little anti-personnel mines. When I rolled up my hiking pants, my legs were speckled with welts. I made for the asphalt.

The next evening, I finally stole a glimpse of the "noble tenderness" and "sensual vision" that Keats had found more or less where I had found nettles. I was staying at a guesthouse on a comically steep street at the north end of the town of Ambleside. Toward evening, I bought my dinner—the customary supermarket sandwich (I carefully checked the expiration date, because taste wasn't a reliable indicator), a yogurt, and a package of Romney's Kendal Mint Cakes (the brown-sugar variety)—circled back to the bed-and-breakfast, and kept walking. The road turned even steeper, reaching, according to the signage, a staggering 20 percent grade. THE STRUGGLE, added a black-and-white sign helpfully. I struggled up toward the top of what I now know to be Kirkstone Pass. The land below me was threaded with gold. Lake Windermere blushed like a ripe damson. In the distance an equally lustrous line of mountains stitched the field and water to the glowing sky. Tucked into a seam in the land, Ambleside looked tiny, with its toy steeple needling the hills behind it. I sat at a bend in the Pass where a farm road turned off and I ate my soggy sandwich (cheddar, lettuce, tomatoes, and pickle relish). The great Power! The landscape was suffused with it. Then there was a rumbling. The Power dissipated into the bushes, while a white Mercedes and two black BMWs, packed with Arab tourists, careened by, whizzing down the struggle toward Ambleside.

| | |

When I come into a large town, you know there is no putting ones Knapsack into ones fob; so the people stare—We have been taken for Spectacle venders, Razor sellers, Jewellers, travelling linnen drapers, Spies, Excisemen, & many things else, I have no idea of—
—Keats, letter to Mrs. James Wylie, August 6, 1818

The morning after Kirkstone Pass, the weather soured. No more golden light, only gray rain. I ate my watery poached eggs with what I liked to imagine was grim stoicism, and prepared to suit up.

My walking companion traveled lightly—that much is known. But the exact contents of his enviably commodious knapsack are a subject of debate. Sources disagree, for instance, on whether Keats' pack carried multiple changes of clothes or only an extra shirt. A likely list can be derived from a ditty he writes for his sister while on the walk: "…a shirt / With some towels— / A slight cap / For night cap— / A hair brush / Comb ditto / New Stockings / For old ones / Would split O!" Beyond any doubt Keats also carried paper,

pens, ink, and a miniature three-volume set of the *Divine*
Comedy. (Brown had a pocket-size edition of Milton.) One
biographer adds a good supply of snuff to the list. Keats also
appears to have had a walking stick, a fur hat, and an oilskin
cape. His boots are of provenance and nature unknown—although it is certain that, unlike my Vasque Breeze 2.0s, they
would have been custom-made by a cobbler, and that the left
and right would have been identical.

It hadn't struck me that I actually needed to equip myself
for six weeks of walking. I had imagined traipsing over hill
and dale in jeans and an old collared shirt. Three members of
my family had to force extensive lists of supplies on me before I took them seriously. At that point, perhaps, I took them
too seriously. The Atmos 65—the number refers to its size in
liters—contained: four pairs of hiking pants (one of which
unzipped below the knees to become shorts); four wicking
shirts, two long- and two short-sleeved; seven pairs of wool
socks and sock liners; underwear; the aforementioned jeans
and old shirt; a wool sweater; a fleece; rain pants, a rain hat,
and a raincoat (for me); a rain cover (for the Atmos); a regular hat and winter gloves; a pocket knife; a steel knife, fork,
and spoon; a collapsible bowl; two Nalgene water bottles;
iodine pills; a two-month supply of Prozac; toothbrush;
toothpaste; liquid soap; antidandruff shampoo; sunscreen;
insect repellant; and a razor (but no shaving cream); a plastic baggie of Band-Aids; sunglasses; a Yale baseball cap; my
passport; an iPhone charger and an iPad charger; an iPad,
containing complete editions of Keats' poetry and prose, as
well as several thousand pages of other reading material and
detailed maps of England and Scotland (Ordnance Survey,
1:25,000 scale); a notebook (though I forgot pens); a facsimile
edition of William Carlos Williams' *Spring and All*; and, in
case of desperation, a French novel titled *Suicide*. For easy
accessibility I dangled around my wrist a large plastic bag
with lunch, snack, and extra water. I was not, in brief, as
concisely packed as Keats.

Once I had enshrouded myself and everything I possessed

in Gore-Tex, I left Ambleside. Keats' route for the day would take me via Wordsworth's house to Keswick at the northern end of the Lake District. I slogged up hill after hill in a steady downpour, stopping to take a selfie in a roadside mirror. Dripping with water and swinging my muddy shopping bag, I looked like an extremely well-waterproofed bag lady. I paused at a large flat stone. This, it turned out, was a "coffin stone," one of a series of rocks on which pallbearers once had rested their loads when taking the local dead to the nearest church, in Grasmere. I, too, was carrying a dead man. His five-foot frame was surprisingly heavy. Perhaps he had rested on this very rock. I sat there too, and briefly unburdened myself of Keats while I checked the map app on my iPhone.

On this day of the walk, Keats called on Wordsworth, whose house was not very far from the coffin stone. But the father of English Romanticism wasn't home for Keats, much to the younger poet's disappointment. He wasn't home for me either—doubly so, because I had gone to the wrong place. Wordsworth had lived at two addresses in the Lake District, both between Ambleside and Keswick: Rydal Mount and Dove Cottage. They both had three-syllable names and sounded equally pastoral. I couldn't keep them straight. Keats had traipsed to Rydal Mount, where Wordsworth lived in 1818. I had gone to Dove Cottage. William had moved five years before Keats had come anywhere near the Lake District. I wasn't exactly doing the best job keeping track of my companion.

Too cheap to pay the £7.50 price of admission to Dove Cottage, and irritated by the swarm of Nikon-toting tourists (supposedly Rydal Mount is less of a tourist trap), I stole into the garden, which also had an entrance fee, and sulked next to the custodial shed. I was alone there, surrounded by lush English plants dripping with pearly English rainwater. There was nothing to tell me it wasn't 1818 (except that Wordsworth had once again taken up residence there). A concatenation of misses, in time and place, linked Wordsworth to Keats and Keats to me. The chain looped back on itself like the ouroboros, the world-serpent that swallows its own tail. It was a serpent of loss. I shut Wordsworth's gate softly behind me. When he stood here he would have seen open land. Now there was a roundabout, a spinning vehicular pinwheel.

I crossed the highway and entered quaint Grasmere. It did not lift my spirits. On the outskirts of the village there was a primary school. In late June in England, school was still in session, and the children were outside playing. They all had raincoats and were oblivious to the bad weather. But as I hurried past, I couldn't amuse myself with that detail. I was too anxious about...Well, did I find any of the little girls attractive? No...Was I sure? Yes...But I thought it was cute that all the kids were wearing raincoats! Yes, because it's amusing that for the British, raincoats are as compulsory as underwear! Well...did I want to see that little girl in her underwear? No! Was I sure? Yes, but maybe I was just in denial...And what if the split-second turn of my eyeballs toward them had been A) noticeable and B) traumatizing... I couldn't escape this obsessive script. I wandered the village. Bought an ice-cream cone. Decided, now that my OCD had put me through the wringer, that I'd wait for the bus to Keswick. On this day in 1818, Keats had visited "two waterfalls in the neighborhood" and went along "Grasmere through its beautiful Vale." He'd missed Wordsworth, but at least he'd walked through this village in high spirits. If he'd seen a village girl playing in her garden, he wouldn't have had to triple-check how she made him feel. He was probably immersed in conversation with Brown; I was immersed in an anxiety disorder with no bearing on reality. As I rode out of Grasmere in the bus, I tried, and mostly failed, to conjure Keats' joy and awe at the mountains enfolding me on every side.

The next morning was my twenty-first birthday. I was not sure how to spend a birthday with neither friends nor family, only a dead poet. So I climbed with him into the hills. It was raining buckets and in every direction, but it didn't matter. I had left my pack with the owner of my bed-and-breakfast, who insisted on calling me "Ellie." I felt weightless. No, I felt as if I had negative weight. There is no better surprise than walking without a pack once you have become accustomed to its leaden pull. In the hills, about two miles outside of town, stand the Castlerigg Standing Stones. A crude henge, assembled by Neolithic Britons to some unknown end, they looked like worn and filed teeth sown scattered in a field. The field in question, when I found it, was marked by an ice-cream truck. But there were no visitors except for me and the sheep who used the giant stones as shelter from the rain. Treading gingerly through the mud and dung, I scattered the sheep. I circled the megaliths. First around the outside of the henge, then around the inside. One by one I touched the jagged teeth. They felt warm and wet and mossy and alive. They were ancient. They had seen everything. They had seen Keats.

Keats called the Standing Stones a "Druid temple." He went to see them as a postprandial treat—"rather too near dinner time," in fact, for his comfort. I'm not quite sure what he thought of them. He writes of "gratification," just a single sentence, and then he moves on. Two years later he remembers them in *Hyperion*: "a dismal cirque / Of Druid stones, upon a forlorn moor." They clearly had not aged well in the poet's mind. Forget the ice-cream truck: for once I was finding something more beautiful than Keats had. I grew suspicious. Maybe I liked the henge only because it was my birthday. Maybe I was becoming sentimental in my old age. But I also felt a twinge of pride. It felt trangressively good to love something Keats didn't. I had not lost myself, either to Keats or to madness. I hurried back to Keswick. In the evening, I splurged at the supermarket and had Scottish smoked salmon from the on-sale aisle for dinner, straight out of the plastic packaging.

Late that night, after the sun had finally set, I turned the lights off and sat staring out at the rainy Keswick night. A single sodium light cut the darkness. Keats and I were alone. By the time he turned twenty-one, he had done hospital rounds, assisted during major surgeries (without anesthesia, needless

to say) and qualified as a medical doctor. He had turned his
back on medicine to write poetry. He had translated the entire *Aeneid* from Latin and published his first book of poems.
He had written "On First Looking into Chapman's Homer," a
sonnet that virtually every English major now has to read. He
had met Shelley and was about to meet Wordsworth. On top
of all that, he had found a flat to let in a hip district of London
(Hampstead—now one of the most posh neighborhoods on
earth). What had I done to show for myself? I once saw Harold Bloom give a lecture in which he declared, "Some poets
develop; others unfold." Keats was definitely an unfolder,
bursting fully formed from the Goddess' cranium. I could
only hope that I was on track to be a late and slow developer.
At least, I thought as I drifted off to sleep, I probably wouldn't
be dead within two years.

The next morning, I fled the Lake District on the bus. Despite the standing stones, I had begun to associate the place, in
its current rainy state of affairs, with my anxiety, and I wanted
to get away as fast as possible. I urgently wanted to cross over
into Scotland. I spent the day and night in Carlisle, an ancient
border city known for a thousand years as a bastion of the
English military. When I arrived, uniforms and camouflaged
vehicles were swarming the city center. A band was playing: it
was Armed Forces Day. I spent the afternoon in the cathedral,
roving alcoves dedicated to the war dead. Carlisle Cathedral
seemed built out of the names of dead soldiers. Keats had
written dismissively about the place, and in this case I could
forgive him the oversight: he couldn't have foreseen the Napoleonic Wars, the World Wars, and all the other bloodshed
that would glut itself on Carlisle's young men. I spent the night
listening to the gulls. They circled the city in crowds, wailing
and sobbing like the unburied dead.

From Carlisle, Keats went by coach across the border to
Dumfries. I took the train, a two-car contraption that announced its nationality in English and Scots Gaelic: ScotRail,
Rèile na h-Alba. Alba: Scotland. I was entering a new world.

From the train window the grass did seem greener. I felt more foreign, more alone, more happy. I was on the lam from everything and everybody except Keats.

My companion's presence firmly asserted itself the next morning. I was wandering Dumfries fully loaded and in full rain regalia, collecting provisions for my day's walk. A young man appeared in front of me. "You couldn't spare me any change, could you?" he asked. I couldn't. The man was visibly pained. "But I thought you were a nun," he said. "A nun?" I asked. I looked myself over, from my Atmos 65 to my olive-drab raincoat to my Vasque Breeze 2.0s. "Yes," he said. "A nun."

If Keats could be mistaken for a razor seller, a traveling linen draper, and a spy, I could be a nun. The poet was right: there was no putting one's knapsack in one's fob.

I V

I'll not run over the ground we have passed, that would be merely as bad as telling a dream, unless perhaps I do it in the manner of the Laputan printing press—that is I put down Mountains, Rivers Lakes, dells, Glens, Rocks, and Clouds, with beautiful enchanting, Gothic picturesque fine, delightful enchanting Grand, sublime, a few blisters, &c—and now you have our journey thus far...
—Keats, letter to John Reynolds, July 11, 1818

Suddenly I was walking with zeal and zest. I was even keeping pace with Keats. My first full day in Scotland, I tromped at least twenty miles. I did not resort to public transportation. No more Lake District tourists, no more motorway: I walked on country roads now, alongside stone walls linking dairy farm to dairy farm, over hills that radiated out on vistas of slowly undulating land. The rain had retreated: a lake of light filled the sky. A stiff wind blew away the reek of manure.

When I was overcome by hiccups (I had a terrible case from eating and walking at the same time), the cows scattered before me. I could make livestock stampede! The air was pure combustible oxygen, and I gulped it. I felt aflame.

My muscles were also burning with lactic acid, and my feet throbbed so much I was sure they were swelling like balloons and would soon burst the seams of my hiking boots. I stopped to rest at the corner of a lonely field. My "wicking" shirt had soaked through with sweat. The sweat turned icy when the wind rippled through, and I shivered and perspired in one grand gesture. It was a febrile amalgam I had experienced before only in illness. This was not illness. It was terrifying and exhilarating, just as the sublime should be.

In some ascetic practices the body is mortified in the hope that the spirit might leave it behind. Ecstasy, after all, means out of body. But I was in body. On foot, the pain and the pleasure were one and the same. My body and spirit hummed and trembled in a single mass. For once, I could sense that my legs and my mind were strung on the same cord. It was, I was discovering, hard to worry in this state.

In a tiny village, I passed a primary school. The children were out for recess. They waved and shouted at me, astounded at this stranger passing through, this creature who was, perhaps, part boy, part young man, part nun, and part Keats. The curious and excited children knocked the needle of OCD back into its well-worn grooves. The girls had bare legs beneath their school frocks...Why did I notice that? Could they have noticed that I noticed, and had their lives ruined forever? Virtually impossible. But did I notice in the first place because I felt turned on? No. Was I sure? Yes. But what if I was lying to myself? I really wasn't. But...This was a familiar convulsion, nothing like the spasms in my back and neck from hauling the Atmos 65. And yet it dissipated after a few thousand paces. I left it behind. The children too. I could not run my mind in circles. I had to press forward. My aching body did not care about imagined sexual deviancy. It cared about thirst, hunger, inflammation. I had never been so grateful for the steady presence of my own trembling flesh, all the way down to my bruised and swollen feet.

The modern American is likely to have trouble imagining an Age of the Foot. Walking has never been an integral part of our experience; our man of the road is Kerouac, not Keats. I met people in the UK who were puzzled by my pursuit of Keats, but few who were puzzled that I pursued him on foot. The walks of the British Isles—"ways," as they are called there—extend to a faint horizon of deepest antiquity. "In a somyr sesoun, whenne I south wente," begins *Piers Plowman*, and we know immediately that the narrator of the great Middle English poem is a walker, and we can guess that the ways he takes through the Malvern Hills are much older still than he. Even in this age of iPhone Ordnance Survey apps, the walking landscape of the Middle Ages survives in law and in fact as much as in literature. Seventy percent of Britain's land belongs to 1 percent of its people—a landed aristocracy for whom the commoners can thank the Anglo-Norman conquests of the eleventh century. The UK government owns only 13 percent of the remainder; in contrast, the US federal government owns 50 percent of Idaho and 85 percent of Nevada. But because so much of Britain's land has been private property for so long, walkers have equally entrenched rights to it: even peasants and serfs had to get around without getting their heads lopped off. In Scotland, any path that has been in use for at least twenty years and links two public places is a right of way: anybody can walk on it anytime, period. In the rest of England, legal restrictions are a little stricter, but nothing like the trespass laws of the United States. If Keats had gone to America with George and set out walking there, I could not have been on the road with him today. The ways and the rights to them simply do not exist.

That said, it would be tricky even for a Brit well-versed in rights of way to imagine the geography of Keats' walk.

To erase airplanes and automobiles from the lay of the land is one thing; to reconceive a world without trains—indeed, without rapid, comfortable travel of any kind—is another task altogether. The horse-drawn coaches of Keats's day managed—at most—about six miles an hour. The much cheaper stage wagons used by the poor maxed out at three miles an hour, which is about as fast as Keats and I could have walked if we hadn't been carrying gigantic knapsacks. Roads weren't smooth planes of asphalt either, and the shock absorber wasn't invented until 1804. Unless you had a horse—and could pay to stable and feed the thing—walking speed was about as fast as you could go.

But that didn't mean that actually footing it was socially acceptable. As a mode of transportation, the long-distance walk had distinctly lower-class, up-to-no-good connotations. It smelled of highway robbers, footpads, peddlers, and vagrants. And so, naturally, walking became something of a fad among the English intelligentsia of the 1790s. All the cool kids did it: Wordsworth, Coleridge, Hazlitt, De Quincey. De Quincey calculates Wordsworth's lifetime-walking-distance total to have been 175,000 to 180,000 miles, which is roughly sixty trips across the continental United States. Of course, walking this far was only fun if it wasn't necessary, and more fun still if you could afford to go somewhere beautiful: Keats, after all, reached Lancaster by carriage. But all the same, the English Romantics embraced the long pleasure walk as a rebellious, countercultural gesture. What the clenched fist came to represent in the twentieth century, the blistered foot might well have signified in the late eighteenth. By the time Keats tied his boots in June 1818, his peers had done a lot of walking, and even more writing about walking. As a Late Romantic, Keats was a second-generation slow-footer.

And so, my five-foot-tall companion in his oilskin cape was being characteristically contrarian. Our Romantic moments were out of step. For this reason, perhaps, my companion simply couldn't allow himself to walk in complete earnestness. In the letters he wrote to his friends and family during the summer of 1818, there is often an ironic detachment from the journey and at least a feigned irritation at the expectation that he will describe it. When Keats describes his walk through southwest Scotland as "Gothic picturesque fine, delightful enchanting Grand, sublime, a few blisters, &c," he is having a little fun at the expense of Wordsworth and friends. But when I walked through the same landscape and felt the presence of the sublime, I really felt it. One-hundred ninety-five years after the apex of English Romanticism, sublimity no longer comes canned, hot off the "Laputan printing press," à la *Gulliver's Travels,* that Keats imagines churning out Romantic filler. I could walk genuinely embodied in a newly rediscovered world of footing slow. My companion could not.

V

> *There was a naughty Boy*
> *And a naughty Boy was he*
> *He ran away to Scotland*
> *The people for to see—*
> *—John Keats, "song about myself" enclosed in a letter to*
> *Fanny Keats, July 2, 1818*

In the rainy town of Kirkcudbright, the day after my exuberant twenty-miler, I discovered I had lost my wallet. That morning, I had woken up groggy and sore and entirely flushed of endorphins. I had taken the bus to Kirkcudbright. I had gotten off, walked around the castle, bought soup in a café crammed with what appeared to be all the local school children, a coincidence that deepened my anxious fog. So I tried to relax by having a pint in the pub. I put my hand in my pocket. I had no money, no debit card, no ID. In fact, I had no wallet at all. "I think I lost my wallet on the bus," I said. The bartender looked the bumbling American over. "Ye'll ne'er git it back," she said. "Th' bus drivers aroond 'ere are awl either senile or droog addicts." Fortunately, mine was neither. At the end of his shift, he passed the billfold on to a woman at the bus company—who, later the same day, delivered it to the door of my B&B on her way home from work. So, I thought, this is what it's like to live in a tiny village. For days after I recovered the wallet, the bus driver would overtake me walking by the side of the road, look at me quizzically as he zipped by, and flash me a thumbs-up. Perhaps he thought it was I who was senile or addicted to droogs.

While I was fretting about being stranded in Kirkcudbright with naught a pence to my name, Keats was busy writing his sister a long letter. He tells Fanny about how tired he is after each day's walk: "when I am asleep you might sew my nose to my great toe and trundle me around the town like a Hoop without waking me." He also tells her, at length, about how hungry he is: "a Ham goes but a very little way and fowls are like Larks to me—A Batch of Bread I make no more ado with than a sheet of parliament..." And, with a prefatory apology ("My dear Fanny I am ashamed of writing you such stuff"), he encloses a song about himself. It is as winsome as the letter itself:

There was a naughty Boy
   And a naught Boy was he
He ran away to Scotland
   The people for to see—

The naughty boy "follows [his] nose to the north," where he finds that Scotland is pretty much like England: "There he found / That the ground / Was as hard / That a yard / Was as long," and so on. He's learned his lesson: "So he stood in / His shoes / And he wonderd / He wonderd / He stood in his / Shoes and he wonder'd." This is not exactly the Romantic Sublime. Poetry, wrote Shelley three years later, "purges from our inward sight the film of familiarity which obscures from us the wonder of our being." But Keats' song is about precisely the wonder, or perhaps the anti-wonder, of familiarity—the opposite of Shelley's claim. I sat on my B&B bed, turning my wallet over and over, and wondered at the wonder I had found in Scotland, and wondered whether Keats would have wondered at it too.

I had breakfast in Kirkcudbright with an elderly Swiss couple. They understood easily that I was hiking to Inverness, but I couldn't convey, in either English or very bad German, the reason why. "Keats," I said. Then I added in German, "A poet." "Ah ja, der Dichter," said the husband. My hopes rose: maybe they knew who Keats was after all! "Englisch oder Schottisch?" the man asked. "Englisch," I said, trying to enunciate—"romantischer, wie Goethe." They looked at me blankly. They didn't know who Keats was, after all. My dreadful German didn't help matters. Much to my relief, the frau changed the subject. "How much," she asked in English, "is Obama loved in America?"

I didn't have much better luck with the Scottish. A vote for Scotland's independence was on the horizon, and the Glaswegian Andy Murray was about to win the championship at Wimbledon. No one could understand why I was tracking an English poet across the lowlands of Scotland—which was home, no less, to Scotland's own Robert Burns. The eighteenth-century poet, author of "Auld Lang Syne," was a national obsession, but I hadn't paid homage to his birthplace, his deathplace, or any of the other numerous Burns-themed shrines/pubs that I'd passed on my route. This, in retrospect, was blockheaded. My lack of Burns-fever not only deprived me of a source of conversation with the locals but also proved patently untrue to Keats. At the time, I thought my companion's repeated allusions, during the walk, to Burns and his assiduous visits to all the Burns landmarks were simply sightseeing. Only later, stateside, did I realize how obsessed Keats was with the short-lived poet whom the Scottish call Robbie or "the Bard." Keats even compares Burns' home to Shakespeare's. Of the Bard (the Scottish one) Keats writes: "One song of Burns's is of more worth to you than all I could think for a whole year in his native country." For the two weeks we were in Burns territory, Keats was looking for inspiration, influence, and the blessings of a dead poet by retracing his steps. He was romancing Burns' ghost while I was romancing Keats'. I didn't even notice that my companion was up to exactly the same thing I was.

For this reason, perhaps, Keats snubbed me. I felt lonely. A day's walk took me out of Kirkcudbright and across the River Dee on the shoulder of the A755; then due north on an old military road to Twynholm, where I ate my supermarket container of sherry trifle in one of the tiny village's two cemeteries; and through a forest preserve that commemorated mysterious criminal activity from soon after Keats passed through ("At or near this point on the night of 17 February 1819 a series of Assaults and Robberies were committed.... Details of this gruesome tale are related in a leaflet available in 'The Murray Centre'"). By the time I emerged from the treeline into the oddly named village of Gatehouse of Fleet, my body wasn't tired (I was getting stronger), but my mind felt very sore indeed.

My OCD had reached full flood. It had become a gruesome tale worthy of a Murray Centre leaflet. In aggregate, I was spending at least three to four full hours a day doing nothing but weighing the evidence about whether or not I was a pedophile. If Moses himself had descended from Mount Sinai and informed me that I wasn't sexually attracted to children, I either wouldn't have believed him or would have found something else to worry about. In fact, in a sure-fire indication that I really had been sucked out to sea, other old *favorite* worries were starting to assert themselves... Would I strangle my family upon their arrival later in the

summer? Would I contract rabies from peeking into a dere-
lict church? Would I get food poisoning from one more noxious sandwich? In classic OCD fashion, each obsession felt
as inevitable and disastrous as the next, even if some were,
from a reasonable person's point of view, objectively much
worse calamities than others. I struggled to have a complete
thought, even about Keats, without being plunged beneath a
wave of anxiety. Each smidge of joy or an inkling of bliss—in
the shape of a Scots pine, a phrase of Keats', or the fantasy
of sleeping with that junior from my Freud seminar last se-
mester—was flattened by a massive breaker of obsessional
anxiety. I knew the exhausted panic of a drowning man. I
wasn't sure I could keep walking.

"You must go on, I can't go on, I'll go on," Beckett writes in
The Unnamable. I wandered aimlessly up and down the main
street, and examined the items for sale in the local store:

FAT BALLS 4 FOR £1.00

GIANT FAT BALLS £1.25 EACH

As I was trying without success to identify whether the fat
balls—which looked like a cross between durians and moldy
tennis balls—were animal, vegetable, or mineral, it suddenly
struck me as urgent that I have contact with human beings
who, unlike Keats, weren't dead. My garbled conversation
with the Swiss couple had been the most face-to-face interac-
tion I'd had since I started walking. I had no Charles Brown
to entertain me. Somebody needed to look me in the eyes
and register the words that came out of my mouth. In W. G.
Sebald's *The Rings of Saturn*, the narrator takes a walking trip
alone on the Suffolk coast and winds up in a mental asylum.
The choice was simple: talk to somebody other than Keats,
or go absolutely bonkers.

After a nap and a dinner of stale, prepackaged Indian
bread from the fat-ball shop, I went to the more promising
of the village's two inns, and sat for a long time drinking

whiskey in a corner. It seemed daunting after these long days of silence to sidle up to the bar and start talking to any of the dozen villagers with their pints. There was one in particular who caught my eye: a beautiful woman of about my age, in close conversation with an elderly man about the health of another elderly man in the village. She reminded me of a girl I once knew who was the daughter of a famous Russian poet. After countless hours—countless days—fretting over the possibility of an improbable world in which I was a pervert, I was in the same room as someone I was actually attracted to! (I was between girlfriends that summer, so I didn't even have to fret about infidelity.) Even my OCD had to concede the point. Keats—who was, after all, a very young man himself—hadn't yet met Fanny Brawne, the love of his short life, but some Scottish dancers did catch his attention. He writes to his brother Tom: "There was as fine a row of boys and girls as you ever saw; some beautiful faces, and one exquisite mouth." I heartily concurred—and, of course, positioned myself at the bar as far from the exquisite mouth in question as possible.

It was not an unsuccessful night: I drew enough attention from the local drinkers that I was eventually introduced to the pretty girl (and everybody else there), and she offered me a crisp. I, in turn, ducked out of the bar and hurried back to my B&B. But my dinner of bread must not have been enough to soak up the Scotch. She had mentioned she was coming to the States. I ran back to the bar, where she was still perched with the old man (he was the cook), and gave her my phone number scrawled on a page from my notebook. "Ah will be thare neist July," she said in what appeared to be all earnestness. "Ah will definitely ring ye." Keats, I'd like to think, was proud of me. Back in my rented room for the second time, I found an email from a close friend, concerned about my solitude and my OCD. Dreamless slumber swirled in: I felt I was being rocked to sleep.

After that, I went to pubs as often as my increasingly sore feet would let me. In the minuscule hamlet of Barrhill—so minuscule I had to stay a mile outside the village, on a working farm—I bought from the pub a Styrofoam carton of fish and chips and a coffee cup filled with the delicacy known as mushy peas. "The weather's nice today," I said to the bartender, making British small-talk as best I knew how. "And may it remain that way for the rest of the week, inshallah," he said. I did a double-take at his Arabic. As I wandered off to eat my mushy peas outside, he called to me in French. I had to come back.

On my return, the multilingual bartender told me he was "only an amateur" (pronounced in a lavishly Gallic accent). Mr. Amateur, in fact, was a retired British ambassador to Saudi Arabia. He was the last British official ever to sign a manumission certificate, in 1979, emancipating a rich but still technically enslaved man in a country (I don't recall which) that had once numbered among Britain's Arab protectorates.

Mr. Amateur had also eaten his wife's afterbirth: "I pulled the doctor aside and asked him, 'What have you done with my wife's placenta?' And the doctor said, 'We are going to give it to the Swedes to make face cream.' And I said, 'No, give it to me in one of those jars.' So he did, and I took it home and fried it up with some butter and bacon, and ate it. It tasted strongly of iron."

"Weel," observed Auld Tom, a truly ancient man who came and went from the bar, drank minute quantities of scotch, and spoke in an impenetrable brogue, "it's whit animals dae, sloch thair ain afterbirths. Ah wis born a farmer, sae ah wid ken, though ah quit farming 'n' became a bricklayer by trade."

The banter, in this pub in the middle of nowhere, was extraordinarily fast and sophisticated. Mr. Amateur: "It was a really fine hospital, I went there for my operation." A local: "Fur yer lobotomy?" Mr. Amateur bought me a pint and began talking to me about the fearsome Scottish fly known as the midge. "It's not midges," he said to me. "It's the midge. Mass noun." "A collective plural?" I asked. "I don't think the words 'collective plural' have ever been uttered before in Barrhill," he said.

By my second pint, I thought perhaps I had actually col-lapsed while walking and gone to heaven. Late that night, I walked back to my farm amid tornadoes of the midge. Mr. Amateur, on hearing my last name, had attempted to set me up with the only Jewish girl he knew in Scotland. He had also insisted I not leave the pub before he had bestowed on me the black bracelet of the SNP, Scotland's pro-secession political party. I had been a naughty boy and run away to Scotland, the people for to see. Keats complains at length about Scotland's dour, Presbyterian character, and he rarely describes a Scot except for caricature or parody. Unlike my companion, I rejoiced in the occasional local company and their brogues. Lying back in the farmhouse bathtub later that night, covered in midge bites, I could not have been happier.

ELI PAYNE MANDEL

V I

In diseases Medical Men guess, if they cannot ascertain a
disease they call it nervous.
—*John Keats'* Anatomical and Physiological Note Book

I walked on forest paths. Walked on dirt paths. Walked on bicycle paths. Walked on back roads with only the occasional tractor for company. Walked on the shoulder of major high-ways. Walked across major highways. Walked through cow fields, potato fields. Walked through dairy farms. Walked over the Ayrshire beaches, past Ailsa Craig, the mushroom-cloud-shape island that made Keats "a little alarmed." Walked over pebble and seaweed and sand and crumbling cement blocks. Walked in the rain, but mostly in the blazing heat of Scotland's second-hottest, second-sunniest summer in recorded history.

I took the bus. Ate innumerable cheddar and relish sand-wiches. Drank nearly as many pints of beer. Slept in one B&B whose owner frequently unlocked my door to check on me, as if I weren't old enough to take care of myself. Stayed in one hotel with a lamp in the shape of slabs of scallop roe. Walked. Took the bus. Walked again. By mid-July, I reached Scotland's Central Belt and its main city of Glasgow, where, according to Keats, "Brown look'd back and said its whole population had turned to wonder at us." I just had a quiet stroll through the old part of the city and a warm glass of Guinness.

Hereto Keats had been my only constant companion. He had dictated, or tried to dictate, my every move. Now—as any good walker should—I strayed, wandered, erred. I shook off Keats for the weekend and went to Edinburgh. When I picked up his trail again, I had new company. I was joined by my mother, her sister, and my sister. We made a formidable quartet, I realized once I had seen our four enormous backpacks sitting in a row. My mother and sister are intrepid travelers. My sister has climbed every mountain over 4,000 feet in the Adirondacks and been featured in the pages of *Adirondack Peeks [sic] Magazine*. My aunt is a marathon runner. Setting out from a Glasgow suburb in our eight-boot convoy, I thought of one of the more bizarre passages in Keats' letters of the summer, a long rumination that begins: "I am certain I have not a right feeling towards Women—and at this moment I am striving to be just to them but I cannot." I didn't care if my imaginary companion was balking at his real counterparts: Keats would have to get used to the women of my family, whether he liked it or not. After all, he had been an orphan since the age of fourteen, and he got to see precious little of Fanny Keats, who was exactly my sister's age. His one healthy brother was sailing to America as he walked, but my family had crossed the Atlantic in the other direction just to keep me company.

I like to think that, in the end, my Women charmed Keats—entertaining, intentionally and unintentionally, as they were. My mother and aunt immediately became mildly addicted to the apple and pear ciders on tap throughout Scotland. No particular brand could satisfy them, only some ineffable ideal: they sampled extensively and were therefore in perpetually good spirits. In addition to her hiking backpack, my mother also insisted on a massive suitcase, the contents of which were never fully identified, that she arranged to be portaged by a surly lorry driver between our nightly stopping points. Every morning, the portmanteau seemed to acquire more and more mass, until sealing it shut required my sister and me to sit on it. My sister turned up her nose at the cider and the suitcase alike. She reserved her energy for making the rest of us look clumsy and slow on the trail. No distance or difficult terrain seemed to faze her. She hardly broke a sweat. Her heart rate rose precipitously only once, as far as I could tell, and the cause was not a steep incline but a fellow hiker who had tied his dirty briefs to the outside of his hiking pack and refused to let us overtake him, no matter how close we got to his heels (and his underwear). It is impossible to satisfy a mother, an aunt, and a sister all at the same time. A comprehensive catalog of their criticisms is far too long to include here, though my smelliness was a *favorite* complaint. I was forever nudged and badgered. I couldn't believe how grateful I was.

After all, I had been walking for weeks with a dead man. One-hundred ninety-five years earlier, Keats had had bountiful amusement in the form of Charles Brown. At one point he wrote to his brother Tom, "Here's Brown going on so that I cannot bring to Mind how the last two days have vanished." As far as I can tell, Brown talked and talked and talked and talked. He complained about the food. He told Keats dirty stories incorporating the names of places they had been ("so touching her with one hand on the Valle Lucis while the other un-Derwent her Whitehaven," etc., etc.). He insisted on a nightly ritual of removing writing materials from his pack in a specific order, a habit that stirred in Keats a blend of amusement and exasperation, something familiar from how I felt about the family trifecta now accompanying me. I am uncertain whether Brown found Keats nearly as entertaining. I am inclined to guess not. Keats was famously moody and introspective. His letters from the trip evince long periods of brooding during which he was probably not paying the slightest heed to Brown's chatter. Between my OCD and my preoccupation with the ghost of this Late Romantic, I probably seemed as intermittently saturnine to my family as Keats had to Brown. In turn, I was relieved for the Brownian escapades of my mother, sister, and aunt. As is so often true of people of a certain temperament, Keats and I were perhaps best not left alone—either with ourselves, or with each other.

Northwest of Glasgow, suburbia yields quickly to the Highlands. A day's walk took us to the base of Loch Lomond, a pristine finger of water whose splendor prompted Keats to insert a sketch into a letter to his brother Tom. (Perhaps the poet was, for once, at a loss for words.) Here I had to part with Keats in order to be more faithful to him. The western bank of the Loch, where he had walked, has become a highway, but the eastern bank is untouched except for a long-distance trail known as the West Highland Way. It was this path that I took with my sister et al. Time, writes Ovid, is the devourer of all things—but time is also the great displacer. Our side of the Loch could have passed for Keats': "the Water was fine Blue silverd and the Mountains a dark purple the Sun aslant behind them." As we wended our way along the water, I liked to imagine Keats and Brown on the other shore. No cars, no trucks, just two tiny figures tramping North.

I had finally reached a part of Scotland where public transport did not go—nor would my sister possibly have allowed me to take a bus, had there been one to be found. The five of us (including Keats) were keeping a pace of fifteen to twenty miles a day. Walking can be an ambiguous term: but this was hiking, not strolling. There were rocks, roots, mud, and steep inclines of both the up and the down variety. Our daily treks were so long that we had to march at a fast clip to avoid running out of sunlight. Above the ankle, I felt supremely healthy. My OCD seemed baffled

by the combination of strenuous exercise and relentless
human contact. It flared at least once or twice a day, but
it was no longer a scorching, baleful sun. My feet were another story. I had assumed that bulbous blisters and stabbing pains were an inevitable consequence of this kind of
hyper-pedestrianism. Hadn't Keats boiled down his walk
to "a few blisters, &c.?" For a notorious hypochondriac, I
was uncharacteristically blithe about the possibility of, say,
contracting gangrene and having my toes amputated. But,
as I wiggled them one evening in the pure distillate of Loch
Lomond, an almost unheralded wisp of a feeling floated
by. Just for a second, a sensible, realistic worry had lit my
thoughts: was it really normal for feet to hurt this much?

On July 19, 1818, Keats mentions offhandedly to his brother
Tom that "Brown could not proce[e]d this morning on account of his feet." On the morning of July 20, 2013, I noticed
that, overnight, the fourth toe of my left foot had grown painful even by the summer's high standards. It was hot and red to
the touch. For the first time since I began walking, I applied
antibiotic cream and a Band-Aid. (Several experienced hiker
friends had warned me to bring moleskin, and one had even
tracked down the British name for the stuff—Compeed. I had
insisted on taking only Band-Aids.) Then we tramped out into
the Rannoch Moor. The Moor is a vast, remote peat bog spotted with hills and mountains that has played starring roles in
the history of cinema as the site of a vicious shootout that ends
the life of a key MI6 operative and the locus for a train-hijack-
ing by the undead. In the best of lights—and, with a noonday
summer sun and no cloud cover, the best of lights was what we
had—its stern and stark beauty made me feel, as if I'd known
it all along, that civilization was a mere trifle in the face of the
open, untouched land.

Stumbling along English military roads built during the
Highland insurrections of the 1700s, I grimaced with every
thud of my left boot on the packed dirt. My foot was staging
a Highland insurrection all its own. I had to scrunch my toes
within the boot to keep the pain at a tolerable level. But even if

blisters had bothered Brown, it had taken far more serious illness to fell Keats, hadn't it? He had kept walking, and walking, and walking, and never once in his letters had he complained seriously of podiatric problems. I was determined (more than usual—which, granted, is not saying much when it comes to my tolerance for physical ailments) not to complain in front of my family. We stopped for lunch beneath the only appreciable cluster of trees in any direction. They shaded each end of a short bridge over a gully. We took photos, ate stale granola bars (our analogue to Keats' abhorred oatcakes), and gulped water. My sister passed me a cherry tomato.

Usually, once I stopped moving my legs, my walking pains vanished blissfully until I started up again. This time, the pain went on a walk of its own. All at once I had a stabbing sensation in my groin, where left thigh met pelvis. This was the kind of pain that causes an urgent need to stand up. I did. Then I urgently needed to sit back down. I am the sort of hypochondriac whose complaints become matter-of-fact when something is actually wrong. "I'm not feeling very well," I said. "No, you're not," said my mother. "Lie down quickly and pull your knees up to your chest," said my aunt, who is a superb general practitioner in rural Vermont and presumably has had much firsthand experience with fainting. The Rannoch Moor revolved slowly around me. Now that I was supine, I thought about all of the horrendous emergent conditions that might be wrong with me. Appendicitis? Wrong side of the body. Testicular torsion? Possible. Incarcerated inguinal hernia? Now there was a nasty probability.

"Take off your left boot, your sock, and all your Band-Aids," said my aunt. People sometimes describe skin infections as "angry." My fourth toe was furious. Red streaks emanated out from it toward my ankle—they were "tracking," in the unintentionally apt medical jargon. "The infection has caused one of the lymph nodes in your groin to become swollen, and that's triggered your reaction," said my aunt. "It's probably cellulitis. You need antibiotics." We were miles from anywhere.

At this point, I experienced my first and only divine visitation. Two middle-aged women dressed in sensible hiking attire appeared from nowhere. They were a Scottish lesbian couple. "Dae yi"ll need help?" one of them asked. "A'm a doctor, 'n' she's a pharmacist." So this is what angels look like, I thought—two slightly overweight Scottish women with butch haircuts, cargo shorts, and medical licenses.

The two seraphim consulted with my aunt, who had also revealed her medical credentials. "He's had a vagal response," said my aunt. "I think he might have a staph infection in his toe."

The angelic couple cheerily drove me to the inn where we were staying the night and left me with a stockpile of drugs. Some of the pills treated illnesses that even I hadn't imagined having. Nonetheless, I developed a high fever. My aunt lanced the blisters on the infected toe with a sewing needle (did she pack sewing needles just for this purpose?), while I sprawled on my bed, shivering convulsively and thinking of Keats dying of tuberculosis in Rome. I felt Romantic myself. Forget about Brown and his prosaic foot problems: I had never been closer to Keats.

Oddly enough, he had written about what was wrong with me (more or less). His lecture notes from the time of his training at Guy's Hospital in London a few years earlier contain this succinct explanation:

Cellular Membrane is a common seat of Inflammation....
The substance thrown out in inflammation is albumen. If
inflammation do not stop the Bloodvessels become affected
and pus is secreted—which collects together into a Cyst.
The next thing is an absorption of the surrounding parts
by pressure. At length the Skin becoming absorbed the
Matter becomes discharged. When the cellular Membrane
becomes killed the disease is Carbuncle.

My aunt is a superb diagnostician. But Keats, too, would have known what was wrong with me, and what to do about it, in an early nineteenth-century way. Did he examine Brown's feet when his blisters became intolerable? Did he lance them with a sewing needle he'd packed in the bottom of his rucksack? How did he take care of his own feet? Even in the swamp of a raging infection, I couldn't help noticing that my OCD had skulked away into some dark corner. An agonizing memory that, earlier in the day, I had thought pointed to sexual deviancy or hidden murderous tendencies now seemed flimsy and preposterous. "In diseases Medical Men guess, if they cannot ascertain a disease they call it nervous," Keats wrote in his medical-school notebook. My toe throbbed, but for once my head did not, as if in observance of a principle stating that agony must be conserved, in zero-sum fashion, even if transferred from mind to flesh. It was a strange relief to have something wrong with me now that any doctor— even one who was last certified to practice on July 25, 1816— could easily understand.

The morning after my Romantic fever, we went by bus to the Accident and Emergency Department of Belford Hospital, Fort William (National Health Service, Highlands). Belford, according to its website, has "an established reputation in the management of trauma, particularly from mountain accidents." Flies buzzed around the examination room. Big-band jazz wafted from a speaker in the hallway. The nurse practitioner forgot to take my blood pressure. I explained how far I was walking, and why. "We'll hae tae fix ye up guid, then," she said. She set to scrubbing my blisters with a viscous yellow solution that my aunt later cheerily mentioned could cause tissue damage. Then she performed some unspeakable scraping procedure with a scalpel. I chose not to observe. Nearly fainting once was plenty for the summer. But whatever the good nurse did, she fixed me up guid, and it didnae cost a pence.

V I I

I often long for a seat and a Cup o' tea…especially now that
mountains, castles, and Lakes, are becoming common to
me—yet I would rather summer it out for on the whole I am
happier than when I have time to be glum—perhaps it may
cure me—
—Keats, letter to Tom Keats, July 26, 1818

Within a few days, I was back on my feet. They weren't pretty, and I had to swathe them in special DuoDerm Hydrocolloid Dressings ("For use on post-surgical wounds, lightly exuding traumatic wounds, and superficial pressure sores"), but ambulation was possible once more. Besides, I liked the idea of soldiering on while my traumatic wounds exuded lightly. Keats would have identified their exudate as albumen, although—to my relief—a dribble of OCD seemed to be seeping out as well into the DuoDerm. Something in acute but minor afflictions can clear the mind. My mind is a master self-torturer, but with my feet in distress it dropped its cruel instruments and focused tenderly on my flesh. As Keats had said of his own time walking, on the whole I was happier than when I had time to be glum. At least for a few days, the fell spell was broken.

As my health, physical and psychological, began to improve, Keats' was on the decline. On my sister's birthday, she and my mother had bid us farewell and returned to London on an all-night bus that promised reduced fares and free onesies. (The ride seems to have been a permanently traumatic experience for both of them.) By the time Keats, my aunt, and I reached the Isle of Mull—by dingy in 1818, ferry in 2013—in the Inner Hebrides, crankiness had slipped into the poet's Romantic heart. Parodying his contemporaries and caviling about oatcakes gave way to more biting complaints. The Hebridean cottages were "wretched." The island walking was "wretched." Even a bagpiper was wretched: "I thought the Beast would never have done." "I carry all matters to an extreme," Keats wrote just before leaving for Mull, "so that when I have any little vexation it grows in five Minutes into a theme for Sophocles." But on Mull he seems to have encountered genuine misery. While my aunt and I enjoyed a lazy bus ride from one end of the isle to the other, Keats "had a most wretched walk of 37 Miles across the Island." Thirty-seven miles is an awfully long way even by Romantic standards, especially when the terrain is rough and the weather very, very rainy. It didn't help matters that Keats was taking shelter at night in local homes, tiny huts whose occupants burned peat for warmth. The smoke, he observes, was chokingly thick, and there were no chimneys.

To top it all off, Keats had a sore throat that almost certainly wasn't as "slight" as he makes it out to be in a letter to his much sicker brother, Tom. Brown called it "violent." The pair of walkers had to hole up for a couple of days upon their return to the mainland. Even that wasn't the end of my companion's affliction. His dreadfully sore throat seems to have brought out a case of homesickness, or at least an acute nostalgia for London life. Referring to the aptly named street on which they lived, Keats tells his brother, "I assure you I often long for a seat and a Cup o' tea at well Walk." He insists that the walking might cure his habitual glumness—the same claim he had made before setting out—but his heart isn't in it. Tom surely could have divined Keats' inward state: even I could, after weeks in his company.

During reprieves from OCD, I start to feel like a real person. Like an unspeakably foul houseguest who has finally packed his bags, my anxiety departs and takes along its delusional terrors. Suddenly, all is still. An invisible hand peels back a film from my emotions, and fires are lit and stoked in the hearths of desire, gentleness, joy. Someone is at home in contented solitude. That someone is me. As the obsessional waves receded in the wake of the toe incident, I began to realize how different Keats and I really were in what we loved and longed for: he was looking for adventure, I was looking for the North. It was true that we were bound tight by our strange and shared endeavor, this grueling walk. But for me the North had an infinitely magnetic allure. The cardinal point sucked me toward it like a lodestone. What Everest or Chogo Gangri are for some young men and women, lowly Ben Nevis was for me; I would rather catch a glimpse in the fog of the rough, gray Hebridean Sea than stand on Kangchenjunga and see the curve of the world. I am not sure that Keats would have agreed.

We both might have been of the Highland persuasion when we first set out from Lancaster at the end of June. But Keats, I think, had a change of heart as he walked. I did not. It is hard to say exactly when and where the North lost its luster for my companion, but the song he wrote in Kirkcudbright for his sister, in which the boy follows his nose to the North and finds it basically the same as the South, is one inflection point. Keats' misery on Mull is another. Certainly, I realized that spending a month all by myself wasn't the brightest idea. But not even the throttling grip of OCD strangled my boreal desire. Chill summer winds and almost endless light (seventeen hours of daylight at Scottish midsummer) made my heart beat fast. I blushed at the stark moorland, loved the peat bogs that literally made Keats sick. This haggard but hardy land could scare me, but fright only made its seduction more complete. In his great poem on the auroras, Wallace Stevens writes of "An arctic effulgence flaring on the frame / Of everything he is." That line and a half, I was beginning to realize, resonated more deeply with me than anything Keats wrote. Landscape and character intertwine, and my companion would have preferred a roundtrip ticket to Rome. (Instead, in one of the most tragic ironies of his short life, he got a one-way trip.) Keats' wit and words still thrilled me, but we were not cut of the same cloth. He, too, was a guest in my house, no more a member of my household than my OCD.

In spite of his worsening illness, Keats dutifully made the short crossing from Mull to the sacred isle of Iona, where St. Columbus first landed, bringing Christianity from Ireland to Scotland. Sacred sites specked the tiny island: a monastery, a nunnery, a royal graveyard, towering Celtic crosses. Keats was unenthusiastic. He reported the sights in travelogue-worthy detail, but without affect. Unimaginably, his description is almost boring. I, however, wandered the island in silent rapture. Iona is a shard of land set in an ocean colored an improbable Caribbean blue. Its weather is uncommonly gentle. There are gardens of Babylonian richness. I stared down a rhubarb plant at least as tall as I was. The ancient monastery, ruined in Keats' time, has since been restored to use by a liberal ecumenical Christian community. I wandered its grounds with a sense of reverence I did not fully understand. Off the monastery's central chapel, a flight of steps carried me up to a thick wooden door. STAND FAST, it says, in a carved and curly script. I had to get on my knees to pass through. On the other side was a room of rough-hewn stone, hardly more than a crawl space. Vines grew through its cracks. Its windows blazed. I sat hunched there, facing the light. I sensed myself go very strange indeed. STAND FAST STAND FAST STAND FAST, said the room. I felt the lambent flare of grace. After a minute, I crawled back out again. I thought through my litany of unspeakable obsessional anxieties. I do not believe in standing fast, I said to myself—right? I believe in Keats, who was here when it was still a pile of tottering rocks. And then I walked on.

When I returned to the mainland at the beginning of August, I said goodbye to my aunt and turned once more to the North. Barely a week of walking remained. I had now had another stint alone with Keats, shorter and less lacerating than the initial solitary exposure, but I was not to be alone anymore: my father was joining me for the final days of the trip. We set out from Fort William in the Highlands, headed up the Caledonian Canal and the Great Glen

Loch Ness for Keats' final destination of Inverness. It was a
spotless day, untrammeled by clouds or fretting. Only my
feet and my ever tenuous sense of direction were sore. I
had planned a gentle day of walking so that my father and
I might enjoy the splendor of the Highlands. This, indeed,
was what we did—until we came to the end of the day's
trail and found ourselves in the middle of nowhere. There
wasn't the trace of human habitation in sight. I had made
a slight miscalculation. As my iPhone's Ordnance Survey
app made all too clear, the inn where we were supposed
to rest our feet was miles away. Public transportation was
a thing of the past and the South. My father and I were so
sweaty and bedraggled that our efforts to hitchhike failed
dismally. There was no way to get to the day's end but by
walking—straight uphill into the mountains.

Family lore has it that, shortly before I was born, my
father became panicked because he couldn't identify any
trees and wouldn't be able to teach me their names—a skill,
he had decided suddenly, that a healthy child could not do
without. It was only fitting that, two decades later, he and
I—die-hard New Yorkers both—were alone together in a
ravishing wilderness to which we could append few names,
let alone taxonomic classifications. Ample sunshine, cool
air, running water, snow-capped mountains: we could identify all these. But green organisms were beyond us. A rose
is a rose is a rose. A rose is every other flower to me. A fir
is a conifer is a spruce is a pointy tree with pine needles.
Are there even fir trees in Scotland? Roses? Surely there are
roses. We might have discussed such matters if we hadn't
been so bloody exhausted.

My father and I arrived eventually in the hamlet of Spean
Valley and revived after tea and cake. But when I took off my
boots and socks, I saw that my walk was at its end. Both feet
were covered in massive blisters. Some were more than an
inch in diameter and at least a half inch in height. They were
eerily translucent and rimmed with white, like hitherto un-

discovered lunar jewels. A number of smaller blisters ringed the larger ones like satellites. The worst were rooted on my heel and the tips of my toes, and together they extended and distorted the shape of my feet such that I was unsure I could fit them in my boots once again. (When I tried the next morning, I had to leave one boot unlaced, the blisters were so large.) The infamous fourth toe of my left foot was looking angry again. The arches and soles of my feet were chafed red. I could not find any podal surface that could bear pressure without searing pain. Even walking barefoot on the carpeted floor of the inn was excruciating. Somehow, in those final miles uphill to Spean Valley, my feet had rebelled once and for all. A summer's worth of footsteps had now incited open revolt. With fifty miles to go to Inverness through largely unoccupied territory, I would have been a fool to go on. Spean Valley had a train station, the last before Inverness. Barely able to walk, I called the walking quits.

It was August 5, 2013. Keats had given up on August 6, 1818. On foot, I was three days short of Keats' stopping point. In time, 195 years minus one day separated the end of his journey from mine. Surely fate and not coincidence was at work: we had both been on the road for precisely forty-four days. "It is a cruel disappointment," Brown wrote of Keats' impending departure. After all, the pair had planned to plod on for two and a half more months and hundreds more miles. Oddly enough, I was content with the decision (not that it was much of a decision). The premature end was fitting. It matched both the incompleteness of Keats's own journey and my own incapacity or unwillingness, the whole summer long, to plant my boots exactly where his once had trod.

It took Keats nine days to return to London. It took me nine hours. The train erased my achingly slow progress of my summer in a matter of moments. Looking out the window as the Rannoch Moor swept by, I felt I was rewinding an old tape. Even the streaks of rain on the glass recalled the bands of VCR interference. The ribbon that had tethered me to Keats for six weeks was unspooling at eighty miles an hour. I dozed off for a few minutes. The ribbon hung taut in the blankness of sleep. When I awoke it had snapped. That night, in London, I caught one last ghostly spark from my companion. I saw Keats standing on the dock in Inverness, pacing as he waited for his boat, swallowing with difficulty, thinking of Charles Brown continuing without him, step after step after step. I saw him like this in a last retinal flash. Then he was gone.

EPILOGUE

"I have been werry romantic indeed, among these Mountains and Lakes."
—Keats, letter to Mrs. James Wylie, August 6, 1818

When Keats, sick and miserable on the Isle of Mull, mentioned his tendency to turn a minor vexation into a theme for Sophocles, he wrote a truth deeper than he probably knew. The name of the most famous hero of Sophoclean tragedy, Oedipus, means "swollen foot." And indeed the Sphinx's riddle centers on how men walk, and with what degree of impediment. In their account of prosody, the ancient Greeks identified a certain poetic meter as the *scazōn,* the "limping one." Ottoman musical theory speaks of *aksak,* a limping rhythm, and even today we still refer to metrical feet, although they are rarely if ever swollen. Poetry and walking have a shared and rich history—all the more so, it seems, when the walking is hard. The march of marshaled syllables aligns with the footfall, the poet's line with the walker's. We do not escape from a long walk or a long poem unbruised. We are made raw, we feel the real road, we founder in the transit of life. Keats did not live to write any major walk poems, nor did he write any major poems while on the walk, unless we count the ditty for his sister, Fanny. One particularly keen critic observes that in that text, "the metrical and semantic units are consistently out of step with each other."

It is as if the poem is running away from its author. I like to think that what Keats discovered, what happened when he "stood in / his shoes, / and he wonderd," was out of step with the poetry he sought to write. I like to think that if he had lived, he would have written a great walk poem, a poem that would have matched the feet of his great lyric gifts to those of his disillusioning and painful walk.

While I was walking with Keats, I was obsessed with a line from Wagner's *Das Rheingold*. *Alles, was ist, endet,* prophesies Mother Earth: all that is, ends. I kept the scrap of song close to my heart. My walk would end, my blisters would end, my OCD would end. I do not now treasure that frighteningly soothing verse. I think instead of Keats' letter to Mrs. Wylie, his brother George's mother-in-law, dated the day he gave up the walk. She had read in a newspaper about a man in a fur hat who fell off a cliff in Kirkcudbrightshire, and she had been fretting that it might have been Keats. "If it was me," he writes Mrs. Wylie, "I did it in a dream, or in some magical interval between the first and second cup of tea." He playfully refuses to refute the rumor. He imagines his return from the dead. And, indeed, his joyous spirits, his preternatural wisdom, seem resurrected after lying six-feet-under for the past couple weeks. "I have been werry romantic indeed, among these Mountains and Lakes," he writes. Three years later, his sore throat gave way to pulmonary hemorrhage, and he bled to death with his friend Joseph Severn at his side. All that is, ends. But it doesn't. A walk does not end. It returns. One foot moves contrapuntally against the other. "It is impossible to prove that black is white. it is impossible to make out, that sorrow is joy, or joy is sorrow," wrote Keats to Mrs. Wylie. Joy, sorrow. Left foot, right foot. After walking itself in a long slow circle unto the end of ages, the ouroboros will swallow its own tail. I will be werry Romantic. I will be werry un-Romantic. I will be anxious again. I will be happy again. Keats will live. Keats will die. I will give him the slip. I will join him once more.

A History of China

CAROLYN FERRELL

DIXIE

Every year at the family reunion—before Cousin Monique comes to your rescue—the uncles sit back in their folding chairs and napkin-necks and ask about your father. They take you in with age-soggy eyes, as you stand before them in a floppy blouson and skirt. You look different now than you did in 1970 or 1981 or 1997—though you still have what lyrical Aunt Vitrine calls your *swan quality*. Cousin Monique had wanted to ditch the reunion for the shopping mall in Auntsville; she has always been your wings and, as such, was born to ignore the uncles: in 1970, she set fire to the truck belonging to one uncle and claimed it was lightning; in 1981, she put Ex-Lax in their pound cake frosting. Now she is nowhere to be seen. There's no reason we can't have fun at the reunion, you told her the night before, when she picked you up at Raleigh Airport. You're right, Monique replied, grinning in the dark, the car pulling faster and faster along the blind curves of the road. Slave food and rockheads. I don't see why that would in any way be an obstacle to fun, cousin.

Your blouson sticks to your skin. The uncles lean forward as if to smell you—girls here only wear that kind of top if they are in trouble—but gradually their eyes drift over the dirt hills across the street, behind the Baptist church. They don't care if you're like every other girl down here: fast Monique and her sisters Mae and Wanita and Tarnisha and Lynette. Her cousins Meggie and Mercy and Shawnelle and Winsome. Their kids LaDonna and Kelly and Juan and Quanasia and Cedric and Colin. Tons more. Monique's mom had given her a fancy name in the hopes that she would be better than the rest. But look what happened, your father once remarked. 1981? 1982?

The uncles want news about him. Word on the road is that their nephew wants to return to his roots in North Carolina. The prodigal son returning—what a laugh, the uncles concur.

You stretch your eyes across the property, exasperating because it is huge and small at the same time and fills you with a familiar hopelessness. Monique and a friend were supposed to meet you at dawn. You all were supposed to slip out of your respective houses (you are staying with Aunt Nephronia, and Monique and Kate are, of course, staying with Monique's mom, Vitrine, two houses down; as a child, this road of relatives fascinated you)—but you over-slept, in part due to the brutally hot North Carolina night, in part due to your tears. Can a dead person ever change? Can time remove a tiger's stripes? Those foolish questions made you weep in your sleep last night; in the days before your father died, you'd been too stingy to say goodbye.

The uncles look at you and say, Your daddy ain't set foot here in near twenty years. But tell him we forgive him if he wants.

You need to tell them that he somehow finagled all the land from Great-Grandma Elldine and left it all to you in a will. Something about an unpaid loan, the land not being worth spit. The letter actually read, But why not enjoy it as your own, Sasha Jean. I utterly wish I could give you more.

The uncles are suddenly worked up in clammy anger.

CAROLYN FERRELL

How come he don't answer when Vitrine call? That ain't no way to be treating your one sister on this earth!

He always thought he was the best at checkers. Well, he got another thing coming.

If he thinking about parking that damn Cadillac in my yard again, he even crazier.

That sucker!

You'd had a dream, coming back to the folks in North Carolina: that you'd get a chance to talk smoothly after they all finished eating and were in good spirits; that you'd lay out everything Bobby Lee's scribbled will said, though in reality it was vague, not more than four sentences. The sun wouldn't be too hot and the children wouldn't be too unruly. Dogs, as they happened to wander back and forth from each house, would not frighten you with their larva-laden ears. This was your dream. In reality, you can't recall a single time that the uncles, in their walking days, didn't eventually get smashed drunk and start fighting with the women. The pig, burnt to a crisp on the outside but pink as a newborn on the inside, would turn your stomach. The same gospel songs would be sung, the same protests as to who would hold the mic, who would gather the children from their hiding places and force them to sing. It's not Sunday, one of them would say, relenting under a smack upside the head. How could your dream stand up to these details? Your dream was like a story that was told in the pages of some huge, incomprehensible book, spread out on a lemon-wax table in the only good part of someone's house or trailer. Everyone sensed it was there but knew how to avoid it.

That and still: you want to find the right time to tell them—what better place for sad family news than at a reunion?—and you're hoping that since it didn't happen last night (your arrival at Nephronia's, with glasses of Harvey's Bristol Cream) or this morning (gluten-free breakfast crepes—à la *The Food Network*—with Vitrine), a suitable moment will come today.

Everyone is in the backyard of Grandma Elldine's decrepit Victorian. Random picnic tables have been set out and on them, flies chill over Tupperwares of mac salad and wings. Curlyhead, feverfew, and false foxglove dot the perimeter but everyone treats them like weeds. Already at eleven in the morning, it is 90 degrees; the relatives fan themselves with their hands until someone drags out a standing General Electric and plugs it (via two extension cords) into an unseen outlet.

I hope my brother don't think we still in the prehistoric days, Aunt Vitrine had said at the breakfast table, her gray wig toppling. I'm learning to eat healthy, Sasha Jean. Buttermilk, no heavy cream. You go back and tell my brother that for me. We all gone live forever, like it or not.

In reality, it should be easy to tell everyone that your father died (in his armchair, surrounded only by his home healthcare aide and *General Hospital* playing on the tablet in her hands). Perhaps they will expect you to cry, and then for you to expect them to cry back. Ancient Hattie Mabel carries a mic (via three extension cords) out to the middle of the yard, preparing to gospel. We can forgive, the uncles say. But hell if we can forget.

You are silent; handed a plate of beans and rice by a young boy; pushed into a chair next to the uncles, in direct sunlight. You mention that your daddy plans on coming down to the reunion next year. That he misses everyone and longs for the red earth of his childhood. The uncles raise their brows and laugh. They tell you, don't lie. Ancient Hattie Mabel removes her hand from your shoulders and starts in with "The Old Rugged Cross." You notice that she still has on her overnight curlers, that her eyes are closed as she sways from side to side, as if in a godly stew. The fragrance of the beans and rice is heavy for this time of day, but still you lift a fork. The uncles say they've never known you to be untrue.

They have heard rumors all these years. Your father, the big gambler, every weekend in Las Vegas, thousands lost. Your father, owner of not one but two homes in Los Angeles. Your

father, the lady's man. He never paid child support. He called
himself a minister on his tax forms and got caught by the government people. He tried talking Grandma Elldine into selling him this property just before she went into Pine Haven
Home but luckily she resisted his advances. He wanted to
tear down the old Victorian the first chance he got.

He got called on by the cops one time for "untoward devi-
ousness." He never said *I'm sorry* to anyone like he meant it.

The uncles tell you not to lie. Ain't no way he's coming
back. Our Bobby Lee is gone for good.

CHINET

The will—scribbled on a yellow legal pad and witnessed
by *Faith Akintola, Dept. of Aging Adult Services, Los Angeles County*—indicates that you're supposed to evict them.
That you're supposed to raze everything and then build a
real house here, with functioning plumbing and privacy
windows. Sit on your newly built porch and look out over
the chicken hills across the street and invite loads of edu-
cated folks over for drinks and perhaps to hear those "short
stories" you've been publishing in graduate school—you can
read them aloud (that is, your father last said, if they really
want to sit around on a firefly night and listen to that crap).
You're supposed to recall childhood summers here, laughing
in Great-Grandma Elldine's post bed with Monique while
the other children went to work tobacco. (Why not make a
story out of that, he demanded. Monique and her slut self.
Lazy, that's all. Monique's sisters and their slut selves—chasing men like firehouse dogs. Those girls belonged to nobody and look where that got them. Four kids apiece and
no guardian in sight.) You're supposed to see why he turned
out the way he did, and why you will never go down that
particular path. Never ever. (You belong to me. My *favorite*.
Forgive me. Forever and ever.)

ROYALTON JAPAN BLUE

In 1961, your father stood outside a small white house on a street empty of trees. He was bowing his head, quite uncharacteristic. But his mind went like: Thank you, God, for this is not Carolina red dirt or Carolina sun. Trees can be planted if people need them, and churches can be fucking avoided by simply watching the ball game on TV.

Your father rocked a carriage with one hand while looking over a brochure handed to him by the real estate agent. *Pomegranate Estates*, it read. *Take a Bite of This Fruit.*

In 1961, the real estate agent had called this Long Island neighborhood a "colored development," shying away from words like *community* or *housing project*, as he didn't want your father—already coming across as uppity—to get the wrong idea. These were normal houses for normal people, the agent claimed—some even had wooden shingles. People watered lawns here, drove cars into proper driveways. There would be no fists here, no spirituals or arms linked in arms or fires or Jackson Five records or Aretha Franklin passion in this part of Pomegranate Village. The agent waved his hand over the sea of three-bedroom-plus-den Cape Cods (there were actually thirty-five on this cul-de-sac) and said, If you all want something to do, think about painting the shutters a different color, or planting a little garden or something. No vegetables, no livestock, no front yard clotheslines. Just a row of marigolds or begonias.

Tell your closest friends, the brochure encouraged.

In the yard of your soon-to-be new house, your father ignored the agent. His job at that particular moment was to keep his eye on the carriage in which you lay. The sun beamed straight into your eyes, and you bawled; the carriage was a foot away from a struggling maple sapling, but your father made no attempt to wheel you into that bit of shade. He was, instead, listening for your mother.

Who was walking around the yard, wringing her hands,
not believing her luck. Not only did the house have more
than one bedroom and a bathtub and basement, it had all
this land. Nearly a fifth of an acre. She imagined planting
the gooseberries and potatoes she'd smuggled from her last
trip home to Laboe. One patch here, another here, near the
culvert. There was that annoying maple sapling in the front
yard by the curb, but in the backyard, there was nothing.
Plenty of room for German food.

In 1971, your mother announced that she hated trees.

ROSENTHAL

You struggle to eat the beans and rice, only to have Aunt
Cathy tuck a bowl of grits and eggs into your lap. For later,
she says, winking. From the corner of your eye you notice
Monique, her brown skin glistening with baby oil, hur-
rying in a dress and bare feet. There was that one time, in
1981, when she duct-taped shut the door to the church and
wouldn't let them out for over an hour. In 1982, she stole
seven dump cakes from the church basement breakfast and
threw them into the branches of the tall pines.

She is flying like a pterodactyl now, large brown wings
outstretched in love. She is coming for you.

CORNING CENTURA

I love it, your mother cried, walking away from the men and
the carriage toward the side of the house. There were huge
lilac trees and a gutsy chain-link fence running from front to
back. When can we move in, she cried, without once turning
her head.

Just out of sight of the men, her hands went back into her coat
pocket; she, too, began a quiet prayer. The house was a mira-

cle—it would be *her miracle*. It was close to the others. It looked exactly like the others. Likely, when you opened every door, you saw the same walls, you noticed that the bathroom was in the same place, the kitchen fan made the same noise. But how fantastic was that? No useless standing out or drawing attention to the wrong things. Being the same meant being the same.

Your mother wandered back toward the front yard. I love this place, Bob, she whispered. Please say we never leave.

Elspeth, he murmured. His hand on the carriage, the baby that was you still bawling.

The real estate agent cleared his throat. It was not often that he saw a black man hold a white woman in his arms and live to tell about it. His own family was Connecticut stock by way of Georgia and New Mexico. We'll take it, your father announced. Bring me the papers.

The agent again looked at him funny; just what did this colored man think, using a phrase like that? *Bring me*—what was he, the fucking King of Siam?

But still, the agent didn't resist. That afternoon the three of them sat together in the office on Main Street in Pomegranate Village and signed the papers. In the carriage, you bawled even further.

AZTEC MELMAC

What your father has left you is a deed to these dusty thirty-seven acres, populated by fallen-down prefabs and trailers, at least seven in total, and at the end of the road, a rusted old church. Faith Akintola sent you a letter with a copy of the signed will you've carried in your purse; the letter (dictated, in fact, to the aide during commercials) continued:

> I'm sorry for
> any way you thought I might
> have hurt you. I love you, Daddy.
> With all my heart. Doesn't life go on?

Monique is scowling at the uncles. Why you talking to these old skunks, she asks? yanking you toward the road. Her face is riddled with egg white, remnants of an acne cure she'd applied earlier that morning. Unlike almost everyone here, she is as slim as a model. Her skin bakes underneath your hand into pure chocolate custard.

You tell her you were just making small talk.

Small talk, Monique sighs, wincing. Those suckers don't know nothing about no small talk. Try making BIG talk and see what happens.

Big talk?

They think they doing you a favor when in reality it's no way to treat a baby girl they supposed to be loving. They think they doing you a favor. I wish I could kill them all.

When you get to the roadside, you vomit in an echinacea bush.

Let it out, don't be afraid, Monique whispers, lifting your sweaty hair from your shoulder. She giggles, but the pulse of her hand is soothing. You knocked up, Sasha Jean? I would be so happy. You don't know how long I been waiting to say to you: JOIN THE CLUB.

(Re: the uncles: later she will claim what she was talking about was the time the uncles were asked to watch her oldest daughters—Monique was doing two shifts at Target— but then fell asleep and let the baby girls wander off down the road—almost two miles on their own. She wanted to kick them in the dick, hurt them so they'd stay awake forever, damn stupid talkers.)

What's going on, Monique asks, as you rest against an oak stump? She smiles. In 1981, she poured sugar in various gas tanks, and then told the uncles it was a case of ornery white men. Girl, it's nothing to be ashamed of, she whispers, clasping your face between her hands. You attempt to smile an answer, but then the bile comes back up. Monique looks into your eyes, unwavering. Exactly what kind of bun, she asks, do you have in your oven?

MELITTA

There was a story before Long Island. In it, El boarded the plane with the Melitta in her suitcase.

She'd never been on a plane before, had never been spoken to by a stewardess bearing peanuts and napkins, had never left her home in the night like some common criminal. The stewardess brought around a cart of drinks, but El shook her head; all she could think of was Bobby, waiting for her at the end of the line, opening his arms to her so that she could melt inside. Liquor on the breath could possibly prevent that melting. The third time around, however, El gave in and said she would just adore a gin and tonic. She'd been gone from the Laboe farm for a little over six hours. Though her suitcase—the one from her dead father—was stowed solidly underneath her seat, she imagined she could hear the Melitta dishes clinking softly against each other.

El had taken the dishes in the middle of the night as her mother slept. She'd lifted the tea and coffee pots from the cabinet in the basement kitchen and wrapped them in a cotton nightgown, stowed the cake platter at the bottom of the suitcase, hoping the cushioned lining would prevent it from breaking. During the fourth gin and tonic, El gazed again out the window and imagined she saw the chocolate-wafer edge of America.

They landed sometime in the early day. The waiting room was loud, strewn with paper cups and newspapers. The sounds of planes overhead rattled the chairs. She stood looking for help, for Bobby, but there was nothing. Eventually, El slumped into a chair attached to a miniature TV; she was hungry and thirsty and tired. To watch the television cost two quarters per fifteen minutes, but since Bob had told her she wouldn't need any money once she arrived, she'd only packed an emergency five-mark bill.

The clock on the wall moved slowly; next thing, it was eight and the sky outside the plate glass was pure black.

The janitor sweeping at her feet told her it was time to close
this waiting area, that she would have to go to Arrivals. He
showed her to the escalator. Good luck, Ma'am, don't let
nothing happen to you.

But she nearly toppled down the moving stairs. Her suitcase seemed heavier than before.

She felt tears form. This country, it was so loud, so ugly, so
wildly placid. She wanted to find a stewardess and ask how
she could return to Germany—to Laboe on the Baltic—because was this how they did things in America? The man
who swore his devotion—vanished like a ghost?

At the bottom of the moving stairs, she quickly saw Bob.
Now Elspeth.

He looked much different than she'd imagined him since
their fifth meeting five months ago: gaunt, mustached, pal-
pable. No longer Bobby Lee—she saw immediately that he
was to be called Bob. *Now Elspeth.*

He reached out a hand to her. No embrace, no tongue in
her ear, no touch of her breasts. In her mind they were practically married, she'd run away to be with him, had taken her
future wedding dishes without permission. She expected Bob
would at least put his hand under her elbow, leading her the
correct way into the future. But instead, he walked in front
of her toward the luggage carousel; and when they got there
and stood side by side, and she reached over to caress his
cheek, Bob stepped back and frowned. *Now Elspeth.* Isn't it
enough you made me look all over the damn airport for you?
Don't you know I have better things to do? Plus, I had to get
up and go to work this morning, unlike some people I know
who spend their days drinking cocktails on Lufthansa jets.

His voice was so different from the voice he'd used in the
aerograms, the one that began each letter with *Baby* or *Dar-
ling* or *Sugarpie* and ended with *Forever Yours.* His last letter,
dated April 29, 1961, had begun *Dear Sugarpie, I saw you in
my dreams last night.* As the luggage began to tumble onto
the carousel, Bob took out a cigarette. Life in America was
tough, he said, did she think she could make it? Did she bring

any money? If she didn't think she could make it, she might as well get back on the plane.

El didn't know why they stood there; she already had the yellow suitcase in hand. As if reading her thoughts, Bob quickly tossed his cigarette. He led her to the exit by her hand. All the while never looking her directly in the face. Had she ever seen a cockroach, he asked, because his mother's apartment, it was a cockroach paradise. His mother's apartment—you couldn't call it a honeymoon suite unless you were crazy—was only one bedroom, with him on the couch, and collards and chicken-fried steak three times a week. Pork chops and gospel radio on Sunday. He hated it, sometimes. But that was what was on the table.

Did she think she could handle that—black life?

Baby, we will live off a love, the letter from April 29 insisted.

Bob wiped his forehead with his shoulder, and El then noticed the large perspiration stains in the armpits. He noticed her looking. Been hot as hell, he said. Here in America, summer's no joke. My mother has a Westinghouse fan, yes. But no air-conditioning, if that's what you're expecting.

The letter from April 29 had ended with the words *I don't know if you will want me once you are on these shores, but I will pray every day that you will. Forever Yours.*

They walked out to the parking lot under a half moon. Bob swung the suitcase into the trunk, and just then she thought she heard the platter crack, the little lids of the coffee and tea pots clatter together. What in the hell you got in there, Bob asked, laughing, as he started the car.

The drive was bland, a few lights sparkling over Jamaica Bay.

CORELLE

Monique makes sure you can stand on your own (how no one else saw you throw up is a mystery) and then leans you against a pine tree, saying she has to go back inside for just a minute; she's afraid Kate (a white girl from Duke who has *forever and a day* wanted to experience *this kind* of family reunion) might have fallen prey to her cousin Stanley. You haven't seen Stanley in years, Monique whispers. But he's still the same. Thinks he's gone get his hands on Kate. But that'll only happen after I get *my* hands on her.

You'll love Kate, she says. You're different.

She hurries off in a cloud of roadside dust and pollen. You imagine Monique finding her white lover and kissing her under a pile of stale pillows, in a wrought-iron bed, under dozens of family photographs—the ancestors. Forgetting about you for whole hours. When you attend their commitment ceremony three years later—only one uncle will come to the church where two females are saying "I do"—you notice the same crystals of love in her eyes, the same spike of deliverance as you see on this day, the last reunion you'll ever attend.

DIME SAVINGS BANK ACCOUNT-OPENER BONUS SET

You were ten years old when you told your mother about the nighttime touching. She rolled her eyes into her head, as if this were the straw that literally broke the camel's back. How could he do this to me? she blurted. Then: Oh, baby.

It was nothing more than a few weeks worth of touching. The moon came out from your Mother Goose window and stared in shock. His finger didn't even make it in all the way. Do you like this, your father asked. No, you answered. It took another five and a half weeks for him to get that through his head.

Ach Du Meine Güte! Heaven, hear me.

Your mother said she would leave him, take you and your brothers back to Germany. There was no way she could stay with a child molester. A monster.

Heaven, don't stop hearing me!

But then weeks, more than a year passed.

OVENWARE BROWN TEN PIECE

When they entered his mother's apartment on Hoyt Street, Bob set the suitcase down. The shower was running, and a woman's voice sang the sweetest melody El had ever heard. *The only way that we can survive, we need the Lord on our side!*

Bob kissed El on her forehead and said, More of this later; he pointed to his lips. The woman in the shower called out to Bob to make his girl comfortable.

Bob took the salami out of the suitcase, holding it to the ceiling. You know, he said, we got food over here too. No need to drag this sucker clear across the world. This here salami is Italian food. What's a German girl doing with Italian food?

El fell on the plastic slipcovered couch and rubbed her eyes. Her stomach growled. And she fell into a faint, a short deep sleep. No dreams whatsoever. Minutes later she woke up to Bob's mother applying a cold washcloth to her face. *What did you eat, Baby? You bony as a bird.*

El slowly raised herself and shook her head; she didn't know enough English without her pocket dictionary to tell the woman that in fact the only thing she'd eaten all day was four gin and tonics. I got a pork chop in the icebox, his mother said. Let me go and heat it up, baby.

Bob turned away. But El could see the Army still leftover in his bones and she felt his anger. Mama, he said. We don't want that country food. Let me show my girl what we got to offer in Brooklyn!

And despite his mother's protests, he lugged El back out in the car again; it was nearly 11. Her eyes were fully open as she rolled down the window. By now, her mother would probably be pulling her hair out, weeping with utter and relentless despair. That's how El liked to imagine her: writhing in regret. Her mother had once denied knowing that the

Jewish girls who came by after the war were starving. They looked fine to me, she'd said, giving all the crab apples to the horses. Bob pulled into a restaurant that had a window on its side and a sullen girl stuck in that window. *Hello my name is Maryann and welcome to Jack in the Box and can I take your order?* Bob grinned at the girl, then turned back to El; Dry your eyes, girl, he said. You making me look bad.

They ate in the car while listening to Ray Charles on the radio. When they got home, his mother greeted them at the door in a caftan gown. El had never seen anyone so smart, a woman who looked like a magazine. You will make my son very happy, Barbara said. She kissed El's ears with lips that felt like firm pin cushions. Bob's mother was thirty-six years old.

She served El a slice of sweet potato pie on a chipped plate with cornflowers around the edge and spread out a blanket on the couch. It's not a fold-out but I hope you will be comfortable, she said. I don't believe in young folks pretending marriage. It's my church upbringing, but don't even mention the word church to Bob! Do, and he'll give you a mouthful.

She embraced her full-on, a mother's hug. Bob's told me only a little about you, so tomorrow I hope you'll fill in all the blanks, Barbara said. And that was the very last thing El heard.

She felt herself lifted into the air. She felt herself descending into the ground. After so many years of no dreams, she was bombarded that night by pictures she hadn't seen for ages. Cows, fires, birch trees, coins.

Dreams are nothing but random images, an elderly Polish doctor would tell her years later. This is how they do things in America.

FIESTAWARE

They want to be nice to you, all these relatives at the reunion in Spring Hope. Cleopatra and Susie and Katrina and Shequanna and Betty. Horace and Clotilda and Tanya and

Dove. They want to be nice, in spite of the way your eyes are your father's eyes, your nose flat brown and wide as his. When you talk, even the younger cousins say they can hear Cousin Bobby's voice come alive in yours. You know these kids have never met him, that they only know him from tall tales. Still, you laugh when they say that if he were to step foot on Grandma Elldine's land, they would kill him with a hatchet.

They can't imagine, these young cousins say, what it would be like to live in California and never see North Carolina again.

No, they will have to carry me out, one eight-year-old boy announces.

The sun is starting to set over the field. You breathe in this air: a hint of sulfuric chicken farm, a drying watering hole but evergreens as far as the nose can smell. A hint of thimbleweed out the corner of your eye.

You loom alone at the picnic tables like an unlit candle. The women and the uncles are discussing an evening service at the Baptist church. Ancient Hattie Mabel wonders if you'd like to come. It's about time you learned the words to all the songs they sing.

But then, deus ex machina, Cousin Meggie comes running from her pickup. A giant cross plops between her breasts.

Sasha Jean, she cries. I been praying you wouldn't forget me!

1964 WORLD'S FAIR COMMEMORATIVE

She is as round as the proverbial barrel, and yet she moves storklike from the truck between the fading aunts and uncles. You've thought about her for years but haven't picked up a pen or tapped on a keyboard. What would those hicks have to say to you? your father once asked. What would they have to say to anybody?

You stopped seeing him, despite his letters, his infrequent calls to your college dorm, your first apartment in Manhattan, your sublet in the Bronx. When you turned eighteen, you announced you were never going to see him again, and he laughed. Sasha, he said. People make mistakes. People get over things. It's the course of life. Grudges are about as real as cotton candy.

But you kept true to your word. Years passed—and then you received notice that he'd died in his sleep. Next to Faith Akintola. In front of her *favorite* show: Luke and Laura, escaping on foot over the top of a jetliner. In the middle of the ocean. During a lunar eclipse.

Meggie squashes you with treacly hugs, doesn't wait for any answers before immediately asking after your mom. Her skin is as light as a white person's; her eyes, round and small (Mongoloid, your father once said), literally sparkle as she talks. She says your mom's name, and her face is quickly awash in tears—she apologizes for not sending any kind of note when she heard of your mother's death. Victuals always heal a broken heart, she says, leading you to the table with the hot sauce steak and loading another plate high. Crispy kale and artichoke hearts. You want to tell Meggie that now you officially belong to her, to them—what use is a girl without a parent to stake her in the landscape? But she is eyeing you up and down; too skinny, she concludes. Your mama would not be happy.

When you shake your head, Meggie frowns. Your mama was the best thing that ever happened to this earth, she says, waving over Aunt Quincy and her bowl of spicy pork barbecue.

HUTSCHENREUTHER

El awoke the next Brooklyn morning not on the sofa but on a huge double bed. Striped sheets had crumpled under her armpits; a thin blanket straggled at her feet. El felt a terrible, lovely ache in her shoulders, in between her legs. Music sounded from the kitchen, from a radio on the table; later in the day someone would say, You mean you never heard gospel music before? Lord Have Mercy!

A car horn screeched the sunlight into her eyes. Bob, she called.

ROYAL DOULTON KNOCK-OFF

Later that day, El would sit in the front pew of the First Church of Christ on Avenue J and nod along as the choir sang, "Going Up Yonder." She would be next to her future mother-in-law; her husband was at home, looking out the window.

The church mothers would cast glances her way, happy that a white person had finally sat in the pews without looking over their shoulder. The pastor, Melvin K. Ritter, commanded the congregation to stand and be thankful; El liked this. She liked standing and begging, slowly, not too fast, the pure act of supplication, of asking things of someone who might just actually fulfill her deepest wishes. Just before his final sermon, he introduced Bob's bride-to-be to the entire congregation.

Child's too small, said one church mother in the pew behind El. Better put some meat on that skeleton, said another, smiling at Bob's mother. Them Krauts do indeed have it bad, after all this time.

When the sermons were done (there were five in all), the church people went to the basement and sat at a long table in front of several platters of minute steaks, cornbread stuffing, and okra; many wrinkled hands took hold of El's, wishing her the best with Bob. Lord knows other girls have tried to get him to change his ways, the hands told her. Hopefully, El would be the lucky one.

SANGO

You and Meggie head to the watering hole—Monique has texted that she will get there as soon as "lovingly possible." Meggie blushes as she stuffs her phone into her bra. She says she's all right with two ladies in love even though there is something creepy about it.

You enter the woods—about a half mile in is the bluestone watering hole, the one that is said (by Aunt Vitrine and others) to contain healing liquids. The trees hang low, and you notice that it is dark but not pitch; you can still find your way. You'd hoped for complete darkness—what would they say when they learned you hadn't said a proper goodbye to the man? Down here, everyone deserves a proper goodbye, hated or no.

You hope for one of those legendary water moccasins to snake its way to your ankle and take out a huge chunk.

Would it be wrong to tell them that the last time you saw your father, you said nothing specific? That the words *forgive* and *forget* never made it past your lips? That you engaged the reams of selves who came before you—the little baby in the carriage, the kindergartner, the science project acolyte—and told them it was time to close up shop, as though your father had never ever existed? He once was alive, and was all things to those former selves. You, on the other hand, despise that idea. Was it wrong to turn your head away from the phone the last time he called? Was it wrong to crunch up the letter in which he explained he'd suffered a major heart attack and needed just a touch of kindness? You hate him for keeping your mother, and you hate your mother for having been kept. You have his last will and testament sewn into a seam of the blouson, sort of like the way slaves traveled with their papers. You'd read about slaves in the fifth grade. Your father tested you on their names for a social studies test. He patted your head when you got the answers correct.

This thirty-seven acres is yours.

Immediately as you step foot under the canopy of trees, you are eaten by mosquitoes. Meg has something in a small flask; she offers it to you, and you take it down fast, lemonade and something bathtubby. Meggie giggles uncontrollably and admits that she's always wanted to visit California and start herself all over again.

But dreams cost, she suddenly moans, her lips puffed out with fake citrus.

At the next clearing, she stops and puts her cheek against your arm. You had the best mom in the world, Meggie says.

You tell her you know.

Meggie ignores you, saying, She saw me on one of your visits—I think you were only seven at the time. Your mama saw me and marched straight to my mama—God rest Evangeline's soul but my mother was a dumbass—and told her I was having a quote unquote rough time of it. That I needed more taken care of. That she only had one Meggie in the world, and what was the sense in ignoring that?

Your mama, she says. She saw my belly bowling out like a sail in the wind. She saw my legs bow and the ringworm on my cheeks blossom like flowers. Your mama saw, Sasha Jean. And she said something. And at that point, my mama had no choice but to *look at me.*

You want to ask her what happened, but Meggie is already walking away. You remember Meggie's family, the father whose eyes were so outlined in whiskey they looked like huge beetles on his face, the mother whose cough shook every house on the road of relatives. Once they both took you to church and called you their adopted daughter—Look at this good skin, they'd said, almost in unison. You laughed when they did this—was 1970 or even earlier?

You arrive at a grove of pear trees, tucked away neatly in this back wood against a small bluestone quarry. Vines everywhere come alive as snakes and then go back dead as plants. This is where Grandma Elldine used to go for her canning fruit. You smell their fragrance, wish to reach for the fruit. Your mama, Meggie keeps saying, If it wasn't for her I wouldn't've been alive.

Your mother died on her way to the VFW nursing home where she was a volunteer. She'd been planning to visit her own ailing mother in Kiel, had even booked her tickets. But then her heart conked out, and she had to be placed in the nursing home morgue. The veterans went crazy, sliding their wheelchairs into walls, throwing food at each other. How could Mrs. Elspeth be gone? And so young?

Try as he might, the Polish doctor in charge could not get those men to calm down for weeks and weeks.

DANSK

You are ten and Fortunoff is the store of dreams. Like your Aunt Vitrine once said to you: don't let your eyes get bigger than your stomach! Well, this is your mother in Fortunoff. She wants everything; as our neighbor Miss Jerldean sometimes says behind her back, Fifth Avenue tastes on a Bowery budget. It is a Saturday when the two of you escape here; your father lies in the backyard with a cold compress on his forehead; it was only the day before that you told your mother about the nighttime touching. In Fortunoff, you and she can forget the world.

Your mother admires the blue onion pattern of the Wedgewood, the clean dullness of the Rosenthal. Are you in the market for bone today, the salesgirl asks. Her tag says EVIE. It's a bit early, but have you seen the Christmas Spode?

Your mother says as a matter of fact, she was in the Christmas mood right now. Who says you can't have Christmas in July?

Here, Evie says, Feel this. Villeroy and Boch, straight from the Manhattan showroom. Hold one of these cups up to the light and you can see clear through, like it's a veil.

Last spring, the Church Mothers of Pomegranate Baptist chipped in to get your mother a set of white coffee cups, a thank-you for being such an inspiration to the kids at Tuesday Teen Services. Who knew that hearing all that talk about life during the Big War would have made such a difference to these young folks? Always mouthing off as if they knew life better than everybody else—thank God for Miss El and her tales of woe at the hands of that Nazi scum! (The Church Mothers were not above occasionally using a swear word in their speech.) Four white mugs, supposedly out of pure Japanese china, had been stuffed in a Christmas box and tied together with twine. I seen those very same mugs in White's Department Store, two for a dollar, said Bob. Why these females have to be so damn cheap? There isn't a damn thing for you in that church.

Evie goes in the back and brings out a soup tureen. This is my personal *favorite*, she announces happily. Her lips, your mother notices, are the color of strawberries.

For those women not afraid to spend a little more on themselves, Evie adds, a bit louder; perhaps she has noticed your mother's thick accent.

The trip to Fortunoff is a major departure. You both were supposed to go to the Fruit Tree, and then to White's for some tube socks, and then to the doctor, the one who will tell your mother that IUDs don't normally fail, and if she is in the family way, it is due to her own recklessness. Then on to the butcher for lamb chops, and finally to the dentist, where she would have that impacted wisdom tooth looked at.

So much to do.

But early this morning, when the dawn was sparkling with a few lights over Pomegranate treetops, something possessed your mother. She waited. She called Miss Jerldean and asked her to pick the boys up from school later—Johann from the first grade, little Keith from kindergarten; she pulled you from your bed and tossed you into the backseat; she drove at the speed limit to Westbury, where Fortunoff loomed like a Long Island Everest.

You've always wanted to come here. You've always wanted to go with your mother. But it would take until now, the day after you told your mother. In the store she doubles over the counter and begins to cry. To you she whispers that the word *finger* literally crushed her spine.

Ma'am, are you OK? Evie asks.

Utter exasperation. Your mother replies she's fine, all the while caressing the bottom of the dark blue salad bowl on the counter. It isn't the blue onion, but rather a blue fleur-de-lis. It is a pattern she is gradually and quickly falling in love with. The small bowl has a rounded bottom and soft, wavering edges. You touch your mother's hand with your own.

Sorry, Ma'am, you can't just buy one piece. It comes in a five-piece place setting. Tureen, large cake platter, medium cake platter, teapot, coffee pot, creamer, sugar additional.

You look up and see the impatience in Evie's eyes.

And can hear your mother's thoughts, loud and clear, funneled into your own head, the small bowl in her hands: how wonderful it would be to run away, with just the girl. To come back in a few weeks for the other kids. But just have this girl, all to myself. To hear what the world been saying all along.

The bowl is hard as a rock.

Your mother purchases an entire dinner service of the unnamed pattern, twenty pieces in all, but says she'll have to come back at a later date for the soup tureen and cake platter. She is, after all, not made out of money.

LENOX

With the first light of her first morning in America, El felt the wind blowing in from the open window. A train clanged by, as if the track were close by. Bob, she called out again.

She found her suitcase in the front room of the apartment, right where Bob had dropped it, and she immediately went for the lock she'd snapped shut after tossing the cufflinks back inside.

The tea and coffee pots were fine, maybe a tiny chip on the edge of one lid. The platter was broken in three places. With glue, it could be restored. A bit of glue and some sun, some fresh New York air. The skyline, the taxis, the restaurants, the department stores. Gin and tonic flowing like a gulfstream toward Jamaica Bay, and from there out to the beckoning Atlantic.

She laid the Melitta dishes—blue pansies etched on a white background—back into the suitcase and went into the kitchen. The radio played soft and loud at the same time. Outside this window, which was covered with an eyelet curtain, a woman and child walked by, laughing.

El's hands felt damp. She smelled like Bob's hair, his chest. Surely there was a tea kettle somewhere in this kitchen. Above the stove a small plaque bearing the face of a black man read: *I've Been to the Mountaintop.*

She would have to shower, she would have to wash her hair.

PFALTZGRAFF

The swim was more delicious than food; afterward, you all rest on your backs on the slick bluestone shore, you and Monique and Kate (high as kites off some pills they borrowed from Stanley) and Meggie, who can't seem to stop crying. Her face has gone back to childhood, with its circles of ringworm and eye dirt. She says she will never get over the day your mother saved her life.

Once, she says, there was a family all living on top of each other in a double-wide but still there was no room. We ate Cap'n Crunch every day and felt hungry all the time. Then this lady appeared out of a cream-colored DeVille. She was wearing a blue scarf on her head, like a turban, and she smelled of lilacs.

Little girl, she said to me. Don't make such a sad face.

She lifted me into her arms, and I could smell baby roses over those lilacs. The powder blue ones, the kinds with the thorns that don't make any difference.

Little girl, she said, Would you like to come live with me? And I was all set to drift asleep, let this fine lady take me with her, away from the smell of unwashed cereal bowls and all the feet of my brothers.

She was better than a fairy godmother. She was cleaner than a queen. There was a pot of summer rhubarb boiling somewhere. And just like that, I recall my mama having words with her. Saying some nonsense about how her daughter was not some African orphan in the desert.

The truth was, I would've gone to any desert.

My mama lived twenty years after that day. You know what happened to me. On her last day at Auntsville Rehabilitation, where she was fidgeting with her kidneys, she told me I looked like a million bucks. How was it I raised such a gorgeous gal, she asked. Her lips were like quarry silt.

You did such a good job, I told her. I didn't want to bring up the cream DeVille. I didn't want to talk about that blue scarf or the queen walking into every house like she owned it. I was afraid of seeing the last drop of my mama evaporate on the spot.

ANCHOR HOCKING HOMESTEAD

Quit that bellyaching, Monique says, laughing. We all been there. We never look back, dummy.

What you need is a baby, says Kate, who is the only one—besides you—who is childless. She adds, A baby to love in the right way.

Monique swats her cheek gently and says, Lucky for us, there will never be a shortage of kids. Take your pick you want another one. Myself, I got three I'd love to give you. And I think Sasha Jean about ready to tell us of the newest addition, isn't that right?

No one waits for an answer: instead, they laugh faintly and remove their wet shirts and shorts. They are becoming mermaids, and for some reason, you can't stand to watch. Is it ever too late? Would swimming be better than a life of feathers? You know you're no different from the rest—so you get up and dive back into the hole, letting its blackness swallow you. Too late: at water's touch, your arms become fins and your legs fuse together. Your belly feels cold as you plough through the underground ripples; your neck has grown bright brown scales. The others don't seem to notice. But moments later, they call out to you, and then dive in themselves.

Do they change? You can't really tell. Eventually, you all swim, however, with the same ease, the same ruffled glide, to a mangrove tree, the roots of which sit like umbrella handles above the water. When you come up for air, you all look strangely bloodless. Tell us, Monique finally says, resting one arm on a root, What would you say, Sasha Jean, to some extra cash?

When you raise your eyebrows, she says, I plan to empty out the uncles' payday accounts tomorrow. I figured out a computer way.

Please don't name me accomplice after the fact, Kate says, swopping over to kiss Monique on the lips. Meggie blushes.

You are quiet, bobbing your head halfway into the water. And then you plunge as deep as you can to the bottom. You can hear the girls shout after you—*Rude Bitch, why can't you answer the question! You gone tell on us?*

It's lonely down below but also green. Pallid, alive. You wonder, as you open your eyes, where all the green has come from. There must be snakes here, you think, as you pull yourself—with fin arms—down farther into the hole.

He will never love you like he used to, your mother told you. But he says I'm his *favorite*.

You are an angel, she replies, wincing. I have to live with that.

Down below, you believe you see your mother's bluestone eyes, feel her farm-toughened hand upon your forehead. In Laboe there is an authentic German submarine on display on the sand; you can read the plaque and you can wail but you can't go in. You look past the motionless sea plants and recognize a knife in your mother's apron pocket.

If he ever says "finger" again, she warns, then lifts the knife
to her breast. You reach out and she vanishes among the
weeds—how could you tell her that he never once even uttered that word?

When you bubble up out from the depth—when you gasp
for air and hold tightly to Meggie's arm—you hear Kate,
speaking in a thick Southern accent, imitating someone back
at the reunion. Hattie or Cathy or LaWanda or Ancient Hattie Mabel. Chris or Daquan or Malik or Harris. You think
they've forgotten you when suddenly Monique nods toward
the reunion noise in the distance and says, If Bobby Lee in-
tends to take back Grandma Elldine's house, he's got another
thing coming. Family is family. We got our own ideas.

You and what army, Kate asks. That house needs bull-
dozed, plain and simple.

It'll be a place for you and me one day, Monique announces, taking Kate's hand and pressing it against her neck.
You and me.

Y'all better cut that shit out, says Meggie. But don't forget
to make me bridesmaid.

They laugh. They touch. Sunbeams try hard to burst
through the woods canopy. You're supposed to evict them all.

Kate says, I like it here. I open my eyes and every day it's a
new surprise.

Only a white girl would say that, Meggie laughs.

Why don't you say something, Monique suddenly asks.

But you're sure you *are* saying something, that words
are actually exiting your mouth and penetrating their ears.
You're pretty sure you're telling them that as of nine months
ago, you inherited everything here, as far as the eye can see.
Thirty-seven acres. You paid for it. You can't imagine ever
wanting to set foot here again.

And perhaps they *have* heard. Monique flips her fins playfully in front of her. We'd miss you if you never came back,
she says, not understanding. This is a sign. They hear what
they want to hear. And that's fine with you. You can never
really be free, but you're already there.

Crows and starlings screech through the landscape. In the distance there is the fragrance of the pig being roasted on the spit. You hear the old shingles peel off the Victorian and land in the elderberry hedge. The house will certainly die.

You clear your throat, make your way to the other side of the pond. The others release themselves from the umbrella handles and follow you, drifting on their backs. A child screams into the woods and waits for an answer. Ancient Hattie Mabel is shouting the words to "I'm Getting Ready."

You all dive again, this time not needing to come up for air. This is the world and there is no need for stealing, kissing, anger at past wounds. This world operates on scales and silt.

You expect it to end. For the fins to melt, the tails to finally recede, the women to call you all back to the tables. Hair will be quickly braided or wrapped into shirts, skin smoothed back into order. You expect that soon you will all tramp slowly and un-eagerly through the forest—Kate will suddenly squeal in horror as she steps upon a harmless worm—and then it will take forever for Meggie and Monique to tame her cries with their hands.

A fantasy arises in which you all continue your walk, even with the brays and hollers of the slave women in these woods, their feet smashing snakes, their arms tattered by thorned vines, their minds agape with the babies they could not afford to carry. The slave women are deafening, the slave women are worse than ghosts. You wonder if your parents are trapped here with the slave women. Would they torture your parents like ghosts in a cheap horror flick? Would that make you feel any better?

But this is all so conveniently stashed away. The world you're in now is all scales and silt. Meggie, Monique, and Kate dive deep, trail air bubbles behind them; their light and dark brown breasts hang over their bellies, not in perfect mermaid style, but in the style of girls who have longed to do this since the day they were born. Their hair floats in the depth like a series of snowballs. They remind you of Christmas. There is swimming, miles of it—and a surprise underground clearing, and giggles over mermaid nipples and moles, and promises, and some hope. Why ever resurface? Why not stay here for all time? Dandelion wine and nougat truffles. You could live like kings.

It's tempting, but not going to happen. *Land ho!* Meggie screams, laughing as she runs on ahead; she'll be the first one to fill up another plate and hug the kids. Kate and Monique touch fingers to lips behind every tree, vow to go to Stanley's room and steal the rest of his "raw material."

And over midnight margaritas on Aunt Nephronia's roof, you tell them (these girls now your girls) in clear, cement words, that you have no idea what your father is planning on doing to the land. But you promise it won't be anything bad.

ROYAL COPENHAGEN

El lifted her hand to her throat and felt the tiniest swell there, like a foamy wave bundling itself to the shore. She would have to go out and see Jamaica Bay up close. She would have to find that chocolate wafer edge of the world, once again.

There in the afternoon sunlight of the kitchen table, El dared not move. She hated the feeling that life was a race—would it be possible to remain here like this, forever? She found a pack of cigarettes behind the toaster and took one out, a race to the finish.

Anyone there, called Bob, slamming open the front door to the apartment. He carried a bag of sweet rolls in his arm. I'm home. I'm home.

She rose from the table, allowing herself to swoon against the wall. Don't I get no sugar, he asked, and she felt oddly moved by his stingy smile.

He buried his face in her neck. I'm a changed man, he whispered. Do you believe?

But El wasn't listening. She was wondering, instead, if her mother had finally noticed that the dishes were gone. She kept seeing the old face, disappointed and yearning at the same time. Not at all the right punishment for the crime.

The Girl Who Lied

UCHE OKONKWO

The first time I saw Kemi she was causing a scene. Everyone stopped to watch—the boarding house staff, the students they were checking in, and the parents carrying luggage into the hostels. In front of the hostels, in the open space where cars were parked, a woman stood by the back door of a shiny Land Cruiser with dark tinted windows, struggling to wrench herself free from Kemi, whose hands were locked around her middle. Kemi was holding on from behind, her body bent at the waist. Her face was buried in the small of the woman's back and her feet anchored in the sandy ground. Dark sunglasses covered the woman's eyes, and she was muttering through stiff lips. The driver's door flew open and a short, harassed-looking man hurried out of the car. He grabbed Kemi around the waist and pulled, his eyes bulging. When he managed to rip Kemi from the woman, he carried her, kicking and screaming, off in the direction of the school matron's house. I wasn't surprised by the laughter that had erupted around me, but I couldn't join in. Clearly she was new here, like me; and she looked about eleven, so she would be a Junior Secondary 1 student, like me. I knew I could easily have been her, holding on to my mother's wrapper and begging her not to leave me in this school in the middle of nowhere.

*

That evening, after a short welcome address, the matron assigned hostels, rooms and bed spaces to us J.S. 1 students, the new entrants. The rooms—each with sixteen bunk beds and lockers arranged along both lengths of the walls—felt dense, the air inside thick with the heat of bodies. The windows were few and small, and the ceiling fans slow. I was shown to my bed and locker and I immediately started unpacking my things, to distract myself from what I would be missing for the thirteen weeks or so that the school term would last. I tried to take comfort in the chattering voices around me, but they were mostly from senior students who were by now comfortable in this place that felt so strange to me. I took a break to glance around the room and take count of the new students—they would be the wide-eyed ones in uniforms that were still crisp like mine, not frayed with time and usage.

I felt oddly pleased to find Kemi sitting cross-legged on a lower bunk bed at the other end of the room, her body appearing smaller than it really was. She was chomping on something out of a red packet and looking into space. I stuffed the last of my things inside my locker and made my way to her bed, where I stood trying to appear casual, looking at her until she looked back.

"My name is Tola," I said. When she didn't reply, I nodded at her boxes, massive and unopened on the floor. "Won't you unpack your things?"

She eyed me for a few seconds before looking away. "When I'm ready," she mumbled through the Maltesers in her mouth.

I waited for her to say more. When she didn't, I said, "You were the one holding your mummy's waist this afternoon. That was you."

She laughed then and looked at me again. "You saw me, ehn? Was it good?"

I wasn't sure what she meant by "good," but I wanted her to know I could relate to how she was feeling. "You're not the only one," I said. "I wish I could follow my parents back home too."

I was surprised when she sneered.

"What, you think I'm a baby?" she said. "Please, I was just playing."

Kemi resumed her staring and chewing and I realized I'd been dismissed. As I went back to my locker I decided that Kemi was a spoiled brat—her mother's car and the big boxes, surely filled with expensive assorted goodies, the entitled, familiar way she chewed on the Maltesers. I told myself I didn't want to be friends with her.

I lay on the narrow bed after lights out, that first night at Lagos State Girls' Secondary School, Badagry, and stared into the dark. I imagined that, instead of standing by and watching my father's old Peugeot disappear after my parents had dropped me off, I had chased the car out through the school gates and all the way back to our flat in Ajah. Traveling down to the school that afternoon, leaving the noise and madness of Lagos behind and negotiating the potholed roads that ran through several kilometers of Badagry forest, my mother had sung along with the radio. My father bobbed his head and tapped the steering wheel to the rhythm, and I looked out the window at the green. Going back home with the car emptied of me, I wondered, could they have heard the songs the same way as before?

I liked to think not. I liked to think that my mother had cried, dabbing tears from her eyes and second guessing bringing me here; and that my father had patted her shoulder with his free hand, comforting her in his quiet way. Here, I was alone. It was dark, and as the room and its people slowly settled into sleep, I let go of the tears I had struggled with all day.

*

The next morning, I woke up to Kemi shaking me.

"It's wake up time," she said, peering into my face. She stood waiting, her towel wrapped around her, empty red bucket in hand, while I fumbled out of my night dress. With the warm weight of sleep still snug around me, it felt natural to follow her, with my bucket, out of the room. The memory of her snobbery the day before had grown distant and I felt a gratitude I could not explain. Her towel, red to match her bucket and slippers, seemed to glow before my eyes, a beacon I could not ignore. In the predawn dark outside, surrounded by other bleary-eyed students, we lugged buckets of water from the taps to the communal bathroom, a square expanse of concrete floor enclosed by four walls and lit by fluorescent tubes.

After surveying the bathroom with disdain, Kemi lifted her bucket and wove through the bathing girls. She led us to a vacant spot by a corner and set down her bucket. She unwrapped her body, folded her towel into a neat square and set it to hang on the handle of her bucket. I tried not to let my eyes linger on Kemi's chest, tried not to think how flat mine was in comparison. Desperate, I cast my eyes downward. A mistake. I couldn't help wondering if the darkness below her navel was a trick of the fading dawn. I set my gaze on Kemi's red bath bowl as it floated on the surface of the water in her bucket. She picked it up and took out a bar of soap that smelled sweet enough to be eaten.

"You want to bathe with your towel?" she asked me drily.

I kept a straight face and peeled my towel off, trying to adopt Kemi's ease even as she watched me. The warmth of my towel was replaced by a crippling self-consciousness as the air hit my naked skin. By the time I had my towel folded Kemi had emptied two bowls of cold water over herself, without making a sound, and was lathering soap onto her skin in vigorous strokes, her teeth gritted against the chilly air. I scooped up water in my bath bowl and held it suspended, away from my chest.

"Is it cold?" I asked Kemi.

"No, it's very hot," she said, her sarcasm as biting as the cold.

I kept my hand hanging and took a deep breath. "I will count to three and then pour," I announced to no one in particular. "One... Two..."

Kemi's hand shot forward and she emptied a bowl of cold water over my head. I shrieked, surprising myself and silencing the other bathers for a moment with the sound. Kemi ignored my glaring eyes and clapped her hands as she laughed, sending soap suds flying.

When she was done laughing, she fixed me with a gaze so solemn it was almost uncomfortable. "Don't worry," she said, "I am here to help you." And then she smiled. "Even if it means bathing you myself."

*

Around noon that day, the J.S. 1 students were herded into the school's assembly hall for the first item on our orientation program: the "School Tour." We were divided into seven large groups, each one led by a teacher brandishing a cane. Kemi and I stuck together and ended up in the same group. Our teacher and tour guide, Mr. Yusuf, had a mustache that threatened to slip into his mouth with every word he spoke. Kemi whispered something about the mustache resembling the brush of a long-handled broom.

Mr. Yusuf led us from the assembly hall to the dining hall to the principal's house and staff quarters. Then he steered us toward the hostels, and just beyond them, to the chimpanzee that I had noticed when I first arrived yesterday but had been too preoccupied to fully ponder. Its head jerked up as we approached, and it watched us, still and alert. We stopped a respectful distance away and Mr. Yusuf pointed with his cane.

"This," he said, "is Chaka the chimpanzee."

Chaka's muscled body was coated with dark brown hair. Its eyes, gold-flecked and somber, held a kind of sadness. It pouted its lips, and then spread them to show yellowish teeth and dark gums. We chuckled as it picked its teeth with a twig held in almost human hands.

"Don't think that because it looks like you, you can play with it," Mr. Yusuf continued. "This animal can be dangerous, so never go too close to the cage."

"If it is dangerous, why is it here?" Kemi asked.

"Good question. But raise your hand next time," Mr. Yusuf said. He licked his lips and continued. "Part of the land on which this great school was established...And when did I say the school was established?"

"Nineteen eighty-four!" we all roared.

"Very good," Mr. Yusuf said with a grin. "But remember to raise your hands. Part of the land that was given for the school used to be a wildlife conservatory." His eyes darted from one face to another. "And who knows what a conservatory is?"

Nobody volunteered an answer. "Nobody?" he prodded.

Kemi sighed and, her voice heavy with reluctance, said, "A place where animals are kept."

"Brilliant! But like I said, raise your hand before you speak, ehn," Mr. Yusuf said. "A wildlife conservatory is a place for keeping and protecting wildlife, wild animals. So part of the school, the extreme toward the principal's house, which you have seen, used to be a conservatory. When the government allocated the land for the building of this great school, the animals were moved, but it seems Chaka was forgotten, or left behind. The authorities never came for it, so it has been here since, like an inheritance. Who knows what 'inheritance' means?"

Kemi rolled her eyes as eager hands shot up. The question got answered and the students were quiet again.

"Can we feed it?" somebody asked.

"No. Feeding Chaka is the job of Sovi, one of the school's caretakers," Mr. Yusuf said. "You will see him around as time goes by. Never feed Chaka."

"Why can't we feed it?" Kemi asked, her hand stubbornly fixed beside her.

"I have just said that that is Sovi's job. You want to try feeding it so it can bite off your finger? That has happened

before to a stubborn student like you. After that incident,
she got the nickname of Philo Four Fing–"

"Can Chaka kill people?" Kemi asked.

By now I wanted to clamp her mouth shut with my palm. Mr. Yusuf seemed to be struggling for words. Kemi filled the silence. "What if it breaks the cage one day and escapes? What if it enters the hostels one night when we are sleeping and goes to somebody's bed?"

"Why are you asking these stupid questions?" Mr. Yusuf said, glaring at Kemi.

"You said we could ask questions," Kemi answered, her face unflinching and guileless.

Mr. Yusuf stared at Kemi a moment longer; then he smoothed his mustache. "Moving on," he said as he started to march off.

The other students, now subdued, followed Mr. Yusuf quickly, me and Kemi falling behind. Kemi met the other students' accusing glances every time, holding their stares until they looked away.

That night, after lights out, Kemi came to my bed. I had just started to drift off into sleep when she tapped my shoulder and whispered to me to move over. I blinked in the darkness, up at where I thought her face would be, and a question formed on my lips and lingered there. With an impatient sigh, she sat on my bed and pulled her legs up, forcing me to make room. I turned my back to her but my eyes stayed open and unseeing. She shifted around for a while, trying to find comfort. And she found it, molding her body into my stiff back. Her breath tickled my neck, and before long I could tell she was asleep. I stayed awake long after, not understanding my need to decipher the language her body spoke in sleep: one of murmurs, sighs, and grinding of teeth, unguarded and unrehearsed.

*

It was our first Sunday at Lagos State Girls' Secondary School, and a visiting evangelist was part of the orientation program. Muslims had been sent to the mosque and Christians, with Catholics grudgingly following, to the chapel hall. At Girls' Secondary School you could only be Christian or Muslim, and attendance at church or mosque was mandatory. Kemi could pick a side, a luxury that many students envied—as they did her well-known last name. She said her parents never went to church or mosque or anywhere. I found this lack of definition unsettling, but Kemi had no problem with it. She enjoyed watching Muslims perform their ablutions with water and had had a Muslim student show her the steps. But she said she liked to dance as well and was looking forward to showing off her skills in church. I had said nothing yet, but I had every intention of persuading her to choose church permanently.

"All heads bowed and all eyes closed!" It was the evangelist. The silence was absolute.

"The Bible says!" the evangelist thundered on, "that there will be weeping and gnashing of teeth! And it will be forever!"

I heard Kemi's frustrated sigh beside me and marveled at her lack of fear, but I didn't dare open my eyes to look at her.

"J.S. 1 students, you might think that you are still very young," the evangelist said, "but you are no longer children; you know right from wrong! God is watching, and all your sins will be played on a big screen in heaven on judgment day. All of you who tell lies, hell is waiting for you! You stole your bunkmate's bath water? Hell is where you are headed! You lied to your parents for extra pocket money? Hell! Except! Except if you become born again today and turn from all those evil acts. Don't wait until tomorrow; what if you don't wake up in the morning? What if, as we are leaving here, the trumpet sounds and God calls His people home? Where will you go?"

The answer was silence, broken only by intermittent sniffles from around the hall.

"Who will come to Jesus today?" the evangelist said, his voice now gentle.

There was rustling and the creaking of wood as students shifted on their benches. I cracked my eyes open long enough to glimpse anguished faces and raised hands, and to see that Kemi's hands were beside her, fingers tapping noiselessly on the bench. I closed my eyes again, raised my hand and repeated the words the evangelist said, inviting Jesus into my life yet again, just in case that other time with my parents wasn't enough. In case my salvation had worn off.

I could breathe easier after the prayer; the air seemed lighter somehow. But the evangelist was not done. He raised his voice again.

"There is somebody here! You need special deliverance from the forces of darkness!"

"God, when is this going to end?" Kemi muttered.

"Yes! Somebody here, they are oppressing you. They come to you in your dreams! Stand up and identify yourself, and be set free!" he said.

The hall remained quiet for a while. Then, "It is me, Pastor!"

I opened my eyes to see Kemi already on her feet, her hands lifted high above her head. "It is me!" Kemi repeated.

Hushed exclamations filled the hall. Kemi's name was in the whispers.

"Today! You will be delivered! Come out, sister!" the evangelist said, thrusting a fist up in the air above him.

As Kemi went slowly to the front, I felt numb with dread. But I also felt relieved that now, without having to ask, I had a possible explanation for Kemi's foray into my bed that night. It must have been these people, these dreams the evangelist spoke of, that had frightened her.

"Tell us what happened," the evangelist's voice was fatherly as he addressed Kemi. "The truth will set you free."

"I have been having…dreams," Kemi started. "This woman is always coming to me. She is very fair, like a white woman, with long hair, and she wears a long gown; a gold and shining gown. And she has a crown, with 'queen of the sea' written on it."

"What does the woman do to you?" the evangelist prompted.

"She is always calling my name, saying," and Kemi said this next bit in a voice I didn't recognize; a booming masculine voice. "'Kemi, Kemi, come and join the sisterhood! You have a mission!' Then I shout no and start running, and she starts chasing me…but…but when I turn back to look at her, her legs are not moving. And she doesn't even have any legs; she has a fish tail! And it's as if she's floating on air, and her long hair is made of snakes. Red snakes with tiny yellow eyes! Then I fall down and bang my knees against the ground, then when she is about to catch me, I shout, 'Jesus!' and I wake up."

"Hallelujah! That is the name of Jesus for you–"

"And when I wake up," Kemi said, "my knees ache, for like two days!"

"The devil is a liar," said the evangelist. "Sister, what is your name?"

"Kemi…Kemi Oyewole-Kamson."

"Sister Kemi, deliverance has come to you today. I will pray for you."

The service ended soon after, but the evangelist kept Kemi a few minutes longer. I waited for her outside the hall, and as she emerged I was surprised to see a smile on her face. It was not like any smile I had seen on the faces of the newly delivered. There was mischief on Kemi's face, and a sense of accomplishment. She gave me a quick wave and I stood waiting, expecting her to join me. Instead, she approached a group of girls standing in a huddle outside the hall. They had also witnessed the service, and as she got closer to them their voices grew hushed and they eyed her with apprehension. But I watched Kemi start talking to the girls, her arms gesturing wildly, and before long their wariness melted into laughter. I couldn't make out any words from where I stood, but I didn't need to. There was a look of satisfaction on Kemi's face as the girls doubled over, holding their sides and laughing. One or two of them even had to grip Kemi to keep from crumbling to the ground. I found a place on the hall corridor and sat, arms folded, my eyes fixed on the floor between my feet. With every spurt of laughter I heard, the urge to go there and drag Kemi away from the girls grew. I wondered what could possibly be funny about Kemi's problem, and why she was turning it into some kind of performance.

After the girls dispersed, Kemi came to me, laughing. "Why didn't you join us?" she asked. "I was telling them about the queen of the sea."

"So that's why you left me here, ehn," I said as I stood. "You knew I was waiting for you."

"You should have come if you wanted to; I didn't ask you to sit here like a statue."

I ignored the sting I felt at Kemi's words and asked, "Why were they laughing? What was so funny?"

Kemi stared at me, a smile slowly breaking out on her face. "Don't tell me you believed it too," she said, her laughter coming sharp and unexpected. "I should be in Hollywood!"

"You made it up? That's not funny, Kemi!"

"But it is funny," she sputtered. "You believed it, and those girls I was talking to just now, they believed it. And the pastor! Did you see the pastor's face? Queen of the sea, really? I almost started laughing in front of him."

It occurred to me then that Kemi was unlike any person I knew. I'd never known anyone to trick a pastor like that, and have him not see through it; never had anyone sneak into my bed without warning and steal my sleep, disappearing by morning and causing me to doubt the verity of the memory.

Kemi stopped laughing. "Do you think somebody will now tell my mummy I'm possessed?" Kemi asked, with what I thought was an exaggerated seriousness. "Maybe she'll think I need more deliverance, and she'll come and see me."

"You need to be careful, Kemi," I said. "What if something had happened to you in the chapel?"

"Something like what?" Kemi challenged, her hands on her hips.

"Like with Ananias and Sapphira in the Bible!"

"Ana who? Look, nothing happened jor. I was just joking around."

"You don't joke with God. I've heard of people who–"

"Relax, Tola!" Kemi said. "I don't know why you're so afraid of everything."

"I'm not afraid of everything!" I started to walk away, hoping that would settle it. Kemi followed.

"You're afraid of God," she said.

"The Bible says we should fear God."

"You're afraid of the matron and all the teachers."

"I respect them," I said, quickening my pace. "It's good home training."

"You're afraid of Chaka the chimpanzee."

"What, you want me to go and hug him to show I'm not afraid? That's stupid."

"You're afraid of senior students. You can't say no when they send you on errands."

"Doesn't mean I'm afraid," I said. At this point I wanted to start running, or stuff a handful of sand in Kemi's mouth to shut her up.

"You're even afraid of your classmates, J.S. 1 students like you!"

I stopped walking, causing Kemi to almost run into me. "That's not true!"

"Ehn? Then that day when Jemila tried to get in front of you on the queue at the dining hall, why didn't you say anything? You just let her, and I could see you didn't like it. If I didn't shout at her and tell her to go and join at the back, she would have taken your place just like that. And you were just standing there, looking at her like a mumu. Are you a fool?"

I choked back my tears and opened my mouth to tell Kemi she was wrong. But my voice came out as a croak. I swallowed and tried again.

"You're insulting me, abi," I said. "Don't worry, I won't insult you back. God bless you."

With that I ran off to the library where I hid my face in a book and cried. Kemi had no right to assume that she knew me so well after only a few days. So I liked to avoid trouble; it didn't mean I was afraid of everything. And what if I always obeyed the seniors; wouldn't that make them like me? Maybe. And was it such a bad thing to let people take my place on a queue sometimes? It was better than starting a fight over it. I wondered why Kemi wanted to be my friend, since she thought I was such a fool. I decided I would keep my foolish self away from her and see how she fared. When she got into trouble, as was sure to happen the way she was going, it would not be my concern. I would watch and be secretly satisfied every time she got punished.

When I heard the bell for dinner, I stayed put, ignoring my protesting stomach. Kemi might look for me in the dining hall, and I didn't want to talk to her ever again. I sat there in the library throughout dinner and night prep—Kemi would see me if I went to class—after which there were only a few minutes before lights out. Inside our room, I had to pass by Kemi's bed to get to mine, and my eyes sought her out against my will. She wasn't there, and it didn't matter. She was probably under the almond tree behind the hostel, reenacting her performance at the chapel for a fresh group of girls. I changed into my night dress and lay on my bed, trying to take up more space than my skinny body needed. There would be no room for Kemi here if she tried to squeeze in at night. I closed my eyes.

When the first bell for lights out sounded, I felt a presence beside my bed.

"Tola."

I said nothing.

"Tola, I fetched your bath water for you, for tomorrow."

I opened my eyes to see Kemi's hopeful face. She said, "There were many people at the taps. You should have seen how I struggled. See, I'm sweating." She wiped her forehead with the back of her hand and thrust the evidence at me. "See."

I told myself I was accepting her unspoken apology so easily only because Christians weren't supposed to hold grudges. I resisted the urge to smile. "Thank you," I said.

She smiled and pushed my bucket of water under my bed for safe keeping. As she went back to her locker I shifted on my bed, to make room for her in case she needed it.

*

We were on our way to the hostels one day after afternoon prep. The sun was beating down on us as Kemi told me yet another version of how she'd woken up in the middle of her appendicitis surgery and watched the doctors the rest of the way without flinching.

"I'm telling you, I saw when they brought out my appendix," she said. "It was so red, but so tiny! And there was so much blood, as if somebody poured a whole bottle of Ribena on me; the big bottle, not the small one."

As we passed by Chaka's cage, we recognized a few girls from our class standing around it, at a safe distance. They were making chimpanzee noises at Chaka, trying to get it to stop picking at its genitals and scare them off. Kemi stopped.

"You people are cowards!" she called out.

"Ha!" one of them replied. "You want to go near him? He will bite you!"

"What are you afraid of? It's just a chimpanzee," Kemi said.

"Oya, you go and touch it now, Kemi the Brave," another girl taunted.

"You think I can't go there?" Kemi asked, walking toward them. "I will go there and I will touch that cage. Dare me!"

"I dare you! In fact, I double dare you!" another girl said, her eyes blazing.

"Kemi, what are you doing?" I warned, knowing even before I said the words that they would not stop her.

Kemi shrugged off her backpack and strode toward the cage. I called out more warnings while the other girls stared,

their skepticism giving way to awe with each step she took.
Fully convinced that Kemi had no intention of stopping, I ran
to catch up with her and grabbed her arms from behind.

"Kemi, what are you doing?" I said. "Stop it!"

She tried to pull herself away but I held on tight, and soon we
were tugging back and forth, like in a strange tug of war. Somehow she managed to free herself enough to turn around and
face me, and with more force than I thought she was capable of
she shoved me away from her. Her face was a picture of twisted
desperation. She didn't even wait for me to hit the ground before
she resumed her march toward Chaka. I watched on from the
ground, too stunned to do anything more.

Chaka raised its eyes as Kemi reached the cage and gripped
the metal bars. Kemi met the chimpanzee's gaze and held it
for what seemed like several minutes. I opened my mouth to
tell Kemi to let go, that she'd fulfilled the dare. But Chaka was
quicker. It sprang from its perch and grabbed the front of Kemi's uniform through the spaces between the bars of the cage.
It held on, banging her body over and over against the cage.
The girls screamed as blood broke through the skin of Kemi's
forehead and nose. They picked up stones and sticks to hurl at
the chimpanzee, but the missiles just hit the metal of the cage
with a clang and fell away. Just as I thought to run for help,
Chaka let go of Kemi and she landed on the ground, buttocks
first. Then she fell back, her body flat on the sand. All the while
she had made no sound.

The other girls reached Kemi, and they took hold of her
arms and dragged her away from the cage. When they had
dragged her a good distance they stopped and surrounded her.
I forced myself up from the ground and ran to Kemi, shoving
bodies aside to make room for myself.

"Kemi! Kemi, wake up," I screamed, trying to shake her conscious. Tears were starting to gather in my eyes, blurring my
vision. The crowd around us was growing.

"Is she…" Whoever it was, they couldn't say the word that
was on all our minds. As I knelt there staring down at Kemi's

still body I knew I should have tried harder to stop her. I should have stood in her way, dragged her away from Chaka's cage if I'd had to.

Kemi's eyes popped open and her lips, bruised and swollen, spread wide in a smile. I found the white of her smile, the ease of it, disturbing, at odds with the blood on her face. She sprang into a sitting position, her head almost colliding with mine. The girls broke into a cheer as someone helped Kemi to her feet and others brushed the sand from her clothes and hair. Like a small wave, the crowd carried her a few meters away, leaving me kneeling, watching the imprint her body had left in the sand. I struggled with a mixture of relief and annoyance as I retrieved Kemi's bag. Chaka had gone back to the mystery between its legs and Kemi, cocooned within her newest crowd, acted out being banged against Chaka's cage. Somebody offered her a tissue and she dabbed it against her forehead and nose, contemplating the blood that came away on it with a pleased look. I parted the bodies and took Kemi by the hand, announcing that I was taking her to the school nurse. The others quickly lost interest, and Kemi and I walked alone to the sick bay.

"Do you think the nurse will wrap a big bandage around my head?" Kemi asked. "Like those ones in films when someone has a car accident."

I said nothing.

We reached the sick bay and I presented Kemi to the nurse. She frowned as she sat Kemi down and started to clean her wounds. "How did you get these injuries?" she asked.

"From Chaka. I wanted to give him a hug," Kemi said. "Because he was crying."

The nurse's hand went still on Kemi's forehead as she stared at her. I turned to Kemi, trying to read her intentions on her blank face.

'That's not true, Ma,' I said to the nurse.

The nurse turned to me. "Then what happened?" she asked.

I swallowed and glanced at Kemi, trying to decide whether to defy her warning eyes and tell the truth. But I concluded that the truth—that Kemi had got herself injured on a dare—wasn't much better than Kemi's obvious lie.

"I don't know," I said, looking at the ground.

The nurse regarded me for a moment. Then she said, "Since you two won't tell me what happened, maybe you'll prefer to talk to the matron."

She stepped out of the sick bay and sent a wandering student to fetch the matron. The nurse returned and started to cover Kemi's wounds with small strips of bandage. Then she gave Kemi some Panadol and water. The matron arrived shortly after.

"I don't know what happened to this student's face," the nurse said to the matron, "and they won't tell me. But I think it has something to do with Chaka."

I stood leaning against a wall, wishing I could disappear into it. The matron's eyes passed over me and settled on Kemi.

"Kemi Oyewole-Kamson! You again?" she said. "Only last week you were punished for misbehaving in class. What is this now? Maybe it's time I spoke to your parents about your behavior." Kemi tried to keep her face glum even as her eyes lit up at the mention of her parents. The matron looked from Kemi to me and back. "What happened here?"

Kemi spoke up quickly. "Tola wasn't with me, Ma. She only helped me to the sick bay."

After giving Kemi a tetanus injection, the nurse confirmed that her injuries weren't serious. The matron then dismissed me and asked Kemi to follow her to her house. I went to the hostel and waited for Kemi, praying she didn't get into trouble. I could only imagine the way I would feel in her position. The thought of having my parents summoned because I had behaved badly felt physically painful.

Kemi was quiet when she returned from the matron's house. She went to sit on her bed and I joined her moments later.

"What did the matron say?" I asked.

"She's not calling my mummy."

I let out a relieved sigh and wondered, considering the good news, why Kemi looked unhappy. "What's wrong?" I asked her. She drew her legs up to her chin and hugged them close. I tried another question. "Why did you do that, with Chaka?" I waited a long time for an answer that never came.

*

I knew she would come to my bed that night, and I was waiting. I heard her approaching and I feigned sleep, resisting the tension that crept into every muscle. Her face felt wet tucked into the space between my shoulder blades, and it occurred to me that she might be crying. I lay still, let her body curve into mine. My vigil began the moment she fell asleep.

*

My mother came the afternoon of the first visiting day of the term, just as she had promised. The parking area in front of the hostels was crowded with cars and the families of students. I had been standing outside the hostels for a while, craning my neck to look up the road for my mother and hoping Kemi would get fed up with this and go inside without me. But she was still standing there, the bruises on her face from her encounter with Chaka now barely discernible against her dark skin, when I made out a figure with my mother's rolling walk.

As my mother approached, it struck me how old and tired she looked. My eyes welcomed the familiar pattern on her iro and buba, but I could see now, for the first time, how badly the colors had faded. I pictured Kemi's mother, her face smooth like a mannequin's, her hips sheathed in denim trousers that my mother could never pull off. And there was that big shiny car Kemi's mother had. For the first time, it bothered me that all my family had was the rickety Peugeot.

My mother spotted me and called out with a wave and a smile. My own smile didn't come as easily.

Kemi followed when I went to my mother. I stepped into her open arms and buried my face in her neck to take in the smells of home, my happiness mingling with my shame at seeing my mother through Kemi's eyes. When I let go, my mother handed me the bag she had brought with her, and I bit back my disappointment at how light it felt. When she was done looking me over—complaining about the mosquito bites that marked my skin and how I'd lost weight—my mother noticed Kemi hovering beside us with a half smile.

"Is this your friend?" my mother asked.

"Yes, Ma," Kemi answered with a cute curtsey. "My name is Kemi Oyewole-Kamson."

I could tell my mother recognized the family name. But she only smiled and, noticing the fading bruises and scabs on Kemi's face, asked, "What happened to your face?"

Kemi laughed. "It's nothing, Ma. I got up one night to pee, and it was dark, so I didn't see the door. I walked into it."

My mother frowned her concern as she examined Kemi's face, clicking her tongue, trailing her fingers around the bruises, asking if they still hurt. Kemi said they did a little, and as my mother fussed some more Kemi's eyes found mine. She smiled a challenge at me, and I could almost hear her daring me to tell the truth about her face.

At my mother's suggestion we walked to one of the school shops to get drinks. As we went, she explained that my father was out of town on business and that he sent his love. She talked about home; how it was so quiet with me and my brother away, and that he was doing well at university. Between all of this, she would turn to Kemi, as if to make sure she was still there, and ask how she was and if her parents were coming to visit. We sat down at the shop with our drinks and Kemi stayed the whole time, making my mother laugh with highly embellished stories of our first days at the school, like how she'd had to chase me around the large bathroom with a bowl of water on our first morning, to get me to take my first cold bath. I watched Kemi charm my mother, part of me thinking I should be upset, or at least a little jealous. But there was a need in Kemi's eyes that was new to me;

and, not for the first time, I felt something like pity for my friend. This feeling was as sure as it was puzzling.

Kemi remained with us until my mother was ready to leave. I took the bag my mother had brought for me inside the hostel, to empty it into my locker, and then I went back out to walk with her to the school gates. Kemi stood to walk with us. My mother told Kemi that she didn't have to go with us if she didn't want to, but Kemi insisted she did. Kemi was quiet as we walked, and my mother talked about her hair salon, and how she had put off hiring an assistant for yet another month. At the gates, my mother held both our hands and prayed for us. Then she asked Kemi to wait while she took me aside.

"Your friend, she is from that Kamson family?"

"Yes, Mummy."

"See, your Daddy and I were right. For an Oyewole-Kamson to come here, this must be a good school."

'Ehn…But the food here is not sweet, and we wake up at five every morning, except Saturdays and Sundays. And the teachers like to cane us–"

"Tolani, stop complaining," my mother scolded gently. "You should be thankful that you can come to school here. You know how much we are paying."

"Yes, Mummy," I mumbled at the ground.

"Don't worry, before you know it six years will pass and you'll finish from here." She laughed, "What am I even saying, by the time you become a senior you won't remember all this your whining. You'll want to stay another six years!"

"No, Mummy," I laughed, snapping my fingers over my head for emphasis. "Never, never, never."

She looked past me. I followed her eyes to Kemi squatting and drawing figures in the sand with a twig.

"Is your friend OK? I hope somebody will come and visit her."

"I think her mummy is coming."

"OK. I hope she is a good girl. Remember what the Bible says about friends—evil communication…"

"Corrupts good manners," I said.

Was Kemi corrupting my "good manners"? I didn't think so. I still prayed every night as my parents had taught me to, though sometimes I would fall asleep right in the middle. I even prayed for Kemi, but for her my prayers were always vague, questioning: "bless her, Lord. Help her...?" Words always failed me, because I thought she needed something, I just didn't know what.

Looking at my mother's face, I wanted to tell her everything. And I would have, before. I would have told her that Kemi made up stories and behaved badly in church; that she disrespected seniors and mocked teachers, and that I had to constantly see to it that she didn't get us both into trouble too often. I could have told her that Kemi liked to hike up the skirt of her uniform when she sat in class, or anywhere, and that she kept doing it even after Mr. Dibia had caned her six times, even when she knew people could see her underwear. I could have told her that Kemi liked the sight of her own blood, cutting her nails so close to the skin that spots of red sprouted and that she no longer bothered to pretend it was a mistake. I could have told her about Chaka, and how even after that incident, Kemi still sometimes walked too close to its cage, laughing when I rushed to pull her away.

But I was not sure my mother would understand that, in spite of all these things, Kemi was not "evil."

"I heard her father has three wives. What a terrible environment for a child...all that fighting and suspicion, and maybe the wives even use juju."

"She told me she and her mother have their own house. Only her uncle lives with them," I said.

"Hmm," my mother was reluctant to concede. "Maybe that's a little better. Still, it's not ideal...Does she go to church?"

"Yes, Mummy." I smiled. "She didn't use to before, but I made her start going."

"Good. Continue to be a good influence on her, you hear. I hope you've been reading your Bible."

"Yes, Mummy."

"Good girl." My mother pulled me close and wiped something from behind my ear with her thumb. Her voice was suspiciously casual when she spoke again. "When did you say your midterm break was?"

"Next two weeks," I said.

"Hmm…OK…" I knew she had more to say and I waited for it. "I saw your matron when you went inside your room with the bag. I asked her and she said students can stay back in school for the break if they want to. They will give you food, just as normal, and the matron and some of the other staff will be here to look after you."

My mouth fell open. I could already hear her next words.

"I think it will be better if you just stay here in school for the break," she said.

"But Mummy, I want to come home!"

She sighed. "I know, but the break is not long; it's only for three days–"

"Ehn, I still want to come. Everybody else will go home!"

"The matron said that there are always some students that stay back. You won't be the only one."

"No, Mummy, I want to come home!" I said as I stamped my feet, tears forming in my eyes.

"My dear, don't cry," my mother said, enfolding me in her arms and patting my back. "It's not that I don't want you to come home, but there is nothing in the house. Your daddy and I have spent so much on you and your brother's school fees, and now we're just managing at home, eating beans all the time. And I know how much you hate beans. There's no point spending all that transport money to come home, and then when it's time to come back there's nothing much to give you. Or you want to come and eat beans with us every day?"

My mother held me close, making jokes about beans, and I knew it was decided. "Be a big girl, OK," she said as I choked on my tears. "We'll come and see you next visiting day. Daddy will come too. We'll buy more things for you, OK? Just manage for now."

After giving me and Kemi final hugs, my mother left. I
watched her through the school gates until she got into a bus.
Kemi and I walked back to the hostel in silence. My eyes felt
swollen and my nose was dripping snot. I felt ashamed and
hoped Kemi would pretend not to notice my face, at least for
a while. She didn't. She said my face looked like a pumpkin
when I cried, and she went on to tell the story of the last Hal-
loween she had spent with her cousins in the US and how the
carved pumpkin had appeared in her dream that night to tell
her a scary story. I let Kemi's voice wash over me, grateful to
her for sparing me, in her own way.

*

It was past six p.m., the official close of visiting time, when
Kemi got the message that she had a visitor. She lit up at
once and sprang from her bed, tugging at my arm and saying I had to meet her mother now. I wondered why the visit
was so late, but I realized that, unlike other parents, the
Oyewole-Kamsons would not need special permission for
this. We hurried out of the hostel and saw the only car left
outside: the black Land Cruiser looked bronzed in the light
of the setting sun. As we approached the car, the driver's
door opened and the short man from the first day, who I
now knew was Kemi's mother's driver, got out. He flashed
uneven teeth at us.

"Ah, Kemi," he said, "how are you?"

Kemi looked past him, into the back of the car. "Where's
my mummy?"

"Em, she has traveled to Dubai, today," he said quietly, as
though he was afraid to be heard. "I just dropped her at the airport; that is why I'm late. But she sent plenty things for you–"

Kemi spun and ran back into the hostel, leaving me with
the driver. After a moment of awkward silence, he let out a
sigh and went behind the car to open the boot. He hefted out
a large bag.

"Please...take this to her, ehn. Her mother sent it."

I held the bag by the handles and turned to leave. Then I remembered the midterm break and told the driver about it; Kemi should get to go home, even if I wouldn't. He thanked me and got into the car. I carried the bag in, panting, and set it down in front of Kemi's locker. As on that first day, she was sitting on her bed with her legs crossed, looking at nothing. I sat beside her.

"Sorry your mummy didn't come," I said. And after a while, "Won't you check what she sent for you?"

"You check."

I opened the bag and found enough in it to last a whole term: boxes of cereal, sugar, tins of milk, cans of sardines, groundnuts, chocolates and chocolate chip cookies, packets of candy, juices and sodas, and even bottled water. My bag had contained a sack of garri, a packet of sugar, one small bottle of groundnuts, one tin of Milo, and one sachet of milk. I opened Kemi's locker and started to arrange the things into it, cheered by the thought that I would get to partake of them. I glanced at Kemi's face and immediately felt guilty. It was a good thing I let her have my mother for the afternoon.

*

That night, after lights out, the other J.S. 1 students in our room gathered around Kemi's bed, as they did sometimes. Kemi sat in the middle of her bed, and the rest of us spread out around her on the bed and floor. The mood was festive in the hostel, resonant with the students' joy at seeing their loved ones again after weeks in school. Nobody was enforcing the rules of lights out. We passed around a plate of somebody's home-cooked food, the glow of a flashlight the only illumination.

"Kay-Kay," one of the girls said. They called her Kay-Kay, these people who were not her friends. "Is it true that you have really seen Lady Koi-Koi?"

Many students said that part of the school was built on the grounds of an old cemetery, and that the school was therefore haunted. Koi-Koi was the ghost lady who always wore white, and a pair of heels that went "koi-koi" on the concrete floors. Stories of encounters with Lady Koi-Koi were widespread and varied, and I doubt that any of us really believed them. Kemi had told her own Lady Koi-Koi story several times; each version was slightly different, but nobody ever pointed that out. They were too taken with her: the way she could switch accents and make her voice scary and then soft, the masks she could contort her face into, how she would stand to act out her descriptions.

"Kemi has told us that story many times before," somebody else said. "Aren't you tired of it?"

"Yes, something new," another girl demanded.

I wished I could make them disappear, these girls who kept pecking at her, looking to be entertained. Some had even taken to calling her KKTV, and it seemed like she enjoyed it, like she craved the attention. But it made me think of her as a fly caught in a spider's web, resigned to its fate. The dignified victim. I was always alone in the crowd that followed us. I was the only one who noticed how the light would sometimes fade from her eyes, right in the middle of a story. I was the one who knew she was as restless in sleep as she was awake. I was the one who sacrificed sleep, those nights she would come to me, to listen, to match my breathing with hers, to make my body into shapes that allowed her to be. These others, they came and went as they pleased, taking the bits of her that they liked. There was an unspoken consensus among them: Kemi was fun, in small, carefully selected doses.

"Have I told you about my appendicitis operation?" Kemi said. There was a chorus of yeses. Kemi continued, "And how I got lost when I traveled to London with my mummy to see the Queen?"

Kemi ran through a list of stories, all familiar, all recycled times over. Then she fell silent, like a deflated balloon.

"No more stories from Kemi," somebody said, with a sigh that was really a challenge.

"Have I told you," Kemi said finally, her voice a whisper, "about The Man of Night?"

Kemi paused, and we grew still with her. The murmuring of the other students in the room faded into silence in my ears.

"He lives in the shadows," Kemi continued. "And...you know how in horror films, something will happen in a dream, but the actor feels it when they wake up? That's what The Man of Night feels like. He will come when you're sleeping. He will whisper things in your ear and make you relax. You can't see him; even if you open your eyes, all you'll see is black. But you can feel his hands...touching you...But nobody will believe you when you tell. You've come again with your stories, that's what they will say. Because you're the only one who knows. You're the only one he comes to at night."

After a long silence, one listener asked, "So what happens next?"

"He follows you," Kemi said. "He follows you everywhere."

Kemi went quiet after that, ignoring their questions and promptings until, one by one, the girls drifted off to their beds. This story without scary voices or song and dance was not the kind they had come to expect from their KKTV. I, too, was struck by this Man of Night, but in a different way than the other girls. Something about him felt real.

But then, it was Kemi, and Kemi could make anything seem real.

*

It was not the kind of day when bad things happened. The sky was cloudless that afternoon, and there was an air of celebration in the school—the midterm break was barely a week away. It was laundry day, and I stood beside Kemi's bed, my arms piled high with clothes, trying to get her to come out with me.

"I don't feel well," she said, her words muffled by the pillow her face was buried in. I was skeptical. Any moment now, I knew, she could be entertaining a small crowd, as though a switch had been flipped somewhere inside her. I was not going to do her laundry for her.

"Sorry, ehn," I said in my sweetest voice. "I'm going to wash by the well behind the hostel. There are too many people at the taps. You can meet me there when you're feeling better."

There were three other girls washing clothes by the well when I got there. I put my pile of laundry on the ground, and then I lowered my fetching pail into the light brown water in the well. The girls were loud and excited, talking about all the things they would do when they went home for the break. I resisted the urge to point out that the break was only three days long and that they couldn't possibly do all of those things in that time. I was still upset about not getting to go home, but a scab had grown over the pain now. It also helped somewhat that Kemi didn't seem excited about the coming break. Whenever I complained about not being able to go, or tried to get her to talk about her plans for the holiday, she would shrug and give a vague "we'll see."

I was rinsing out my clothes when I saw Kemi approaching in the distance. I noticed she wasn't carrying any clothes, and I looked back down at my washing. I knew that if I looked at her sulking face long enough, she would persuade me to do her washing yet again. When she got to me, I would try my best to avoid that face.

I heard the screams first, and then there was a splash. I looked up to see the other girls rush toward the well and I followed, fighting to disbelieve what I suspected had happened. My fingers felt wooden as I clutched the rim of the well and leaned over to look inside it. Kemi was there at the bottom of the well, the water reaching to her chest, looking up at us. There was a patch of red on her right cheek where her skin must have scraped against the sides of the well. Other than that, she seemed unharmed. I did not let myself imagine what might have happened had the well been deeper, with enough water to cover her completely. One of the girls ran off to get help as more students, alerted by the screams, approached the well.

"Kemi! Are you OK?" I called down. "What happened? How did you fall inside?"

Another girl, one of the three who had been by the well earlier, glanced at me. "She didn't fall," she said. "She jumped."

It shouldn't have made sense to me that Kemi would jump into a well, but it did. The well had a high concrete rim; it would be difficult for anyone to fall in by accident. And then there was that time with Chaka, and the feeling it left me with: a sense of the inevitable. I had never thought of Kemi sitting at the bottom of a well, staring up at the world, but seeing her now, I got the feeling that it was always going to happen.

"Move away…make way," the matron panted, running to the well. I saw some of the tension on her face ease when she looked inside the well and saw that Kemi was conscious. She grabbed the closest girl she could reach.

"Go and call Sovi immediately!" she said. "Tell him to come with his strong rope."

The matron shouted questions down at Kemi as we waited for Sovi, the caretaker. But Kemi remained silent and lowered her gaze to something in the water. Sovi appeared shortly with a length of rope coiled around one shoulder. His walk was not any more brisk than usual, and he was wearing the brown shorts and once-white singlet that seemed to be his only items of clothing. He glanced into the well, his face not registering any surprise at finding a girl inside it. Then he looked up and started to whistle a tune as he considered his surroundings. He walked toward the tree that stood not too far from the well, and he took the rope from his shoulder and tied one end around the tree's trunk, tugging at it to test its hold. Satisfied, he lowered the other end of the rope into the well, where part of it disappeared under the water. Sovi gripped the rim of the well and eased himself over slowly, one leg finding a foothold first, and the other joining in. Then he transferred his grip from the well's rim to the rope. His muscles bunched and strained as he made the torturous journey down the well, finding footholds to support his weight as he slid lower on the rope.

When Sovi finally stood in the pool of water at the bottom of the well, Kemi looked up at him. He said something to her and she nodded and sniffled. He helped her up, but when she tried to stand on her own she crumpled back down with a scream and a splash. Sovi turned his back to Kemi and squatted in the water. Kemi held on to his shoulder, grimacing as she arranged both arms around his neck and aligned her body with his back. I wished I could have been the one to go down to her rescue. Sovi patted Kemi's arm and took a deep breath, preparing himself for the climb. Then, wearing his resolve as proudly as he did his brown shorts, he held on to the rope and started up. As he climbed higher, I noticed that Kemi's right leg was hanging limp.

When Sovi emerged from the well, the matron unwound Kemi from his back. I fought my way through the watching students to Sovi's side, where Kemi was laid down. Her clothes were dripping wet and tears escaped through her eyelids, which were squeezed shut against the pain. I tried to comfort her with words I do not now remember, but if she heard me she gave no sign. At the matron's direction, Sovi lifted Kemi off the ground. They started toward the sick bay and I followed, leaving the gawking students behind. I tried to catch Kemi's eyes but her face was turned away from the world, buried in Sovi's chest.

Sovi put Kemi down on a bed in the sick bay while the matron talked with the nurse. Kemi kept her eyes closed, and I could see the muscles in her cheeks work as she clenched her jaw. I knelt beside the bed and stroked her hair, watching the wetness from her clothes spread through the bed sheets. The nurse briefly examined Kemi's leg and shook her head. Kemi was scooped up into Sovi's arms again, and the matron, the nurse, Sovi, and I hurried toward the matron's house. There Sovi gently laid Kemi across the back seat of the matron's car, and the nurse and matron drove toward the school gates.

*

A few hours later, we stood in a file, us four witnesses, before the vice principal, the matron and Kemi's mother.

"You girls were there when it happened?" the vice principal asked from behind her wide desk, looking at each of us in turn.

"Yes, Ma," we answered.

Kemi's mother sat on the other side of the vice principal's desk, her back turned to the vice principal, eyeing us. Her face gave nothing away, and her eyes reminded me of the tinted, polished windows of her car. The matron stood beside the vice principal like a guard.

"Please, Ma," I asked, surprised that I could, "where is Kemi?" I wasn't sure which of them would answer, but I didn't really care.

"She is in the hospital," the vice principal said, looking slightly displeased. "She broke her leg, but other than that she is fine. Now, tell us what happened. Kemi has refused to say anything."

The girls looked everywhere but at the panel of adults.

"Did she fall into the well by accident?" the matron prompted. "Did someone push her?"

"There is nothing to be afraid of," the vice principal said, impatience creeping into the soothing tone she was trying to adopt. "Nobody is going to punish you for anything you say here."

"She fell, Ma," one of the girls said.

"It's true, Ma," the others agreed quickly. One added, "She was bending, to draw water, then she fell inside the well. That's all we saw."

I was not surprised that they would lie. We all knew that saying Kemi had jumped could get her into trouble. The vice principal and matron looked relieved. Kemi's mother's face stayed blank.

"Well," the vice principal sighed, "the doctor said she will be fine once her leg heals. We thank God for that."

"Good thing that well is not very deep," the matron said.

"Or we might have been telling a different story now–"

"She jumped," I said. I felt every eye in the room turn to me, but I kept mine on the wall behind the vice principal's head.

"You said what?" the vice principal asked.

"Kemi jumped," I said. "Nobody pushed her, and she didn't fall in by accident."

Kemi's mother leaned forward and fixed her eyes on me for a long time. When she finally spoke it was to say one word: "Liar."

I looked at her then and saw something flicker in her gaze. Seeing her struggle to believe her own accusation, I almost felt sorry for her. Then I remembered Kemi's face after she'd been carried out of the well; hers was not a face made for tears. My sympathy could lie only with Kemi.

"She jumped," I said again.

Maybe if they knew she had jumped someone would try to see beneath Kemi's surface, see the trouble that I had sensed but could not understand. Maybe somebody could help fix her—and not just her legs. Maybe she would be all better when she came back.

"You can go," the vice principal said after a long silence.

We filed out, careful to make as little sound as possible, me ignoring the accusing glances the other girls threw my way. Outside the office, the girls went ahead and I paused just beside the door. I heard the matron say that I couldn't be sure of what I had said, that eleven-year-olds weren't in the habit of throwing themselves into wells.

As I approached the hostels after prep that evening, I saw Kemi's mother's car. I wondered if she was still in the vice principal's office and, if so, what they were talking about. Kemi's mother suddenly emerged from the hostel gates, rolling one of Kemi's wheeled boxes on the ground. Behind her, the driver carried Kemi's mattress in a bundle on his head. He offered an apologetic smile when he saw me.

*

Kemi's bunk stayed empty the rest of the term. I made promises to myself: I would be a better friend when she returned. I would do her laundry all the time; even her home work, if she wanted me to. I would share in her pleasure when the other girls gathered around her, calling her KKTV. I would make her sleep in my bed every night, and we would never fight again. If she would just come back.

*

One day in the middle of the second term, a new mattress, with its new owner, found its way to Kemi's bunk. I wanted to rip this girl and her mattress to shreds and make her know she did not belong there. Kemi had left her imprint in that space, and this stranger could never hope to fill it. Nobody could. Instead I cried. And I slowly started to accept that Kemi was not coming back.

I have asked myself, in the years that have passed since the day I last saw her, would I have told the truth if I had known then that it could mean never seeing Kemi again? I would like to say yes, that I was capable of putting her needs before mine; that I would have suffered the loss if it meant a chance at saving her. But I don't know this. Maybe I would have taken a broken Kemi over no Kemi, and closed my eyes to all the things I didn't then understand. Or maybe I could have loved her into wellness with time, all by myself, and changed the story. This is what I tell myself some nights.

Bones

LISA HORIUCHI

Kyle Waller was retired from his job at InvoTech for exactly twenty business days when he found himself crouched at the helm of an old fishing boat, sputtering across the jade skin of the Mopan River in Belize. The boy Oscar was at the stern, manning the rudder while the woman from Florida and her teenaged son sat athwart, withering in the heat, heads shrouded in sunglasses and safari hats, noses white with zinc. The farther they traveled up the river, the more the jungle canopy thickened with poisonwood and breadnut, blossoming bribri, florets of tamarind spreading like parasols over the river's breach. Along the bank, iguanas sunned themselves on the mudstone flats.

"Oscar," Kyle called, turning to show the boy his profile. "How long before we hit Bullet Tree Falls?"

"I think so fifty minutes," Oscar shouted over the throaty rattle of the motor. "About fifty, but maybe more, actually."

Kyle glanced back to get a good look at Oscar's arm and bare wrist, brown from the sun and his Mayan lineage.

As expected: no wristwatch. Kyle felt a wave of agitation tickle the nape of his neck, but the boy gave him a double thumbs-up and smiled so broadly and so earnestly that Kyle suppressed the impulse to bark out an order. Old habits died hard.

"Well," he said, checking his own watch. They'd left the lodge at Benque Viejo at nine in the morning. It was already ten twenty, and the day felt as if it were running away from them. Still, he held up an appreciative hand and dipped his chin in deference to the young captain. "Looks like we're making good time. Good job, Oscar."

The late-morning heat arranged itself around them, invisible, viscous, aboriginal—a solid thing you could touch. Kyle gave his arthritic fingers a callisthenic stretch before hiding his aching fists in the pockets of his shorts. He grumbled into his shirt collar and looked back up, squinting at the murky green river ahead.

"Mr. Waller, you're on vacation," the woman from Florida said. "Why the rush?"

Her name was Cheryl, and her son was called Diggs, after a great-great-grandmother of Norman descent, a nineteenth-century émigré of alleged prominence. Kyle had gotten an earful last night at the lodge, over happy-hour cashews and plantains washed down with 100-proof Jaguar Juice. Cheryl's sun sign was cancer; she was ten-years divorced and ran a specialty cake shop out of a crawfish joint in Kissimmee; Grandmother Diggs was on her side of the family, and so on. Kyle recalled business-school classmates with inherited Christian names—Baines, Palmer, Reese—a ritual of the wealthy. He imagined her kid at Harvard. It was an absolute absurdity. Diggs had black-dyed hair that hung in knotted strands below the limp brim of his hat, and his sunglasses—large Audrey-Hepburn shades trimmed in tortoiseshell and worn ironically—obscured his eyes and his angst-ridden secrets. Kyle felt a passing shot of relief at never having had children of his own.

"Why the rush?" Cheryl asked again.

The outboard motor stammered and spat, slowing the boat. Oscar muttered something in Spanish—not a curse— and hit the powerhead with the bony base of his palm. It resumed its low rumble, and the boat lurched back on its course, sending Cheryl stumbling in her seat, making a frenzied grab for the gunwale. The ride stabilized and she caught herself, shimmying up straight and pushing at the bridge of her sunglasses, pretending to adjust the tip of her hat. Diggs looked portside where two Caribbean women, one old and one young, were pulling ropes of laundry out of the water at the river's edge, while a toddler in soiled Fruit of the Looms waded in the shallows, waving.

Kyle lifted his palm to the child as they passed.

"I need to get to the bones before dark," he said.

*

Kyle had met the osteologist on one of his cool-down drives twenty business days ago after his last non-fight with Patty back in LA. Like all their arguments, it had hardly been a fight at all, only the beginning of one—Kyle, having no interest in bringing his work personality home, had removed himself from the situation with great efficiency. They'd just returned from his retirement party, and she was talking nonstop as she tended to do after a drink or two. And while she was in the bedroom doing whatever it was she did in her post-party haze—unbuckling sandals, emptying her purse, unrolling stockings—he retreated to his office to make a quick phone call to Bernie. It was midnight and outside the window of propriety, but he'd overheard a troubling conversation in the men's room at the Ritz, and now it was an infuriating itch he had to scratch.

Bernie answered the phone brightly, but when he heard his old boss say the words "lost inventory" something in the tenor of his voice tightened.

"It's under control," Bernie assured him.

"The exposure was supposed to be four hundred thousand," Kyle said, lowering himself into his smoking chair. He used his toes to kick off his patent-cap Balmorals, and he stretched his black-socked feet out onto the plush of the antique Khorassan carpet, a staple from the old days. "Not four million. Apparently nothing's changed—the VP of Operations is the last to know about the goddamned operation. I have to spy on you bastards in the head to get the inside scoop on anything."

"People talk shit in the pisser," Bernie said. "'Talk shit in the pisser.' See what I did there?"

"Bern. This is big."

Patty appeared in the doorway in a nightshirt and soft pants, her hair in a scarf. She was holding up a bottle of Glenfarclas by the neck, brazenly, like a cowboy of the Old West.

Kyle waved her away.

"No offense, Kyle," Bernie said over the phone. "But. Remember what we celebrated tonight? Everybody made speeches? Your wife got drunk? You got a watch. A good one."

"Work doesn't end when you stop working," Kyle said, stupidly.

Patty stood there, giving him a close-lipped stare, her scotch-holding arm dropping like a weight. Bernie, too, was silent on the other end of the line.

"We're talking my legacy," Kyle said. "Is what I'm saying."

"I'm zonked," Bernie said. "Do you mind horribly if we talk tomorrow? Even later if you like. It's…well. You're on permanent vacation. You can retire the 'Czar' shtick for a change, go have fun."

"Control that inventory, will you? For me."

"All right, boss. All right. Great party. We should hit the links sometime."

"Sounds fine," said Kyle.

He hung up the phone and braced himself for Patty. She sauntered in, dangling the bottle like a loaded gun in an

amateur play. "Boy oh boy howdy," she said. "This is fresh.
The freshest of the fresh fresh fresh."

Kyle put his smartphone on the armrest of his chair and covered it with his palm. "We lost a boatload of inventory," he said. "I mean a cataclysmic amount of raw goods."

"How do you 'lose' inventory exactly?" she said, working around his outstretched legs to slump into an old loveseat nearby, pulling her feet up under her rump like a child. "Sounds suspicious. What kind of things are these things, anyhow?"

"PCBs. Fuses. Toilet plungers. Don't worry about it."

"Can't they just…I don't know. Look for them?"

While Kyle calmed himself by counting silently in his head, he watched Patty's eyes wander around the small room—to the handmade shelves stacked two-books deep, the bureau-plat desk and its stockpile of restaurant receipts and Post-It notes, the words *Patience, Attention, Praise* framed and leaning on a strip of case molding, finally landing on the set of blurry wall photos from their last trip together as a couple—Milan, more than a decade ago. He'd canceled a show at La Scala to visit a struggling vendor on the outskirts of the city and gotten into trouble back then too—and for what? For doing his job? Providing for her? He saw his wife now, looking shabby and worn and eerily like his mother, sitting there aslant in the folds of the couch, liquor bottle in her lap, her gaze aimless and her face shimmering with a thick layer of cold cream. He counted to nine, then ten.

"First of all," he said, his count complete, "it's not quite that easy to 'find' things on a Fortune-500 manufacturing floor. Second of all, it's a lose-lose. If we find the inventory, it's four million dollars in carrying costs. If we lose it, it's shrinkage. A colossal unanticipated expense with a meager tax offset. At best."

"Sorry I asked," Patty said.

"Well, I suppose it's not a question of 'we' anymore," he said, digging his knuckles into the hollows of his eye sockets and rubbing them in slow circles. He opened his eyes wide, as if in astonishment, but the room was a fog—of hazel light, spines of books, the shape of his wife—so he shut them again. "It's 'they' now. We, they…any which way it's goddamned sloppy. It's their godforsaken duty to mind the shop. Shameful, is what it is."

"Stupid, stupid Patty," his wife said. "Stupid Patty to think that when Kyle retired, Kyle would actually stop working."

"Kyle's not working," Kyle said, eyes still closed. "So let's all relax."

"Always there to save the day," Patty said. "Thank God for our knight in shining vicuña wool blend. A regular superhero. When the hell is someone going to rescue *me* from my tree? I'm meowing, Kyle, I'm meowing."

Everywhere he went, it seemed: grownups acting like children. Shirking responsibilities and checking their common sense at the door, diving head first into kerfuffles of every kind. He didn't need his wife piling on too, with her juvenile compulsions and childish carping. He waited in the quiet of the room, and when it seemed his wife wasn't going to speak again, he blinked his eyes open, stood, reached his fists up to the ceiling to stretch the long sinews of his knotted back, and he left.

Kyle changed out of his tuxedo into a pair of pressed jeans and a golf shirt and got in his car and drove on autopilot toward his regular late-night haunt—Plus Ça Change, a Westside bistro owned by a friend of a friend—but when he realized it was shuttered for the evening, he made an impulsive judgment call to try the late-night taqueria next door. All he wanted was some down time, a place to collect his thoughts, a quiet corner where he could sit for a moment and figure out his next move now that the last forty years of his life had come to an abrupt close. In the words of his old life coach, it was time to design a new playbook for the upcoming season.

Inside the taqueria it was long and narrow and dimly lit by Moroccan lamps hanging from the domed Quonset-hut ceiling. A row of two-tops cut from unfinished pine ran along one side, an ebony-and-pleather bartop along the other. The walls were lined with unintentionally comical portraits of famous Mexican luchadores, painted in a primitive and colorful Mesoamerican style. The big, lazy fronds of Asian ceiling fans turned and turned in the gloom.

There were only four other people in the establishment. A bartender, female, in a tight tank top and a full-sleeve tattoo, scrutinized a receipt behind the bar. In the corner of the room, at a table farthest from the entrance, a couple sat side-by-side, so motionless in the dusky light as to appear either asleep or in deep consideration of their love. The fourth was the osteologist, Brenda.

She was sipping liquor from a set of sampler glasses lined up on a stone tray. Kyle took a seat at the bar, leaving an empty stool between them.

"Kitchen's closing if you want food," she said, tilting her head toward the bartender.

"I do," said Kyle. He didn't, but he felt beholden to the rhythm of the conversation. He waved the bartender over and asked, "What's good?"

"Kitchen's closing," the bartender said as she approached, slinging a terrycloth towel over her shoulder. "Guac's made here. Carne asada tacos."

"Gimme two," he said. "Please. And a club soda?"

The bartender leaned away from him and rapped her knuckles on the wood top with an air of finality before jogging off to the far end of the restaurant where she disappeared behind a swinging metal door.

"You come to a place like this," Brenda said, looking sideways at the bartop in front of Kyle, "and order soda? The food here sucks, just so you know. Tequila?"

She raised one of her sampler glasses in an offering, keeping her gaze low.

"I don't drink," he said.

She lifted the glass to her lips and smiled into it before tipping it back and swallowing the shot whole. "Agh," she said, bringing her chin to her shoulder. "Smooth."

The contours of her face were determined and cross and her hair was cropped close to her skull in a pixie style. At thirtyish, she was too old for the cut, it made Kyle think of cancer.

"You celebrating something?" Kyle asked.

"Celebrating?" she said with a lippy grimace. "It's Saturday night. It's what we do on Saturdays. And Sundays, and Mondays. Most Tuesdays. What are you…a recovering alcoholic or something?"

"Nope," he said. "Though I will say back in the day it did take the edge off."

"And now?"

Kyle flicked the tips of his fingers with the nail of his thumb, looking up at the menagerie of painted luchadores, their black eyes gleaming from behind the cut-holes of their masks. They were supposed to look menacing, but they only looked anxious, as if they were bewildered by their own circumstances.

"These days, I like the edge," he said. "I need the edge."

She dropped her head at an angle toward him, her face shaded in the red lamplight. "Well that's spooky," she said.

They introduced themselves—first names only, barfly etiquette—and with their names out of the way, there was a new, subtle intimacy between them. If someone were to have walked in at that moment, it would have seemed there were now two couples in the taqueria, one skulking in the dark and another sharing a moment of quiet conviviality at the bar.

She shifted over to the stool next to him. "Know who you remind me of?" Brenda said, reaching over to slide the tray of tequila samplers across the bar top. "Indiana Jones."

"Earlier I was wearing a tux. You would've thought more James Bond."

"Whoa," she said, with a rasp of a whistle. "Player."

"Just grownups playing dress-up," he said. "It was a party. They threw me a retirement party."

"Oh yeah? Must've been fancy shmancy. A regular corporate hoe down. What the hell are you doing here, anyway? After midnight. I asked you that already. Didn't I?"

"Geez, now that I'm retired, I'm wondering," he said. "What's next on the agenda?"

Brenda's face opened up in a sardonic giggle. "The next item up is as follows: Meeting Adjourned. Forever."

"Laugh it up," he said. "Old people's problems are somebody else's cute sitcom until you wake up one day and the shoe's on the other foot. Literally, because you're so senile you don't know which foot is which. That was an actual episode of *The Golden Girls*. Which you have no idea what I'm talking about, I'm sure."

"What were you, some kind of banker or something?"

"Vice President of Operations," he said, with an odd feeling of pride, now that it was all over. "They called me *The Efficiency Czar*."

Brenda attempted a spit take, but she was too clumsy and dry in the mouth to pull it off.

"What, it's not so strange," he said. "Efficiency is a way of life. In any job—any situation, really—there are an infinite number of possibilities. Do you want the beer or the tequila or the wine or the bourbon? You could have them all, I suppose, but it would cost money and make you sick to your stomach. So you have to choose one and be OK with walking away from the others. It's a question of seeing what's possible and committing to what's practical. It's the key to being successful in anything you do. Efficiency was my life's work. That's awfully maudlin. I realize."

He watched Brenda sadly as she put her hand around her last little glass, tipping it toward her and frowning into the drink as if she'd discovered something floating on its surface.

"It's true," she said to herself. "Retired people do die when they slow down."

"Die?" Kyle said. "Nobody's dying over here. I've got a full bank account and no kids pulling at the old purse strings. This is when life begins. I'm ready. Raring, even."

Brenda jerked back, suddenly alive, making a full, sloppy turn on her stool as if her entire body were a half-step behind. "You *are* Indiana Jones. But not like, from way back, when he was all studly with his whip and cargo pants and stuff."

"Gee. Thanks."

"No, I mean the way he'd be now." She patted at the air in front of his face as if to fan her ideas his way. "Older, but still adventuring. Is that a word? Looking for your next project, say."

The bartender appeared with two tacos wrapped in foil and a highball glass filled with clear soda. "That'll be eleven dollars," she said. "Speak now or forever hold your peace, Arturo's closing up for real."

Kyle reached into his pant pocket and put a twenty on the bar. "Keep it," he said. Then to Brenda, "Guess I could do worse. Harrison Ford's a solid actor."

"No, no," she said. "No. No." Her foot missed a rung as she shifted her weight on the stool, sending her body slumping briefly forward. Undaunted, she put a light hand on his arm to steady herself. "Not Harrison Ford. *Indiana Jones*. And boy, Indie, do I have a story for you. Listen. Have you ever been to Belize? Do you know anything about bones?"

*

The dock at Bullet Tree Falls was painted turquoise and peeling in ragged strips in the relentless moisture and sub-tropical heat. Kyle made an off-handed comment about it to Oscar and the boy replied that a dock was a place of wel-coming—like a floor mat in a home, it was meant to receive you, make you want to stay.

"But the foot traffic," Kyle said, stomping for emphasis on the weathered wood with the sole of his trail boot. "The traipsing alone is bad for the paint. But then you've got all the rainfall too. It doesn't make any sense, no? Gimme a day with this thing and I'll have it stripped and sealed and ready for a thousand tourists."

But Kyle remembered he wasn't here as a tourist, or even as the Efficiency Czar. He was the Older Indie, here in the jungle on a mission.

Diggs climbed out of the boat and brushed past Kyle,
knocking him in the shoulder, his mother trailing behind.
Oscar, playing the willing role of the good-natured local,
shook his head at his guests' antics while he secured the
boat to one of the dock's two rusted cleats. His hands moved
expertly around the bright nylon rope, as if each finger were
proficient in its own unique task; watching him, Kyle appreciated how little he himself knew, about an array of things,
and how much more there was to learn despite his age
and maturity. It was an awareness that made him feel both
helpless and hopeful, and more than anything it made him
want to ditch his extra cargo and get on the road toward El
Pilar—and Brenda's legendary bones.

Two weeks ago, he'd called Oscar and offered him what
seemed a meager sum—seven thousand dollars—to loan
him a car and get him a map to the bones near the Guatemalan border. Patty's consent to his solo trip was mani-
fest in her silence; to her credit she wasn't in the habit of
requiring approvals for his various pursuits—out loud,
anyway. Oscar accepted his proposition and the cash ex-
changed hands last night during happy hour, on the back
porch and away from prying eyes. The owner of the Mopan
River Lodge, a pale, brittle woman around Kyle's age who
haunted the rooms of her resort in bohemian dresses and
oversize sunhats, was very much in the dark—about the
deal between Kyle and Oscar, and about there being any
bones at all. Kyle guessed she was a rich American WASP
who paid Oscar fairly and on time and had no interest in his
life away from his day-tour duties at the lodge—and neither
did Oscar have any inclination to delve into her first-world
problems. The boy had a utilitarian view of his job, as he
did of the North Americans who came to visit each month,
but he was also considerate, loyal, and intrepid, just the
kind of young man Kyle would've hired back in his days as
a budding line manager. He had the brief, distasteful notion
that Oscar put them all—the lodge owner, Kyle, Cheryl,

Diggs—in the same category of privileged ignorance, and the thought sent a full-bodied shudder through his spine.

Cheryl and Diggs were huddled under the pink blossoms of an ancient dogwood, sheltering themselves from a light rain that was beginning to tap and patter around them—against the dock, their windbreakers, the lush green canopy. Kyle couldn't wait to be rid of them so he could continue on his quest. A footpath of tamped-down grass and mud trailed away from the embankment and disappeared into a copse of fruit-bearing trees. Kyle walked toward it with his backpack slung over his shoulder. He looked back at Oscar who'd finished hitching the boat and was giving the hull an affectionate thump of his hand.

"I've got the map," Kyle said. "Where's the truck?"

"My car is in town," Oscar said, waving the others toward the path. "It's close. We walk down there—and there's Paslow Road, actually."

The town of Bullet Tree Falls was just beyond the thicket of trees that lined the natural levee of the Mopan River. As they walked the path, raindrops making tiny divots in the mud, the forest quickly opened up and a village appeared in the clearing below, with homes scattered among clusters of towering cohune palms, a broad dirt road cutting through the fertile expanse.

"What map?" Cheryl said, hoisting her Bloomingdale's shopper over her shoulder and shading her face from the rain. As far as she knew, they were spending the day in Bullet Tree Falls—not going off the beaten path with some mysterious map. She and Diggs removed their shades and squinted like moles into the bright mist.

"The moisture's nice," said Kyle to Oscar. "Steady rainfall's nice."

Oscar nodded, absently, as if he didn't care or know exactly how to talk about the rain. Like Alaskans and the snow, Oscar almost certainly had thirty-seven words for rain, but it was something at once too mundane and too essential to serve as a topic of conversation. To these people,

rain was like money, like air. Kyle held his palm out to feel
the raindrops on his skin.

"He's ditching us," said Diggs to his mother. "He's looking
for a skeleton."

"Mr. Waller?" said Cheryl.

As they reached Paslow Road, Oscar walked ahead of them
with spritely urgency. He was carrying very little gear with
him—an American fanny pack, a multipurpose knife hanging from a steel-ball chain around his neck, a lightweight
oilskin slung around his waist. "I think so Mr. Waller has
someplace to go to," he said, calling back without turning.

"I'm running an errand," said Kyle. "I need to bring
something back for a friend."

"Running something from Central America for a
friend?" said Diggs. "Sounds dubious."

"My house is over there," Oscar said as they neared a
patchy lot set back twenty feet from the edge of the road, a
lime-green shanty sitting at its center and an antique blue
F-150 parked under a thatch out back. The rain surged, then
eased, as if it had been shut off by hand, leaving a glimmering
sheen all over the valley. A sudden chittering of birds broke
out from the treetops, and in the distance, where the rainforest pushed into the perimeter of the village, the hoarse calls
of howler monkeys rose out of the mist.

"We'll come with you," Diggs said.

Kyle kicked himself for mentioning the bones on the
boat, for being carried away by the romanticism of his expedition, for showing off. "You're right about it being a dubious mission," he said, speaking to Diggs but looking at his
mother. "Dangerous."

From his fanny pack, Oscar dug out a set of keys secured
to a small leather switch and handed them to Kyle, nodding
toward his truck. "Go up to Main," he said, pointing to a mac-
adam road that bisected Paslow a half-mile north of where
they stood. "On Main there is a crossroad. Straight takes you
to Santa Familia. Don't go straight. Go to the left. Then nine
miles you drive, and then you'll be there. El Pilar."

"Got it," said Kyle. "Straight on Main, left at the T. The rest is on the map, yeah?"

Oscar nodded. "Come back by four o'clock. Please. We take the boat back to the lodge from here. It gets dark by five-thirty, actually. So please. Remember."

Kyle heard it before he felt it—the drizzle, as it resumed— pattering on the hood of his jacket, the leaves, the wood siding of the pastel houses, the thatched roofs. In seconds he was peering at Oscar through a full sheet of rain.

"Four o'clock," Oscar hollered over the rainfall.

"You're not wearing a watch," Kyle yelled back.

Oscar dug into this fanny pack again and showed Kyle his iPhone.

"Nobody uses a watch anymore," Oscar said with a laugh, oblivious to his T-shirt soaking through. "Or maybe this is just in Belize?"

*

On their way out, Brenda stumbled in the doorway of the taqueria, righting herself by holding on to the doorjamb and horse-stepping over the sill, one foot before the other. She had insisted on getting some air, and Kyle had taken a long swig of his club soda, leaving his tacos at the bar.

Brenda stopped just outside the taqueria with heavy-lidded eyes, her skin cast in a sickly shade of green from the neon sign above their heads. "MEXICAN," the sign said. Kyle reached out to hold her elbow but she swatted it away.

"I'm good," she said. "I just...I'm good."

There, standing in the eerie wash of neon, Kyle felt the pull of an involuntary sense memory: Vegas, 1982, a girl at his side, a straight flush on the table. He was there for a bachelor party, not his own, and it was the only time he'd seriously contemplated stepping out on his marriage. Thirty some-odd years later he couldn't have picked her out of a lineup, but he did remember how tall she was, and what she smelled like—Oriental spices with the creamy undertone of cocoa butter. The other thing he recalled was the indelible kindness of her expression, the tilted head and the squint of her eyes, which seemed to reveal not only care but curiosity, pity. He had won his poker hand and she'd grazed his wrist with the tips of her fingernails, and in his imagination there was a flash-forward of room keycards and the undoing of buttons and the brine of sex and the flagrant light of morning, and after he had a chance to live it—the next eight hours in a moment—he'd declined, willingly, and without regret.

Now he watched Brenda dig into her purse to produce a Marlboro Red and a plastic Bic. With her cigarette lit, she took a long drag and propped herself up against the building's brick facade. She let her cigarette-holding arm dangle toward the sidewalk and held the inside of her elbow with her free hand. She turned her head and exhaled a high-velocity breath, careful not to blow smoke into Kyle's face.

"Boy, have I got a story for you," she said. "Let's walk."

As they strolled down Cedar Avenue, navigating a pattern of dark and light under the glow of the city's Victorian streetlamps, Brenda told Kyle that she, too, was celebrating the end of her career, although in her case it hadn't been a matter of choice. An archaeologist specializing in bones at the local Museum of Natural History, Brenda had recently lost her job and had been booted out of something called the SAA, which Kyle understood to be some sort of social club for natural scientists.

"It's a society, not a club, Jesus," Brenda said, "it's a really big deal. They set guidelines and standards for forensics and stuff, there's educational outreach. They have an ethics committee. It's not as if they hang out at the school gym sipping spiked punch waiting for a dance partner. Seriously, dude."

"Ethics?" Kyle said. "As in, should we or shouldn't we dig up tombs and risk the wrath of local hordes and mummy curses? I know all about archaeology, I saw the Tutankhamen exhibit in San Francisco in 1979. There was a lot of gold. Why'd you lose your job?"

"Tutankha-*moon*," Brenda said. "Because I told them if I saw one more Paleolithic fly, I'd punch myself in the face. It was always microfauna, microfauna, twenty-four seven. Here's how it works, OK? I find this flea, sitting next to a big, strange fuzzy thing that's got everybody scratching their collective archaeological head. So I analyze this flea for weeks and months and years, and after eons of staring at it, I finally identify its taxonomy and when I do, fifty other people deduce that the previously unidentified fuzzy thing is probably fleece from a blanket or a rug, because this particular flea only lived on sheep. Then they alert the presses and it's so sad, because this small little flea that I spent years analyzing is the biggest victory ever for the museum. I left my job because it was like heating a pot of water with a match and waiting around for it to boil."

"Sounds inefficient," Kyle said.

"It's called synanthropy," Brenda said with an aggressive pull and exhale of her cigarette. "Discovery by inference is a legitimate approach to paleo-environmental reconstruction…but whatever, that's beside the point. The point is this is not my job, to study bugs."

"For God's sake, Jim," said Kyle, "I'm an archaeologist, not an entomologist."

"Exactly. Who's Jim?"

They came upon an urban park—a patch of grass less than a thousand-foot square with an enormous stone statue of a crouching angel in the center, encircled by four iron benches. Brenda dropped her cigarette on the pavement, snuffed it out with her booted toe, and grabbed Kyle by the elbow, leading him in. He liked the way it felt, to be guided somewhere, somewhere dim and mystifying and full of promise. He recalled Patty on a day in 1976, at their old ranch house on Polaris Avenue in Foster City, when the first snow had begun to tap against the bay window of their living room. The light patter soon intensified, growing into a flurry, and then a full-fledged snowstorm, and in the middle of this absurdity—a snowstorm in San Francisco—Patty questioned nothing. She only grabbed Kyle by the wrist like a child and led him into the yard, where they joined hands and spun and spun, their sneakers soaking through, their exuberant faces obscured by the white noise of the blizzard. A day in history. They were in their mid-twenties then, newlyweds.

Now Kyle observed Brenda, who, while not at all like his young wife of yesteryear, called up something of his distant past, of being drunk with possibilities. She walked toward the center of the park, sulking like a child in the fuzz of her intoxication, overswinging her arms in a failed effort to convey purposeful sobriety.

"You deserved to lose your job, you know," he said, only half teasing. "I hate to say it. Your boss gives you a task, you do it. It's an affliction of your generation. I'm not pulling punches here. The museum, your little club—they have a point."

"Atta boy, Mister Man, kick me when I'm down," Brenda said, choosing a bench and scooting down to the edge to lean back and observe the sky. A single star blinked above them, maybe Venus, barely visible through the midnight haze. Kyle joined her, leaving a small, respectful distance between them, his knee grazing her purse. From where they sat—behind the great statue—the angel's hunched back looked vaguely sinister, as if it were lying in wait, its soapstone robes cascading in a froth behind its enormous form.

"Lookit, know-it-all, I got kicked out of the SAA for an entirely different reason," Brenda said. "This is where the plot thickens, and if you're a good boy, I might reveal Act Two."

"I like second acts," Kyle said. "It's where all the meat is."

"They told me I was getting obsessive and unrealistic—that I was losing my grip on reality and my profession as an archaeologist. The truth of the matter is that it's about job security—these yo-yos make a living off their incremental, infinitesimal work. Well, I'm all about the Direct Hit. I'm about Going Big. Like they say, go big or…or…" She brought the back of her hand to the tip of her nose and rubbed furiously at an itch before slumping her arm back down and resuming her position, staring at the smog overhead. "Forget it. Forget I said anything."

"No, no," Kyle said, touching her shoulder for a moment. He had the passing notion that he hadn't spoken with anyone at any length about anything besides his own work in a very long time. He watched Brenda breathe under the light of the smoggy sky, her chest moving slowly, regularly, as if she were asleep. "Tell me. Seriously."

She sat up as if possessed, her enthusiasm restored. "OK." She brought her arms up by the elbows and shaped her hands around an invisible ball. "I've got a line on some bones that are going to make history."

"What is it? The missing link?"

"Better," she said. "The original link."

Brenda twisted around to paw at her purse, but she kept her eyes on him. She found her pack of Marlboros and shook one out, dropping her gaze to light the cigarette in a single, shaky gesture. She took a fast drag and talked as she exhaled, words and smoke tumbling from her lips.

"A family of Guatemalan farmers discovered it in a cave on the border of Belize," she said. "The near-complete remains of a humanoid *three times the size of Homo sapiens*." She waited for the words to catch. "They found the skeleton of a giant."

She tossed away her barely smoked cigarette and reached for Kyle's hands. The sour bite of tequila was still on her breath and her eyes were glazed and dilated, irises quivering as her drunkenness reached its manic peak. But there was something in her grip, tenacious and steady, that made him pay attention.

"I may be hammered right now, but you have to listen to me. This is not a fairy tale like the SAA thinks. Go home and read your Bible. It's in the Book of Genesis." She lifted his hands in both of hers as if making a sacred offering to the gods. "This skeleton is hard evidence of the Nephilim: the legendary progenitor of all humanity."

They left Cheryl behind at Bullet Tree Falls where there was a wide variety of afternoon activities to enjoy, where she could shop, brunch, and, if she were feeling especially adventurous, go inner tubing at the Parrot Nest Outpost, where she could glide uncontrolled through the rapids of the Mopan until a cable that stretched across the breadth of the waterway caught her like an F-14 coming in for a landing, five miles down the river.

"A regular day at the spa," she'd said, coolly, to Diggs. "I didn't come all this way to this godforsaken place to spend the day alone like a drunk frat boy. This day was for us. No way are you going on a wild goose chase in the Latin jungle with this guy. Who is he? Do we know? 'Kyle Waller.' A fake name if I've ever heard one."

It was a standoff.

Diggs had refused to budge from where he stood in the patchy grass outside Oscar's house, insisting that he come with Kyle. And Oscar—sensing the liability of leaving Diggs, a minor, in the hands of another guest—suggested that the three men make the trip up to El Pilar while Cheryl remained in the village with Oscar's family. At the beginning of the deliberations, Kyle had said, simply, *no*, as had been his way in the office, and when that didn't take, he added, "It's dangerous, I'm making the trip myself," and when that, too, met with further obstinacy from Diggs, Kyle was stunned and dismayed to find long-forgotten emotions—passion, rage, exasperation—enter the tenor of his ordinarily calibrated voice.

"I paid," he said, ragged. "When everybody ponies up their own goddamned money, they can have a say."

He walked to the truck and climbed in, started the engine. But when he felt the thump-and-scrape of Diggs scrambling in the truck bed behind him, he knew he had to give in or risk losing daylight. Within minutes, they were on their way to El Pilar, the three men abreast in the truck's cab, their gear secured under a tarp in the back. As he pulled off the dirt road, Kyle felt a modicum of pity for Cheryl. He watched her dejected silhouette shrink away in the rearview mirror until Oscar's mother appeared in the yard, carrying a package, or maybe it was a baby, leading Cheryl away from the road and into the house.

Kyle had insisted on driving, at least, and Oscar conceded, but now, barely five miles out of Bullet Tree Falls, he was beginning to regret it. The road was deeply pitted from year-round rainfall, which in and of itself would have been of little consequence if it hadn't also been for the bank of gray thunderheads moving toward them like a distant, roiling ocean, and the landscape, which grew more and more inhospitable as he drove. Familiar signs of civilized Belizean life—the jungle A-frames, the local *iglesias*, the single-room bars, the unfinished concrete foundations, even the empty lots cleared of vegetation and set off by chicken wire—were all becoming less frequent and were soon replaced by impenetrable tangles of meaty green vines, prehistoric ferns, strange fruit and stranger trees carpeted in lichen and moss, thick as pelt. Kyle became unnervingly aware of the fifteen-year-old sitting next to him, aware of the burden of his adolescence. Once on the road, Diggs had pressed him for the details of their destination and the nature of the quest, but Kyle did not respond and the boy knew not to ask again.

"This woulda been more epic than the Grail Quest, every bit as romantic and ten times as pragmatic," Brenda had lamented on the walk back to their parked cars outside El Toro Taqueria, kneading her palms in a showy display of vexation. "But I can't afford to make the trip. The locals get you coming and going, you know, it's like extortion-level shenanigans." Something about Brenda's fantastical Arthurian tale took hold of Kyle in the well of his belly and clamped down there. He pushed her for details about the excavation site. It was restricted, but a young man named Oscar, a local who was intimately familiar with the terrain, had been willing to take her there—for a price. Though he'd never seen it himself, he'd had a rough idea how to get there, and confirmed the rumors of a newly discovered cave system dubbed "The Den of the Ancient Child" on the border of Guatemala just south of the unexcavated Mayan city of El Pilar. By the time Brenda put her key in her car door, gazed up at Kyle in the lamplight and asked—pitifully, earnestly, humbly—for seven thousand dollars plus airfare and incidentals and a Canon 5D for taking high-quality photographs, Kyle had already resolved to make the trip himself.

As thunderheads neared and the low-hung skies opened once again in the lightest of sprinkles, Kyle remembered the camera in his backpack, secured in the truck bed by a set of Oscar's strong-line bungees. He steadied the vehicle along the pocked road for another hundred yards when a clearing appeared—a primordial site of lush grass five acres wide and set off by the ever-encroaching jungle and, emerging from the canopy, great swelling hillocks, handfuls of them, lifting and surging in a gentle semicircle around the glade, coated in a tapestry of green. They were in northern Belize, where they could be only four miles out of the nearest village and be swallowed by dense, uninhabitable terrain.

"Just grabbing the bag," he told the others, tugging on the door handle.

"Wait," said Oscar, and something in the thin wire of his voice made Kyle stop cold.

A vein of white lightning appeared in the distant sky, reaching down from the looming cloud bank and disappearing before it could touch the tops of the cresting hills. Like a child, Kyle counted the seconds in his head as his mother had once taught him. On five, a crack of thunder broke out across the plain.

"One mile," Diggs said. "Lightning's close."

Kyle eased the door open and took a breath of air, thick with the mineral scent of dirt and rain, his denim thigh quickly soaking through. He pushed the door open and, in three calculated steps, dropped with a splash into the muddy road, mounted the running board, and hopped into the truck bed. He straddled the dark mass of travel gear and unhooked the bungee, feeling with his fingers under the sopping tarpaulin for his backpack. Recognizing the bag's familiar canvas skin and the bulk of the camera body tucked inside, he hoisted it up and out of the mound, slung it over his shoulder, and reattached the strong line. The rain was hitting him now in wet, violent sheets. With a hand on the tailgate, he heaved his body up and jumped out of the truck's slippery bed and into the wet gravel, circling quickly back to the driver's-side door. Another flash of lightning illuminated the sky, followed immediately by a tight crackle of thunder that seemed to twist and coil around itself until it exploded in a full-throated roar. As he reached the door another emphatic report cut through the endless pulsing rhythm of rain—a single airborne peal followed by two more in rapid succession. In the cab, Diggs made a small bounce in the seat to make room and Kyle swung his legs in, slamming the door and the door lock behind him and tossing the bag over Diggs' legs and into Oscar's lap.

"What was that noise?" Kyle said in the relative quiet of the cabin, the rain outside continuing to drum. He wiped his face with both his hands and gripped the shift knob, grinding it into drive; he thought he could feel the tires under the chassis, spitting gravel.

"You should drive, I think, just keep going," Oscar said quickly, craning his neck behind, into the road, the clearing to the side, out into the hills beyond.

"That was not thunder," said Diggs, rocking in his seat, ignoring the steady drip from Kyle's jacket.

Kyle flipped on the windshield wipers and gave Diggs a side glance. "You OK?"

"Hell yeah, I'm OK," he said. "You OK?"

"What was that noise?" Kyle said again, forcefully now, flipping the wipers to their maximum setting. He shrugged forward to see through the frenzy of the wipers, which seemed to be doing little more than smudging rainwater across the glass. He stole a series of brief looks at Oscar, who was sitting

upright, gripping the grab handle with his brown fist, his body
tense and alert. "Where did it come from? Oscar."

Oscar gave a small, private shake of his head. "I thought I saw something earlier. A car, up on the road. I think so it turned into the jungle."

As Oscar spoke, Kyle saw them cross into the road about fifty yards ahead: four men in camouflaged rain ponchos and heavy boots, rifles slung over their chests, waving their arms broadly, fiercely, gesturing for them to stop.

"Serious," Diggs said, "this is serious."

"OK, my man," Kyle said to Oscar, reaching past Diggs and pushing him in the shoulder. "Time to step up. I don't know anything about this Central American, guys-in-military-gear dynamic. We have choices. A. Turn around and hightail it the hell out of here. B. Stop. Or C. Which, is there a third choice? The answer is we don't know. Answer, answer, Oscar. Answer quickly."

"Slow down," Oscar said. "Stop."

Kyle brought the truck to a stop and the men descended, two on Kyle's side, two on Oscar's. They motioned for Kyle to open the door. Kyle shook his head, but he heard Oscar say behind him, softly, as if it were not his own voice but part of his exhaling breath, "Open it."

Kyle undid the manual lock and pushed the door open and the men were on him, yanking him out of the cab, shoving at his shoulders and his back, hustling him forward. He felt the hard iron muzzle of an M-4 in his spine, guiding him away from the car and toward the edge of the rainforest. The others were being corralled behind him. They moved quickly in the downpour away from the road, splashing in the gravel and trudging into the tangle of trees and thigh-high grass.

They kneeled abreast in the mud—Kyle, Oscar, and Diggs—sheltered by the leafy cover of monstrous cotton trees. The scent of recent lightning, ashy and acidic, wafted in the air around them, and there was something else—the sweet burn of gunpowder.

Kyle dug his knees into the wet earth. He kept his head down and his hands locked behind his neck as he'd been instructed, and he knelt, immobile, watching a pair of combat boots pace in the mud. A pit of anxiety grew in his stomach, cramping and knotting, settling in. He thought he could feel Diggs, feel his fear, as he crouched silently on the other side of Oscar. The rough edges of a shout formed in his throat but it got caught in the thick of his saliva—and after swallowing it down, Kyle was only capable of managing a timid question.

"Can you let the kid back in the truck?" he asked the boots.

"No." The owner of the boots nudged Oscar with the butt of his rifle.

"*Dónde vas?*"

Oscar spoke clearly, without fear. "*Vamos de camino a las cuevas.*"

"*Cuevas?*"

"*Uchben Chanpaal*," Oscar said. "*Cerca de El Pilar.*"

"*Quién está pagando?*"

Oscar shook his head.

"*Quién?*" the man said.

Oscar lifted his chin toward Kyle.

Kyle felt the barrel of the man's rifle under his own chin, lifting his head up, tenderly, like a lover. The man was stocky, clean-shaven, and dressed in head-to-toe camo gear, a bucket hat pressed down on his head. A splatter of moisture breached the canopy above and hit the man in the rim of the hat, and on his cheek. He wiped it away with the back of his hand.

"What's your business there," he said, in clean American English. "At Uchben Chanpaal?"

"I'm just going to take some photos of the excavation site," Kyle said.

"This cave is off limits to tourists," he said.

"I'm not really a tourist," Kyle said.

"Oh yeah?" The man spat in the grass. "What are you, then?"

"I'm here on an errand," Kyle said.

"If you're not part of B-Var, you're not welcome," he said.

"The cave is being excavated by the federal government. How do you know about it?"

Kyle looked at Oscar, and back at the man.

"A friend told me about it. Back at home. She's a scientist with an interest in ancient civilizations."

"Her name?"

"Brenda," he said. "I'm not sure about her last name."

Oscar snapped to attention and peered at Kyle through the intermittent raindrops dripping through the trees.

The man nodded. "I see. Brenda, no last name. She must be a very good friend." He grinned at the other men and they shared a laugh. It was ugly and mannish, their rings and watches clinking against the iron of their rifles. Their leader withdrew his weapon, slinging it back over his shoulder.

He reached out his hand and pulled Kyle up, indicating to the others to assist Diggs and Oscar. "These are not the best of times to be playing games of buried treasure," he said. "We are Belizean special forces. *Tenemos problemas màs grandes.* We have bigger fish to fry."

Kyle stood, feeling light in the head. He put his hand to his temple and rubbed, anchoring his feet in the muddy soil to keep from stumbling. "Your English is excellent," he said.

He turned to Diggs, rising up from his knees, pink in the face, hands still looped around the back of his neck. "Y'all right over there?"

"Yeah," Diggs said, bringing his arms down and shaking his hair out of his face. Oscar put a protective arm around his shoulder, but Diggs shrugged it off.

"It's the national language of Belize," the soldier said, heartily. "And I was born in Fresno, California. I'd better have good English."

The pack of men climbed out of the forest and into the road, their boots navigating the puddles in the gently waning rain.

When they reached the car, patrol commander Sergeant Esteban Campos put one hand on the small of Kyle's back and extended the other for him to shake. Kyle took it.

"Listen, sir," the sergeant said. "It's not wise to come down this way, into our country. It pains me to say it. But we're days away from making the US Blacklist. The Zetas cartel is here now, occupying our land, moving product through northern Belize and Guatemala." He motioned to the other side of the road and into the hills as if to approximate the path of the runners.

Kyle nodded, uncertain how to respond.

"Yup," the sergeant said, with a vigorous nod of his own. "Take one last look at Paradise. You won't see it again. Unless us good guys prevail. Eh?" He laughed and chucked Kyle in the shoulder.

"Thanks," Kyle said, although he wasn't sure what for.

Back inside the truck, Oscar took the wheel. The engine turned over with a rumble and he pulled carefully off the embankment, maneuvering the truck in a large U as the tires crunched the road. From the passenger seat, Kyle watched the small group of soldiers congregate in the reflection of his side view mirror. They were moving swiftly, climbing one after the other into a rusted-out flatbed that had at least a decade on Oscar's old Ford.

"I won't tell your mom if you don't," said Kyle to Diggs, as Oscar set a course for home.

Diggs reached into his jacket pocket for his sunglasses and put them on, casually, flicking damp hair out of his face. He leaned his head back and pretended to sleep between the two men.

"Mr. Waller," Oscar said, but the words were barely out of his mouth when a great white bird the size of a seagull and twice the bulk thudded into the windshield from the sky. Oscar hit the brakes and the three men swayed forward with the force of the sudden stop.

He put the car in park, and as the engine idled he bent close to the windshield to inspect the dead bird, grimacing and rubbing at the glass with the ball of his finger. Diggs lifted his glasses with his knuckles and, seeing nothing of interest, returned them to the bridge of his nose and lay back against his headrest in exaggerated repose.

"Is it cracked?" Kyle asked.

"No," Oscar said, opening his door and jumping out, the wet gravel crackling under his shoes as he headed for the back of the truck.

He returned with a large yellow chamois skin and a crowbar and walked around to the front of the vehicle. Kyle watched through the windshield as the young man made a strenuous lean over the broad hood, laying the skin out flat at the base of the wiper blades and using the crowbar to tease the carcass away from the glass.

As he worked, Oscar called out to Kyle through the open door.

"This person Brenda," he said. "She is how you heard about Uchben Chanpaal?"

"Yeah," Kyle said. "She said she spoke to you on the phone. You had your differences. Which is not surprising."

"She is your friend actually. Yes?"

"I suppose," Kyle said. "More like a daughter. Or someone else's daughter. Why?"

Kyle watched Oscar roll the bird onto the cloth, its neck bent angrily at the base, its single visible eye open in a fishlike gaze and rimmed in a wrinkled membrane of electric blue. Unlike Brenda, he wasn't in Belize for fame or retribution or self-righteousness, and though he had a notion that he'd share his discovery with her once he was back in the states, he hadn't given her much thought since arriving in Central America. But now that Oscar was invoking her name, he felt a surprising gratefulness toward her for leading him here however unwittingly; he felt indebted to her for giving him something to do.

"She never mentioned she was a scientist," Oscar said, dragging the cloth and its bounty carefully down the slope of the hood. "She called me all the time to talk about the cave, the bones. She wanted me to take her for free, for nothing, and she had no money even to come to Belize!" He clucked his tongue in a rare show of irritation as he brought the bird to the edge of the hood and carefully folded the chamois around its mass.

"Anyway," Oscar said as he worked, "she wanted to make a Hollywood picture with big money she kept saying she didn't have yet but she would get soon. I think so she wanted to explore the cave system with her own eyes for a movie idea she was working on. In the story, a girl archaeologist discovers the giant bones of an angel—this is not a real archaeologist but a pretend character she was going to play. The lady Brenda, the actress."

"Actress," Kyle said. "She's an actress?"

"She was very foolish," Oscar said. "But I think so her idea is very good. The female Indiana Jones. He was very popular with the children of Belize."

He came to the open door with the bundle, which he lay gently on the truck's bench seat. "We are sixty miles from the beach," he said. "Very strange to find this bird here. I wonder what it was looking for, so far away from home." He lifted the edge of the chamois to reveal the dead animal, its brilliant blue beak and red jowls, its webbed, gleaming, ruby-colored feet. Diggs stirred beside Kyle, peering over at the bird with feigned indifference.

"It's a red-footed booby," Oscar said.

"You can say that again," said Kyle.

"It's a red-footed booby," Oscar said.

Diggs slumped back in his seat with a grunt. "Epic," he said.

With the bird packed away in the truck bed and the sun cresting behind a silver bank of clouds, Oscar bore down on the accelerator with the urgency of a working stiff keen on getting home. Diggs sat in the middle and Kyle brooded in the passenger seat, chin in palm, face pressed against the glass. Two miles down and on the Western side of the road, Kyle spotted a sign of life—a lone plot of land cleared out of the jungle, with the unfinished concrete foundation

of a single-family home protruding like an abandoned machine out of its center. It was the way jungle families built
their houses, bit by bit and with every dollar earned; Oscar
had told Kyle that when money ran dry, Belizeans simply
stopped building until more came in, forging their lives in
increments the best they knew how.

The Ford barreled down Main Road, and a wan but insistent
brightness followed them, burnishing the truck's hood with a
transcendental glow. Leaning into the window and the flaking
leather of the passenger door, Kyle felt a wave of fatigue sweep
through his bones. He wondered whether he would bother
to tell Patty about the soldiers, his failed attempt at heroism,
about Brenda, about any of it. The mere thought of the conversation exhausted him. He was sure she'd make some typically
snide comment about middle-aged men—heroes stuck in the
back half of their lives—a message shrouded in humor and wit
with a black, cheerless truth at its core.

He imagined her now, sitting in his office, which she ad-
mitted to doing when he was away, sipping lukewarm tea
from her "Kiss Me I'm Irish" mug, though she was neither
Irish nor particularly affectionate, and he was suddenly relieved at the thought of coming home soon. It wasn't that he
missed her exactly, but he was glad his wife wouldn't have to
bear the news that she'd lost her husband, either to Mexican
drug cartels or to the twin perils of adventure and romance.
Patty wasn't one for melodrama, and it seemed cruel to subject her to it so late in life. He'd phone her from the lodge—of
this he was certain—there would be cool pauses and faintly
mocking comments to endure, but at least there was this one
known item on his agenda. As he watched the road outside
his window, Kyle was seized by a brief rush of queasiness as
he realized he wasn't sure what he'd do once he got off the
plane bound for home. There were possibilities, practical and
impractical. He could learn Mandarin. Adopt a dog, pick apples. He'd have to remember to ask Patty whether apples were
still in season this time of year.

"I'm not dead yet," he said aloud, the nausea abating.

Thinking his guest was still distressed by their roadside encounter, Oscar gave a reassuring cluck of his tongue. "We weren't really in any danger."

Kyle reached across Diggs and poked the barrel of his two fingers into Oscar's bicep as the young Belizean grasped the wheel in his sure hands, eyes fixed on the road. "Good job, Oscar," Kyle said. "You really kept your head back there."

A mile later all signs of dampness and rain were gone, and, as they rode in silence, awash in the flush of the storm's aftermath, another plot of land with another concrete foundation appeared, and then another, and another, until soon the jungle brush gave way to grassy expanses and dirt roads, and finished homes dotting the landscape with bursts of Caribbean color. There were chicken-wire tracts, several in a row, and bars advertising Coca-Cola and Belikin Beer, a Baptist Church, and rock doves picking at the sand outside the River Mist Inn. Kyle watched two men walking cautiously away from the main road, each balancing a twin-size mattress on his head, and at the intersection of Main and Paslow, an old woman in bright orange moccasins and a traditional Mayan *huipil* was selling mangoes out of a van. And there were children. Lots of them, emerging from buildings and side streets like fauna in the springtime, without their parents, as if all the grownups were still hibernating in the caves, unable to escape their dreams. The children came alone, in pairs, in small groups, holding hands, pointing at the truck, murmuring to each other, their smiles showing missing teeth.

"Look at that," Kyle said, to anyone who cared to hear him.

"Kids," said Diggs. "They sure know how to goof off on a Sunday afternoon."

Kyle thought they'd never stop coming, or perhaps he'd simply not noticed them before. He liked the thought of recognizing something new. There were so many of them, the children—children carrying enormous babies by the crooks of their armpits, children rolling wheeled toys along the leaf-clogged rain gutters, sharing bags of candy, cradling half-naked dolls, sitting on rail ties outside the Chinese grocery, children chasing wiry brown dogs down alleyways, children chasing each other, squealing as they ran.

The Critic

TIMOTHY PARRISH

The Twerp's new record has been playing for hours, but it seems like days. It seems like it's been playing his whole life. His ears have turned red from excitement. It has *that sound*, the one he has been describing his whole life.

In this room of rooms, the walls have walls and he lingers in them with fingers like a blind person reading the Book of the Universe in Braille. Hours he has idled away feeling their ridges, thin pieces of cardboard holding discs of vinyl and shellac. Each one has a name that he does not need to read to know. A tomb could give him no more comfort than this space made from years of his listening.

From the floorboards his hands drift over the edges of the records above him. He puts letters to the sound. The A's, the B's, the C's: an entire alphabet that speaks in the code he has given it. He takes the sounds of music and puts them into sentences. When the music is lost, when the records can no longer be played, when we have lost Creation's power of electricity, his words will be read and the sound shall live in them.

Candles shaped into figures of rock stars—Elvis, Jim, Van, Johnny Rotten, and the Twerp—yield him light for his lucubrations. A tiny desk hardly bigger than the ones issued for schoolchildren sits beneath more shelves of records and a few books. An outlet in the wall powers the trusty record player his parents gave him—no retro models for Markowitz. His was the genuine article. It had never once broken in its more than fifty years of use. He expects it will outlive him. As for the latest updates in sound technology, which seem to happen daily, he lets his wife handle that. She runs her music through her iPad. She insists he would like the new sound universe. CDs are almost all extinct and records are trendy again. She tells him what is cool. She always knows. He needs to know, since he still publishes his views via an online blog that she uploads for him.

Everything happens in here. It's his closet, his chambers, that is. He retires here to issue rulings, and later his wife disseminates them to the world. From Berkeley to Cambridge, he can lecture wherever he wants, and he does. It's always the same lecture—it's about the records he can't quit hearing. For nearly fifty years, he's been the acme of hip. Anything he writes, we read. Would we even still know who the Beatles were if it were not for Markowitz? He's a genius of listening. Think of Aristotle going to a play, except Markowitz had better material. Elvis, Little Richard, Robert Johnson, Sleater-Kinney, all the greats. Often he thinks their many voices are just the coded signals of a single voice. Some days it's as if his brain is a radio and some alien force is at the knobs.

In one form or another, he possessed every important record made since 1918, and possibly earlier. Not all existed in their original format. The 78s had been transferred to 33 and 1/3 RPM, or, in some cases, compact disc, that abomination of sound and culture. For years, other record aficionados had told him the 78 was the ultimate sound. But to Markowitz the Holy Grail was the Elvis 45 on Sun. He had all five. If his house were burning down, that's what he would save—after his wife. He did have one 78, framed in the house entryway, a Robert Johnson record one of his readers had given him. He had never played it.

Not long ago, an acquaintance had come across an original 78 of Geeshie Wiley. Hearing her bird voice through the noise of the imperfectly preserved piece of shellac was like... he couldn't find words for it. Like listening to Sappho sing by the sea. Christ, what that must have been like! That would be the ultimate bootleg, short of having Achilles on Electric Guitar. In his files was an essay he wrote about Achilles as the first punk rocker. He never published it for fear that references prior to Thomas Edison would compromise his cachet as a pop critic. Once, he had written a book on the Luddites as Punk Rockers and no one had read it. He had no reason to believe Achilles would fare any better than the eighteenth-century sheep herders. Only the Twerp, he thought, would like the essay, and he saw no reason to gratify him.

Fact. More great art had been produced since his birth in 1941 than was produced during the span that separated Aristotle from Benedetto Croce. Markowitz reads aloud to himself, having just written this thought into his Listening Notebook. He had filled hundreds of such notebooks—his wife kept them in a special climate-controlled annex in the backyard. A hundred lifetimes of listening were pressed against the walls of practically every room in his house. He could never exhaust it.

Jesus, just limit it to the years between 1956, when Elvis first appeared on The Ed Sullivan Show, and 1970 and the claim holds. 1970 was the decisive year and not only because it ended the greatest decade since time was first marked in calendars. That was the year the Beatles broke up and the Twerp released that piece of crap he called *Self*—or whatever it was called. But why remember that piece of...that piece... that piece of junk?

He gazes at the shelf where his books are. Randomly he pulls one out. One of his works on the Twerp—his fourth or fifth one, he doesn't remember. There was even a blurb from the Twerp, but it was covered by a discount sticker, so he didn't know what it said. He reads aloud the notices. "Brilliant." "Illuminating." "Not since Nietzsche heard Wagner has there been such a synergy between artist and critic." That one was his *favorite*. "Nearly as powerful as the performances they describe." That one he could do without. "One waits the next album just to read what Markowitz will say about it." He supposed it was a compliment.

He sits up, or maybe he is lying down, it's hard to tell, letting the *sound of the sound* wash over him. A record has been spinning for hours but for now its motion has been stilled. He rests as still as possible in his room where no laptops or iPods or iPads or loaded iPhones exist to torture him. He is listening, intently, to that lost sound he has learned to cherish, which is the silence between sides. He listens, he luxuriates, he experiences the living vibrations of all that had been given him to know that had not been given to Aristotle, Horace, or Longinus. Think of it! Coleridge, Arnold, even Thomas Stearns Eliot (the Little E, he called him, to distinguish him from The Big E) had never had occasion to remark upon the poetry of Chuck Berry or describe the grain of Little Richard's voice. He should thank his lucky stars he was born when he was born.

But it's not like it used to be. These days he was tired. The tone arm wasn't lifting like it used to. When was the last time a new record had made him sit up and take notice? Geeshie Wiley had been his last crush and tombs were robbed to find her. Christ, they didn't really even make records anymore. Consequently, most of the records he played now were already playing in his head and had been for years.

Sometimes, he hears the Twerp's voice speaking from the silence. It's the queerest thing. He can even hear it through the car radio—it doesn't matter which station he is tuned to. "Aw Gabe," the voice rasps, "I didn't take that review seriously. You did what you had to do. Don't worry about it." At the time, the Founder had been pissed. Who was Markowitz—who was anyone—to ridicule the Twerp's work?

The review had jump-started his career, but his heart often twisted to recall it. A few words and he'd reduced the voice of a generation to a pile of steaming dog poo. The power of

criticism! It gave him an edge. People loved the insolence of
it. After getting away with that, he could say anything, no
matter how outrageous, and the public's perception of his
brilliance grew.
The summer of 1970—how could he forget? The Sixties
were over but who wanted to admit it? Markowitz thought he
was the only one who knew, but the Twerp knew too. The eyes
said so. Markowitz didn't want to see what the Twerp was seeing. Great artists were always surprising you and making you
look stupid after the fact. So he asked himself, what if I treated
the Twerp as if he were an object. *Render him inert through the
power of my language.* If I can put my words into his mouth, I
can steal his power. His words become mine. I can do anything
I want with him. Pick him up, put him down. Say he does not
exist, say he does. You can't leave art to the artists, because then
who would know what it meant?

What he actually wrote no one knows. It's just that one sentence they remember. An instant classic—it would have gone
viral had that been possible back then. It had gone viral—
fifty years later. Every day since the Internet was invented,
he has searched his name, the Twerp's name, and "piece of"
and read about himself all over again. People were wrong to
think it was obscene. It was highly intellectual. The language
he had borrowed from Marcuse or Brown—he couldn't remember which. And he had simply asked a question. What
is this piece of...?

It wasn't even the sound that had perturbed him. It was
the album's cover. He hated it—a portrait of the Twerp by
the Twerp. Its eyes weren't level. It looked like a child's sketch
drawn over by a man. Markowitz suspected the picture made
fun of the viewer. And then parts of it sounded like a Frank
Sinatra album. Fuck the rat pack. They weren't the Sixties.

Sometimes he wondered what his career would be like had
he not asked his famous question. But then Markowitz would
not have been Markowitz. He'd be somebody else. It was just
as well. He saw that between the two of them, the Sixties were
up for grabs. They made more sense if he took them.

The work of art stands above the artist. The critic must be prepared to murder the artist to save the work of art. Whenever he felt guilty about that review, he reread those words. They had been the original epigraph to the review. He had to leave them out because the Founder said he could not begin a review by quoting himself. It made no sense, he said, because no one knows who you are. Not then, they didn't. Now I get away with it all the time.

He had meant to kill the Twerp, only symbolically of course, so he would make the kind of music Markowitz liked. The Twerp had left better material in the can—Markowitz knew because he had heard it. But the Twerp had his own ideas. Worse, he kept cranking out records, many actually *ickier* than the one he panned. In return, Markowitz decided to really kill him. He composed a brilliant obituary that would be the final word on the Twerp the instant it was published. Around 1980, he considered publishing the obituary to test the power of his words. Instead, Markowitz kept updating it, a secret obsession, writing long reviews, assessments and reassessments. He read them aloud to his wife. Parts of it he leaked out when the Twerp did something particularly mind-boggling, like turn himself into a Christian. To the Twerp's pronouncement of being Born Again, the critic replied, in print, you're dead to me, and everybody else. The Twerp won a Grammy that year, but Markowitz didn't have a television, so he didn't have to watch it.

He fantasized about issuing the Twerp's death statement, but he knew the Twerp couldn't be killed. He survived records that for others would have been suicide statements. It was as if some spirit were present, always ready to resurrect him from whatever guise he had just worn—and then give him a new one. With the Twerp, you chose among incarnations and believed in the one that spoke to you. Whatever his doubts and heresies, Markowitz, despite himself, remained a believer—in his vision of the Twerp. Every five years, he published a new book about how great the Twerp used to be. The Sixties forever renewed and the Twerp its Dionysius.

Don't think he didn't listen to new music. He did—record companies sent him stuff all the time. He just had so much music in his head it was hard to cram anything else in for more than the time it played. Except when goaded by the Twerp's miscreations, he had not actually felt like writing a new review for years. He had greeted the new millennium with books about the Morrisons—Jim and Van. He argued that both artists had peaked in 1979—the genius part was that by then Jim had been dead for eight years. The Van book was a monster to complete because he had committed himself to writing a chapter for every album. The last twenty chapters covered Van's career since '79, nearly thirty albums! Each chapter was the same. This sucks. This sucks. This sucks. The book was actually very High Concept. But the research had been agony.

Recently, he had decided to write books that focused on individual songs—a chapter a song and preferably songs he heard a long time ago when his brain was still empty. Since the fact of his listening was at least as important as the song being played, his books were spontaneous research treatises on his own brain. *Markowitz Listens* could be the title of his *oeuvre*.

As he was always looking back, the Twerp kept on. The Twerp was unfathomable. How did he do it? He shredded his past every step of the way. The Twerp didn't give a punk's fart for hip. He gave that up when he painted that stupid picture of himself. All those great songs Markowitz revered the Twerp now sung as if he had forgotten what they had ever been. You couldn't understand the words! And he toured all the time—the so-called Never Ending Tour, as if death were not part of his process or as if he was trying to erase everything he ever did. For the most part, Markowitz avoided his shows. He was there for the '74 tour, which he loved. Oddly enough, he saw him the night Obama was elected president. The show was awful—he didn't even sing the song about the changing times, but that night, he almost believed the Invisible Republic of the Sixties he had long dreamed was at hand. He thought maybe the Twerp would reveal it. No such luck.

In principle he was indifferent to live shows. The studio recording was *the record,* which preserved the undying aura of mystery. Everything else was approximations and simulacrums of the real thing. Musicians made so many mistakes live. They hurt his ears. His distaste for live music notwithstanding, he had contrived to acquire—at considerable personal, albeit tax-deductible, expense—nearly every Twerp show ever bootlegged. Hundreds of them. He kept them in this closet along with all of his other listening treasures. He never played them. He liked to think the Twerp lived in here with him like a ghost that at any moment Markowitz could command to appear like a genie from a bottle.

It didn't happen that way, though.

*

At the curious point where our strange tale properly begins, he has been possessed by the record on his spindle. I don't use the word lightly. While his cherished *sound of the sound* was washing over him, a demon escaped the apparatus and went into his soul. These things happen—but Markowitz did not know it. He knew very little at this point. He had been listening to the Twerp's new album—a unique tribute to Frank Sinatra and other great crooners of the past. Side B just kept playing, over and over. The machine allowed the repetition. It was pleasant, like drowning is said to be.

The strange thing is that Markowitz never meant his life to come to this point. He had vowed never to play the record that now seemed to be dreaming him. Known for his fearlessness as a critic, Markowitz had been wary of this record. It had filled him with dread like nothing he could remember. The Twerp had gone awry many times before—hadn't he made a career of pointing this out?—but this time was too much. *Frank Sinatra!* It was the last death of the Sixties. The idea was more offensive than the Born Again records. What was next? A Christmas album? As a favor to the Twerp, he was going to keep this out of his secret obituary. He meant to refuse delivery of his examination copy.

What he didn't know was that years ago the Twerp's manager had forbidden the record company from sending Markowitz his records. Since then, his wife had been buying the new Twerp records and leaving them for him with his mail. When he entered the closet that morning, he saw the Twerp's Sinatra release on his turntable. He accepted it as an act of the G-d in which he did not believe.

He slotted the needle into the groove. A tingling in his groins—this happens whenever a record grabs him. He had not felt like this since Johnny Rotten. For a brief time, no more than a handful of seconds, he nodded off like a junkie because that's what happens when your soul has been seized. He had felt it before.

1956. The year of his birth. He is twelve years old. The radio, his midwife. A Wop-mop-a-lu-bop-a-wop-bam boom. Tutti Frutti. All Rooty. An atomic bomb going off in his head. Eternity cracked open, and like a virus from Paradise, the sound of the sound did come upon him.

How did such a miracle happen? Was it Little Richard who gave him these new ears or did they sprout from his head in the very instant they were needed so that he could receive what had been given? Such questions are difficult to answer and happily beyond the scope of this narrative. Let's just say he came alive, the radio was his mid-wife, and that Gabe, an unusually clueless fifteen-year-old whose existence until then had consisted chiefly of perfect grades and the approval of his parents, suddenly found himself in the realm of perfect being. Words can't describe this state, though G-d knows he would spend his life trying, which ultimately accounts for his gigantic oeuvre. How did he react to this, to this, to this gnosis, if I may borrow a word from another source? His reaction was surprising, given his character. A perfect, still silence. Like the moment before Creation, perhaps. Personally, I would like to presume he experienced gratitude, but as this is a true account, I will not guess. He knew in his heart, and now I employ a word that did not come easily to him but for when he was listening to *Never Mind the Bollocks* and then he never said it aloud, grace, which he called Rock and Roll. It did not cause him to marvel. For the first and last time in his life, he attempted to dance, but his feet became entangled and he fell upon the kitchen floor. No matter. Twice-born Gabe raised himself up and let the music wash over him like light.

Stumbling in the brightness, he discovered a vertical line existed that could move left or right, and then the sounds changed. He felt like G-d or His little brother. He made the line stop when he heard what he liked. He ruled the world. The Everly Brothers, Jerry Lee Lewis, Wanda Jackson, Buddy Holly, Fats Domino…the spirits came when called. The cities of the Americas were at his command. Memphis, New Orleans, Toronto, and someplace in Mexico he couldn't pronounce. In this box no one has died. The past mixed with the present and the races did too. Jimmie Rodgers and Howlin' Wolf. Hank Williams, Muddy Waters, the Carter Family. He turned a different knob and the sound became so loud it blocked out the world. Its volume could not be registered because his brain amplified it to a power beyond dreams. The aftershocks didn't stop. The sound, or its echo, took him to the world that existed before the world was G-d's to name. It played as he slept and went into his dreams, never to escape. Its power possessed him so that he wanted to possess what it yielded. He dreamed he was the world's radio. Or its DJ. When his parents gave him the record player as a Chanukah gift, it was as if he ruled the world. He might have prayed in gratitude but the thought never occurred to him. He believed the world had become his to name.

He had been chasing that feeling ever since. Paradise. At an age where other boys were learning to masturbate, Markowitz was getting his fresh kicks listening to the radio. He never did learn to masturbate, preferring to develop his prose style instead. His lifetime of writing had sustained his listening euphoria, but now he asked himself if the two activities were as integrated as they had always seemed. Maybe he had written himself out. Behind his ennui was a question he dare not ask. What if everything he had written had covered the sound, not revealed it?

All of his *favorite* artists were dead, one way or the other, except for the Twerp. Sure, some continued to live, like the Stones, but they looked dead. Instead of a genius tailor, they had a genius embalmer. And Rock and Roll heaven had been turned into a fake cloud! Imagine! The dead stars, the live stars, and all of the nonentities that time or his reviews should have rendered unknowable, had been brought together in this so-called cloud where it was supposed they would live together. Every day this cloud had to make room for something else because bands now had the means to record themselves. They could not sell what they made, but they could stuff their music like so many electrons into this cloud with Mozart, Bach, Geeshie, and everyone else. The world was losing its need for critical discernment. The cloud was rendering him obsolete.

Some cloud. It wasn't anywhere and didn't come from any place. You couldn't see it. You couldn't touch it. But it streamed music like G-d's piss for all to hear. It existed somewhere on your computer, which was connected to forces in the universe that you could only know through its medium. You affixed its pods to your ears like some sort of *goyishe tefillin* and let its virtual sound fill your head. Apple had monopolized the human ear. Virtual music for virtual people. iPods, ha! iPutzes is more like it. Their brains were in their laptops. They didn't know what they were hearing.

Heroism was not exactly a component of his DNA, but the critic could not help fantasizing about taking over their machines as he had wanted to take over the radio when he was a kid. He would be the voice in their heads and he would save them. *Wake up, dumbfuck! Just because your head is in the clouds doesn't mean the music is in your head. The music is in my head, not your head, and if you listen to me, very carefully, I will save you.*

Ah, but who was going to save Markowitz from this re-cord, this fucking Frank Sinatra tribute album, spinning in his head, carrying him away to some airy cloud he has never known or dreamed? It sounded so...so...so...he didn't have the words. He flipped the pages of his notebook. *The record always ends and you have to live your life in its echo. And then issue reports of what you remember.* Inside his head he heard different words, a tune, a lyric, a chorus of voices sighing *give me the beat, boys, and soothe my soul / Markowitz wants to get lost in that rock and roll.*

He would drift away if he could, but he didn't know how to do it anymore. Writing had bound him to the world and not the sound. He still had books to write and lectures to give. He had contracts, appointments, booked flights, you name it. These days, he was just so tired, as if he had come to the end of something he could not name—a potentially terrifying state for a professional critic. Week after week for years he had issued reports from this closet. What if he just listened with no other obligation than to hear? What if—and here his consciousness flickered like lights going on and off—what if he could just un-write himself? He'd read Derrida. He knew it was theoretically feasible but practically impossible. If he could go back to the beginning and start over, would the same things happen or could one small act change everything?

He imagined calling the Founder with a suggestion. "Hey, I have an idea to pitch. Let's re-review that album I panned— Jesus, no, not the Christian one. The other one. You know. The piece of shit one. We'll advertise that I am undertaking an act of historical-critical restoration unknown in pop jour-nalism. FIFTY YEARS LATER, MARKOWITZ VOWS TO RELIS-TEN TO EVERY RECORD RELEASED IN 1970. AND PRONOUNCE FINAL JUDGMENT. "But that's what I thought your last three books did," said the Founder. Although the conversation was imaginary, Markowitz's feelings were hurt. "OK, Gabe," he heard the Founder say. "Tell me. Would you change your position? It's the only way we'd have a story." Markowitz sniffed. "To predict an end would compromise my critical integrity." "Just what I thought," the Founder answered. "You haven't heard a new record since 1979."

What's on your iPod? college kids were always asking. *I don't have an iPod,* he liked to say, as nonchalantly as possible. It was worth being the greatest critic since Aristotle to say that whenever he could. He was a listener, a human so to speak, not a pod. Whatever his shortcomings, he had remained true to the original mechanism of his origins. Every record he ever reviewed he heard first on this player.

The kids who came to his talks he didn't recognize. Some invasion of the ear snatchers had taken over their heads. They didn't hear what he heard no matter how hard he tried to tell them. The *sound of the sound* was what he loved. He had written the phrase in his notebooks to express his fidelity to something he could hear but not quite name. Before music became digital and lost itself upon its own virtual asshole. It was an emanation, a giving off, a cosmic secretion that caused Markowitz to believe there was more to the world than his own thinking about it. The culture had lost it, but, Jesus, this new Twerp record had it. The Twerp knew what was what.

Listen to this! His voice was shot. He sounded like someone's dead grandfather, but it was beautiful. The lyrics came to life as he sang them. And they weren't even his! The greatest songwriter of all time was using other people's words to do his work. A critic could not get away with that. A critic had to use his own words. It was the only way to be original. Markowitz realized he had never heard these songs before, though he thought he knew them well enough to think they were silly. The Twerp's album was making him double back. He had thought the album was a stupid prank, but it had mystery too. Through these songs, the Twerp was unmaking himself and revealing the *sound of the sound* in places where the critic didn't think it could exist. Markowitz nearly felt like an atheist seeing G-d for the first time.

He held the album cover up to the Jim Morrison candle. The Twerp hardly resembled "ol Blue Eyes." He looked blue—like a Blue Note album. How did the Twerp get so old? Craggy faced like his voice. He flipped the cover over to peruse the recording information. The name of the engineer vaguely rang a bell. From his pocket he took out his cell phone, flipped it open, and called his wife, who was down the hall watching a documentary about the Sex Pistols. She was waiting for the parts where her husband spoke.

"Hi, sorry to interrupt."

"It's OK. I paused it. You were just about to come on!"

He sighed. Sometimes his wife's loyalty oppressed him. "I have a favor to ask."

"Sure, but what are you doing? You've been in there a long time. It's not your bowels, is it?"

"I'm in the closet."

"With the Twerp?"

"You could say that."

"One of these days you really are going to leave me for him."

"Can you Google a name for me?" He gave her the name and in a few seconds learned that Al Something had been a recording engineer since before rock and roll. Markowitz was surprised he was still alive, let alone functioning. He had produced Sinatra records in the fifties and sixties. Of course the Twerp would know. "I should have known."

"Should have known what?"

"It's not important. I'll be out soon. Goodbye."

Did Sinatra ever have the *sound of the sound*? He didn't know Little Richard from the Pope. But this record had it, G-d damn the Twerp! *What does the Twerp know that I don't?* Christ, he thought, his record collection is probably bigger than mine. It has to be—he must have all of Sinatra's records. I wonder how many 45s he has. Probably has 78s too. He'd read somewhere the Twerp had a whole warehouse full of them.

See the critic stretched out on the floor. His lips are moving, at least I think they are, so he must be singing. A song he had forgotten has taken him over, again. His wife heard him from down the hall and smiled. She had always liked Sinatra. He was surprised he knew the words, but he didn't have a choice in the matter. The sound of them was perfect, like the old days before CDs. It was perfect, like a new 45, the first records he ever knew.

A new 45 had been a lifeline to ecstasy, better than any drug. Not that he had tried any, since Markowitz had always paid attention to whatever his parents told him. When it came to experience, Markowitz was something of a prude. But his ears knew adventure. It was more than a click. You heard a song on the radio and you ventured out into the world to find it. The hit side was magic and the other side was mystery. You played the hit side forty, fifty times before you flipped it over to discover its other side. The element of the unknown created an excitement that was unbearable, delicious.

From the record came a spark, that speck of the pneuma, that jumped off the needle and into his ears and somehow went through his body until his soul came forth. The records brought him to life. Without them he would be nothing. He would be like everybody else.

The old Chess records, the Sun records, and anything recorded near New Orleans were his first *favorite* sounds. They had an intensity, power and suspense. They yielded a vibration that seemed to come from his own mind. It activated something hidden within. To play a record was *to put yourself inside the sound*. You became the engineer of its expression. This realization, which occurred about three hours after his parents bought him his first record, became the philosophy of his writing. It meant the records did not exist until he heard them.

And the amazing thing was, you couldn't wear them out. Records degraded but their sound never did. They crackled. They hissed. They seemed finite but what they possessed wasn't. A static surrounded the music like the nimbus around a halo. Their use became part of the sound. The materiality of presence, he called this noise, shortly after reading a Marx reader in graduate school. The phrase later became famous. It launched, he often laughed to think of it, a thousand dissertations, each one citing his small treatise, "The Record and the Mark of History."

Not even Markowitz grasped the *awesome totality* of the *sound of the sound* until one day when it was suddenly erased. Who erased it? The record companies. He was sitting at home contemplating the impending demise of Punk and wondering what the next Big Thing would be when a shipment arrived. Several boxes of CDs, along with complimentary CD players, speakers, amplifiers, the works. The first disc he tried, which also happened to be the last disc he would ever play (his wife played the household CDs), was *The CD of JB*. James Brown. The Mighty Man with the Master Plan. The Big Bad Boss with the Real Hot Sauce. The Godfather of Soul. A true original—it's why the rappers all sample him. For authenticity. If James still sounded good on this thing, Markowitz reasoned, so would everybody else.

Queuing up the disc in the player, he felt like the pilot over Hiroshima. A terrible detonation was on the verge of ignition. He couldn't bring himself to punch the button that made it play. What if he couldn't escape the blast? He pulled down his copy of "Night Train," on the King label. He wanted to hear the original 45 again before entering into the new medium.

The second between when the needle is set in motion and right before it finds the record's groove is ecstasy. He hopes the needle never finishes its falling. An eternity slips between the passing moments. Not like punching a button. He waits for the sound to jump out at him, alive as ever. A crackle and a pop, the prelude to bliss. A sharp snap of the drums, the thump of the bass, the horns' beautiful counterpoint, like Louis Jordan's bands, and he was dancing a little despite his innate lack of rhythm.

Night Train!

A thought comes between him and his body. Dancing, even alone, made him self-conscious. He reaches for his notebook and the words flow. It gives me a shiver to copy them here. *There's something deeper than the music and its mere notes! There's more than the band or James' glorious buzzsaw voice namechecking the cities along the Atlantic seaboard. Only a record can sound like this. You can't hear it live. You can't be there to hear it. You must be here, in this room, with the record player spinning. What is it? It's the Sound of the Sound! An atmosphere the record catches and preserves. To know it, you must have a record player picking up the signals encoded into the disc in 1962. No other technology can preserve and release it. It would be like trying to eat the same knish twice.*

The needle lifts—the song stops—but he returns it to its groove. He loves the manual labor involved. He feels like a worker. It's a tether that ties him to the sound. He plays it twenty times, maybe more. He wants to play it for the first time—before the Twerp, before the Beatles, before the Sixties ended and the world went to shit. Secretly, he wishes the album had never replaced the single. Something vital had been lost. He would never admit the thought in print, especially as it would refute one of his most famous essays. He had been the first to argue that the album represents the greatest transformation in dramatic art since Aeschylus added a second character to the stage and reinvented drama. No way was he taking that back.

He flips the record over. "Prisoner of Love." This time he doesn't bother dancing. He just starts writing. *The single is the purity of the form. Twin sides oppose each other to reveal the Truth. The confirmation of the Manichean heresy. The elevation of matter to spirit—the essence of everything.* I'm just giving you an excerpt. I'd wear my fingers out if I typed it all out.

On the label, he sees printed the numbers 3:03. A song's duration cannot be measured. Time ceases as it plays. As long as the record moves the needle, the world stops its moving. The words help him forget that it's 1983 and Reagan is President and the Clash is disbanded forever. The Beatles still exist and the Twerp, G-d damn him, is a Born Again Christian. A three-word phrase for moron. But he knew what was what and it was breaking him. The world had ended almost fifteen years ago. He was living in its aftermath.

Memories exist in the future, as well as the past. You have to go into the future to discover your past. I mention this because in the interim between "Prisoner of Love" and punching the CD button, Markowitz hears strains of the Twerp singing Sinatra. "Full Moon and Empty Arms." He feels strange, like a bird flying toward the stars. He forgets where he is and punches the button.

The bombs fall. Chaos erupts. He feels radiated and becomes a ghost to himself. What the hell is this? Strings and horns and loud yelling in Italian. He listens, utterly perplexed, for perhaps a minute before he realizes it's a movement from Mozart's *Don Giovanni* and not, as he had at first suspected, a baroque remix of "Sex Machine." Transfixed, he lets the disc play. What's this called? *Recitativo accompagnato!* He's an expert in rock and roll, but Mrs. Markowitz did not raise an ignoramus. He recognizes, pressed into the Brown disc, the Karajan recording he used to hear as a child. It's terrific! He writes a note to himself to remember to get someone to send him the LP version.

Then his head starts to ache—not from the Mozart. His sensitive organism designed for subtle listening contracts something like botulism. The music sounds tinny, processed, canned like rotten tuna. The sound has no atmosphere and its absence drowns the music. He recalls reading somewhere that the CD is indestructible. You could slice cheese on it and it would still play. Well, this sounds like sliced cheese and salmonella. He punches the advance button, seeking James, but hears only more of the opera, sequenced out of order. He keeps punching to last track. Finally, James bursts forth. "Maybe the last time, do-dee-wop." It sounds terrible, worse than the Mozart. Christ, what will the medium do to Little Richard?

Dreck, he said. *Dross*, he had spat. *Traife*, he yelled. Words from his grandmother. He didn't use them around his wife or his books either.

To relive his headache, he writes his review. His critical apparatus is so perfect he wrote only first drafts. *This new medium is a fraud, a mass deception unequalled since Hitler, a corporate trick to make our music disappear, an example of the contempt in which the corporations hold authentic expressions of the American vernacular. The compact disc, it doesn't matter which one you play, is a bad opera: the inglorious production of American cheese being pressed into transparent plastic wrappers and turned into sound.* I remember that essay as if it were yesterday. I felt smart just reading him. I say I felt smart but really I felt dumb. That's what a critic can do. He makes you feel dumb for what you don't know and then he makes you feel smart for agreeing with him. I didn't know the compact disc was an offense against Culture until he said so. I'm sure I wasn't the only one. I threw mine out and never got another one. And were you ever in the Berkeley area, in the eighties and nineties, and found yourself in a store that sells used compacts discs, chances are you bought one of his. Because he dumped every free one he got from the record companies. Except for the ones his wife kept. She still has a room full of them.

His review didn't stop history or CDs either. There are limits to everything—even the Higher Pop Criticism. And now the Twerp is singing him, lifting him really, and the words are in the language of Frank Sinatra. This record is fantastic. It's like it used to be only better. Markowitz almost never sings, not even in the shower, but right now the Twerp is opening him like a Roman sewer. All of his shit is coming out today.

He has the strange thought that together they are singing the Kaddish. The words are wrong but who cares. It's like a radio where one signal drowns out another. Markowitz's mind is a library of old songs—it was the Internet before the Internet was the Internet. This one derived from the slaves but crackers in Kentucky adapted the words and copyrighted them. Some Italian had the first hit with it. It wasn't Sinatra. Who was it? Oh, yeah, Frankie Laine. He preferred Ray Charles' version. He had forgotten Sinatra had done it.

The Twerp never forgot anything. His knowledge was in his voice, which croaked, smilingly, like it issued from a living corpse. Was the Twerp ever alive or was he just a ghost he had dreamed along with everyone else? *Christ, what if I am his dream? What if we all were?*

Just that one time did he meet him. Summer of '63 at a folk festival of some sort, nothing like the rock-and-roll records that had borne him. He was home from college. He knew almost nothing about folk music—back then he was still obsessed with posthumous Buddy Holly records. It was the first concert he had ever attended, which may account for how overwhelmed he was. It took place at a fairground near his parents' house. His wife—they were not married yet—invited him. "Who's that little twerp?" he had asked when the performer hit the stage. He'd meant no offense. Something deeply affecting about the performer had struck him. The little fellow was wearing a dirty hat, jeans, work shirt, and boots. He looked like a Walker Evans photo in color. He didn't even look grown up. His guitar seemed too big for him. Around his head was a cheap circular wire with a harp attached to it. It didn't remind you of a halo. It looked like a contraption affixed to him by a charlatan dentist. By his offhand manner, he seemed to say, anybody could do this. Might have been you. But it's me. Too bad. "Shhh," his future wife said. "You'll know him when you hear him."

From the opening notes, Markowitz is mesmerized. He struggles to ignore the other person on the stage—a beautiful woman with long black hair and a guitar. Next to her the Twerp sounds off key, his guitar playing irregular. He whoops and hollers like a hillbilly. The joyful uncouthness unnerves him. Markowitz thinks he is an amateur and wants to laugh. Gradually, without knowing it, he becomes accustomed to the performance until he forgets anyone in the world exists but the two of them. Strange as it sounds, he let himself fall in love—not with his future wife, whom he loved already,

and not with the Twerp, who scared him, but with his own
future, which was emerging like soldiers marching from the
little twerp's mouth. Markowitz was one of them. Already he
is writing in his head.

He sounds like everyone and no one. Proteus with a guitar.
He sings like a changeling. He sings like Marlon Brando acted.
A method actor whose dramatic art is lived in the moment.
You would never believe he was not the character he per-
formed, even if you didn't know who it was. He's everyone and
no one. Little Richard dressed up like Woody Guthrie. Elvis
with a harmonica. He is everything I must learn to say.

Alas, he didn't possess his notebook, so his thoughts remained unwritten. He spent the rest of his life trying to
formulate them.

The woman's dulcet tones irritate him. She grates on his perfect ears. Her pure tone, her perfectly plucked notes, clashes
with the other one's barbaric yawping. He must tune her out
to hear the other's pure stream. He wills her to leave the stage
and she does—it was his first inkling of his critical powers.

Unshackled, the orphan strums a song that Chaucer
knew—"Barbara Allen" it is called. He looked it up in the
library later. As the song left the singer's mouth to enter his
ears, Markowitz felt a tingle not unlike a gathering orgasm,
and then he became somebody else. A seventeenth-century
Englishman, to be precise, which was no small trick given
who his parents were, sitting in a tavern with long dirty hair.
He stank and he was aware that he probably could not read.
His whole body ached from physical labor. He suspected he
was a sheep farmer and that suspicion explained the smell.
He did not mind. Metempsychosis became Markowitz.
Except for his record player, his life to this point had been
frankly boring. Through a window the sunny sky suddenly
became gloomy and dark and for a second he saw the ghost
of Chaucer's "Knight" ride past. In the corner, a minstrel was
singing. Despite the ache of his body, not to mention the
smell, Markowitz's being quivered with joy. It was the singer

who was doing this to him. Haints—the dead—lived in the singer and were exploding from his mouth and into Markowitz's ears.

The singer stopped singing, but Markowitz didn't know it because the song still played in him. He had not been reborn, since, technically, rebirth was for Christians. Nonetheless, he was no longer quite himself. A new knowledge possessed him concerning the transmigration of souls. His mouth, however, was full of sod. Although dirt covered his eyes, he felt he could burst from his clothes. The black earth yielded to gray sky and he saw level before him a briar twirling with a rose bush blooming. He crawled toward it…lutes and hurdy-gurdys ringing in his ears. Unbustled hedgerows protected the graves, and he slithered through them toward the roses where two headstones lay. Those two, whoever they had been, weren't getting out. Only he had. He plucked a rose with his teeth. Then he noticed a fresh grave, unmarked by any stone. He realized the purpose of his resurrection. The hurdy-gurdy played louder. His future rose before him in her remembered face, and he could not bear to think there were already worms in his love's eyes. He crawled through the twined bushes, his body terribly scratched and his mind upended by fear and dread, toward the fresh grave. He feared its contents. How could she die before he did? He experienced mystical intimations. He realized he had become a song and need not fear his love's death. Songs, even the schlocky ones, were an endless web—an aerie grid in which the world was caught. The stuff of everything, which he knew to be History, became trapped in it and then blew through.

His mouth tasted like flowers and he knew the past was as air. Nowhere and everywhere all the time. You had to hear it to see it. This revelation was nearly unbearable and Markowitz did in fact expire. No one noticed—not even his future wife. From the stage the singer witnessed the listener's death, though, for he knew the feeling and could recognize its symptoms. It had happened to him many times, but he had learned to master it. For this reason, he was an artist. Markowitz obviously wasn't and the singer felt compassion for him. He blew his harmonica at an unbearable pitch until he saw Markowitz jolt back into this world, unconscious but breathing, seated next to his living love.

From behind the stage the sun's dying light cast the singer's form into a shadow that covered the crowd. The singer's shadow-head stopped at Markowitz's dreaming head. From the heavens, the pair seemed to converge. It may have been the singer knew this, since he was keen to see how his listener was reacting to his resurrection. For his part Markowitz was simply trying to breathe. The immediacy of the experience had punctured something in him. In his body he was gasping and for a moment he thought he heard Little Richard's voice mingled in the folksinger's. It was like being present in the force that spins the record or inside the click on the knob as Little Richard's voice bursts from the box. The living thing itself. Perception at the pitch of passion. Disoriented, Markowitz wondered where his record player was.

Something was happening to him and he didn't know what it was. The sky flickered and he thought he was fainting. His breathing was labored, almost choking. He was alive enough that he thought his life was ending right here in the twelfth row. What would his tombstone say? *Here lies Markowitz. A Fan to the End.* The disgrace of it galvanized him. He let everything within out. He threw up. The people in the next row caught his spray. His future kept passing before him and he was a helpless witness to it. It was like it had already happened and there was nothing he could do to change it. The articles, the books, the guest professorships.

He saw the stage was bare. His future wife was rubbing his back and talking to him. She led him from his seat to the men's room so he could clean himself. He stared at the face in the mirror and acknowledged that it was his. From afar he heard an echo of a song. It sounded like "Barbara Allen," it sounded like "Tutti Frutti," it sounded liked "The Night We

Called It a Day," or was it "That Lucky Old Sun"? He used to hear that one on his parents' radio before he knew what the radio was. He turned from the mirror and walked toward the sound. The face in the mirror remained, watching him. They would meet again.

The sound was leading him but inside, some part of him remained, obdurate, writing—if only he had his notebook! *The song chooses the singer to sing it, just as it chooses him or her to hear it. To the song, there is no difference between singer and listener.* Transmission is all. The truth is I copied these words straight from his own lips one afternoon after meeting him at a reading in Portland, Oregon.

Songs trapped in the record were souls to him; he was always waiting for the one that would carry him away. He kept walking, following the song in the air, until he came upon a picnic table shaded by an old oak tree. He lay down on its bench and stared into the gloaming. A half-sleep overtook him and he dreamed he was sleeping on a burning mattress and he could not wake up.

But this time he does wake up. And he is not alone. Beneath the tree, a booted heel on the bench next to Markowitz's head, stands the Twerp. His blue eyes seem to possess a life independent of the body that housed them. It's a wraith, he thinks. He feels transparent. It's unnerving to be observed sleeping. His greatest fear is to be caught unaware. Suddenly, he wants to defend himself—to lash out. Your voice is weird. Your harp hurts my ears. I prefer rock and roll. These ripostes remain in his head, though the Twerp hears them and inwardly shrugs.

"It's you," he said.

"For some time now."

"I just saw you in there."

"I just saw you in there."

The exchange renders Markowitz mute. Three eternities pass before the Twerp relieves him of his silence.

"What did you think?"

"I liked it."

"What did you like?"

"The rose and the briar."

"Yeah, that's a good one. I maybe like 'Moonshiner' better. Uh, did you catch that one?" The Twerp knew he hadn't.

"No, I must have been daydreaming." Markowitz was chagrined by his answer. He made a mental note to remember to look up the song and tried, somewhat desperately, to think of something to say.

"What are you thinking when you sing?"

"Nothing. I'm just singing. What are you thinking when you are listening?"

"It's hard to say."

"Hey, you don't happen to have a cigarette, do you? This is my last one."

"I don't smoke."

"Too bad. I have to get back soon. Joanie wants me to do an encore with her."

"What are you going to do?"

"'The Times They Are A-Changing.'"

"I don't know it."

The singer laughed. "Nobody does. Joan doesn't know it either. I just wrote it." He inhaled once more and flicked the cigarette at the critic's feet. "Soon everybody will, though," he added and walked off.

Markowitz did not remember returning to the show or even finding his date and taking her home. He missed the song's debut performance, though he was present. His wife kept the ticket. It is somewhere inside this closet.

The next day, he was at the record store asking about "Moonshiner." Saying the word yielded the same thrill as knowing the password for entry into a speakeasy. A secret passage seemed to open as soon as he said it. The clerk pulled out a copy of *The Anthology of American Folk Music, six long-playing records*, and pronounced it the "real thing." Markowitz mentioned the Twerp's name. "Poser," the clerk said as he handed it over, the one record they had in stock. "Play *The Anthology* first."

For months, these records went into his dreams and he

awakened morning, noon, and night to their visions. The days before Rock and Roll! The stuff of Creation.

He listened vaguely, without precision. Often, he couldn't make out their strange accents and dialects. The performers were white, black, and Indian. Some songs were in French—Cajun. They yawped like the Twerp did. As he played the six sides back to back, the singers didn't have a race. Not like Markowitz. Maybe it was because one song led into another with no explanation of how it came there. Even the songs in English sounded foreign—like History was a radio and its frequencies had been all jumbled together. He put the thought into his notebook and underlined three times.

Someone named Smith had created the anthology. Markowitz was in awe of him. This guy was the great redactor—a version of the poet who had preserved the *Iliad* or the old Jews who had made the Torah. Markowitz wondered if he could ever match this man's power as a listener.

And the performers! Who were they? Were they ever alive or had Smith's dreams taken material form just to take him over? Markowitz, I hardly need add, was subject to possession—it was his gift as a critic. At times, he felt like a lost son discovering an inheritance that has been waiting years for him to find it. The sides' glorious cacophony caused him to think of the end of *Gatsby*—so many things did, it was his *favorite* book—when the narrator imagines America just before the *Mayflower* landed. That fresh green breast of land and all those lapping waves. The same sense of impending discovery graced these recordings. They made him feel as if America had already existed before the Europeans arrived, just waiting for someone to record it. *The Invisible Republic*, he wrote. *The country behind the country. The world behind the world. The dream that we are and must become again.*

And in that little flight of inspiration, the Sixties and its undying voice was born. If that decade lives, it lives because of him. His essays on the Beatles, his book on the Return of the King in '68, his writing about the Twerp's secret America, made us understand that we had lived through the second era of the Great Masters. Italy in 1650 had nothing on America in 1970. But, alas, there is more to life than art, and Markowitz would tell you that stupendous transformations in art occur alongside revolutionary moments in history. It is therefore worth mentioning that while Markowitz was discovering his Inner-America, the Sixties were happening all around him. At a movie house, he had seen the Twerp in DC marching with Martin Luther King. It jolted him. He was jealous that the Twerp was changing history with his guitar while Markowitz was just a beginning graduate student trying to understand Marx by day and American music by night. He told himself the Smith records were tuning him in to History at a Deeper Level. Its Old Time People, as he called them, were as old as Barbara Allen and lived in a realm where History was Utopia. He had seen it! And without consuming a hallucinogenic, they took him there on amazing trips! In his daydreams, which had become increasingly frequent, he had stood on the Atlantic shore with other Indians, holding an eyeglass of all things, watching for the boat marked History. He rode with slaves on ships to America and then turned the *Mayflower* around, sailed east to locate the root of Appalachian fiddle playing.

From the Blue Ridge Mountains to the Scottish Highlands the spinning records carried him until once he saw Barbara Allen's boyfriend and her father eating gruel and drinking ale at a dingy pub where he may also have seen Tom Jones holding Sophia's muff. He tried to strike that latter image from his mind. He saw fog rising toward the sun and disappearing to reveal rich, dark fields speckled with cotton and slaves singing on ships sailing backward into a land he could not quite see. History is a boomerang, he realized, moving forward and backward, and if it were not, neither the past nor the future would ever be known. When the Cajun songs played, he saw a red-beans-and-rice joint where he had eaten once as a child when his parents had taken him to New Orleans on a family vacation. By then, his notebook was filled, so he didn't write this vision down. Years later, they would all appear in his books.

He hadn't known he was an American until he heard these records. Until that time, he had just been a white guy, which meant he had no history but the oppression of others. Technically, he was a Jew too, but he tried to forget this. Some distant cousins and aunts and uncles had died in the Holocaust, but he'd never known them. Uncle Dave Macon was his uncle. Old Henry Thomas was his grandfather. While the record played, he could choose his ancestry. He could make these records his story. The voices he heard were lost relatives, with whom he could reminisce simply by playing their records. They had been born just after the Civil War and he could hear them in his apartment!

Markowitz played the records and looked for the rock in the sound. Each side was a striated matter of many colors and surfaces. He was a sound-geologist and the needle was his pick. The original recording equipment was primitive, and by the time Smith recopied them, they had become corrupt. It sounded like it had been pressed in 1863. There was no way to remove the hiss from these scratched recordings. *The past cannot be eradicated from the noise of its own generation. Its sound is familiar, comforting. In the beginning…it all comes back.* "Tutti Frutti." "Mystery Train." Those he had worn down until the present were simply his ears quivering. The hiss they yielded was the breath of his listening. Markowitz listened and the past returned freed from its conflicts and quarrels.

The hiss, he wrote, *is the sound of the past, of History Itself, embedded in the recording. The performers themselves are nonentities, democratic flotsam, like you or me, who happen to be caught in time by the recorder. Yet, history blows through them like they're Gideon's trumpet.* It was a lucky coincidence Smith had found these records and an even luckier accident they were ever made in the first place. So what if some of them went to great effort to get to Grafton, Wisconsin, or Bristol, Tennessee, to record. America was wherever you broke ground. Probably, one of their cousins or neighbors could have come and it would have been the same thing. Because—and here his thought awed him—the music the Old Time People heard as kids was never recorded and so on to every generation all the way back to the Big Bang, which for all anyone knew was just G-d or some force like Him singing in the shower. But the traces of that force remained *on his record player* in his graduate student apartment for him to contemplate and interpret as others before him had deciphered the graffiti in Egyptian tombs.

Were he capable of praying, he would have fallen on his knees and thanked his Maker for giving him the chance to encounter these living wonders. But, what the hell, anybody could acquire them. Only he, and maybe the Twerp, could hear them. He put his hand to his heart and addressed the empty room. "Through these voices," he declared, listening for an echo he could not quite hear, "I shall speak!" The resounding silence deflated him. It just needed a little rewrite, he decided. "Through *my* voice these voices shall speak." That was better. *I am the past's receptacle*, he wrote in his notebook.

When the past and the future bend to meet in your present, G-d is said to emerge. In Markowitz's case, the Reverend J. M. Gates was singing "You Must Be Born Again." The future critic couldn't understand a word, whether because of his excitement, the record's quality, or the strange, or the Reverend's strange (to Markowitz), Negro dialect is difficult to say. A light seemed to emanate from the rotating disc, which Markowitz, in his near madness, associated with the Sun record label but may actually have been the bare bulb that hung just above the player. In this ecstatic moment, he realized that the flaw was necessary to the design. He saw the order of Creation made, or remade, in a record. Approximately eight years after his first one, he experienced his second birth.

Strangely, it was at this precise moment that the Twerp's voice came into his ears. The room darkened. For the briefest of moments, he felt estranged from himself—the same way he would feel if someone were to tap on his shoulder to cut in while he was making love to his wife. He strove to drive the intruder from his head. And then he realized (again) he had been hearing the Twerp the whole time, for months, ever since he had come home from the record store, since the concert, really. He felt deflated, but then his critical faculty awakened to the critic's orgasm. Alienation becoming insight. As orgasms go, it was a dry one but what the hell. It was the best he could manage.

The mirror he had left behind the day he saw the Twerp appeared before him. In it he saw the Twerp singing, at the same time, all seventy-two songs of the Smith collection. Markowitz heard every word, though the Twerp sounded as if he had swallowed twenty-seven dead folk musicians whole. The Twerp was the player and he was the listener. The Twerp was his own age, after all, only a little shorter. They were twins, of a kind, and thankfully not Siamese. They had the same ears. He had mastered these records too.

Briefly, he doubted his calling. Since "Tutti Frutti" blasted from his radio like cities falling down, some small part of him had wanted to make that same sound—or perhaps have that sound channel through him. Must he be the listener? Was one role more important than the other? I need never be a musician, he said to himself, because making music would never be sweet and intoxicating enough for me. Through the canals of my ears I shall venture into the ether and return with the thick volumes of my reports. The Twerp can make the same trip and have it come out records and concerts. My music will live in words—like Homer, Joyce, and the rest of those guys. Somebody has to write it down or else how will history know?

Music is transient, but the feelings it provokes are of the eternal. Look at Little Richard or Elvis. Their songs are so dumb nobody would claim writing them but for the royalties they gave. A-wop-mop-a-lu-bop-a-wop-bam-boom?! What the fuck is that? It wasn't even a word, since no one could spell it. True genius requires explaining what the dashes conceal. Their brains, whatever their quality, were irrelevant to their achievement. Performers have a certain vitality—like animals—and they just let it out. Maybe that's all the Twerp had too—an idiot at the mercy of deeper forces that only Markowitz could understand and explain. He could hear the future whispering. It said, what is Markowitz without the Twerp? That's the wrong question, he riposted. What is the Twerp without Markowitz?

He sensed then that one day he would dwarf the Twerp in stature. In the future people would read his articles and buy his books instead of listening to the Twerp's records. Sometimes, they would read his articles in order to justify not buying the Twerp's records. Some wags have claimed that behind Markowitz stands the Twerp, dwarfing him, they say. The Twerp's shadow. Perhaps I am too sensitive on the topic, because that day in the bookstore I asked him if he were but an excrescence rolled off and picked up from the Twerp's fingers. I used nicer words, naturally. The critic stared at me for some time. I appreciated his thoughtfulness and looked forward to receiving his eloquence. At last he spoke. He said it was the next person in line's turn. I wheeled around to see who it was. No one was there. When I turned back around he was gone. Some lower frequencies had intervened between us and carried him away like the revenants he saw when he played his *favorite* records.

All that remained was the vision his eyes revealed to me in the instant before he tricked me. A dream had leapt from his head to mine and I copied it down into the notebook I had lifted from his briefcase not five minutes earlier. In this dream, Markowitz ventures to achieve that which only the boldest critic ever imagines as possible: to locate the origin of inspiration and then to describe its topography for all of us who will never know it. In his dream, he realizes he need only follow the Twerp through all of his influences and the Twerp will lead him to History's Promised Land, perhaps even the Invisible Republic. Stifling his fears that his journey will obligate him to enter the womb of Mrs. Zimmerman, Markowitz senses that the way through must be the record player. Where else could it be? He listens to each Twerp record to discern its origins. And then, unerringly, he traces each source record back to another source record—no other listener could do it, except maybe Harry Smith—until he's left the era of recorded music, traveled through minstrels and troubadours and epic poets and all the way back to Dionysius. Undaunted by the orgies he witnesses, since he was a happily married man, he travels on seeking the invisible attributes of song. He moves over dreams lined with rocks like Roman roads. His perception of traveling through layers of history and time yields to a sound, a rhythm, or perhaps a humming, which carries him up and up and up beyond every semblance of this material world. It's a tune he almost recognizes, and it takes him to the realm where every song is connected to every other song. I nearly fell into his eyes looking at it. Inexplicably, I knew that what was in his eyes I could see and he could not. I wish I could tell you the name of the tune.

Fleecy heaven full of angels and smoke that did not burn and white cushions everywhere upon which eternal beings are sitting and listening to the same tune, getting louder now in his ears. His heart for a moment falters. He wants to turn back, or wake up, but the song pulls him along. The heavenly fog dissipates and at the far end of the room he sees the Unnamable on His Throne. G-d. Jehovah. Yahweh! His beard white and long like a sheep's belly or that of Karl Marx, nodding to the thrumming, strumming of the angel, or is it an imp next to him. The rhythm has words and he hears a verse about sending down a cloud. That's it! The name of the song is on his lips when he realizes the imp singing is the Twerp, and then the song leaves his head like a hit record falling sud-

denly from the charts. He becomes self-conscious. Yahweh
nods at him. He finds a notebook in his hand. What the hell
am I doing here? he wants to ask. He realizes, wrongly, that
he has been fingered as the little Jew assigned to rewrite the
Bible. Has the Twerp got me this gig? No, he learns, that's too
big a job for him. He's been called in as the editor of "selected"
sections. *The New Song of Songs: Records for a Desert Island,*
Third Edition, Revised, G.M, Ed. Probably not even worth
a book tour. After that, his task is *to get right the Twerp's role
in Creation. If you don't get it right, Markowitz,* the bearded
One says, *we're going to turn you into a rabbi and make you
start life all over.*

At that point, Markowitz fell from heaven. It could be
said that the Sixties had awakened him from this nightmare
for, in the nick of time, that marvelous decade, the greatness
which will never be repeated, delivered unto Markowitz, as
it did to everyone, an answer.

Beatlemania! It erased everything, including, happily, that
dream, which had terrified him to his entrails. Before the
Beatles he bowed liked everyone else. The Beatles were Cae-
sar marching into Gaul. They were like Mussolini, like Hitler—their presence brought forth crowds who craved to fall
at their feet. The Beatles brought people together—and made
them all say the same thing at the same time. Compared with
the Beatles, no one knew who the Twerp was. They were
the Sixties incarnate, and they revealed to him that History
appeared in the *Pop Moment.* He capitalized the phrase for
dramatic effect. You've read his books, so I don't have to tell
you what a Pop Moment is. Let's just say it's something like
the cloak of Perseus seen by the gods. It covers everything
and makes it disappear by virtue of its own expression. It has
nothing to do with the past, or, frankly, the present either,
except as the assertion of its own ubiquity. It swallows reality,
you included, and then you reappear as its grateful reflection.
It could be said that Markowitz had already experienced this
process through the Twerp, but as I am his biographer, not
his analyst, I will spare you such reflections.

Millions shared Markowitz's obsession. Though he was not alone, his love for the Beatles is perhaps the most anomalous part of his story. Here he was—the first white kid on his block to own a record made by a Negro, a cognoscenti since the age of twelve—surrendering his intelligence to the joy of mass culture. What a relief it was to know for once he agreed with everyone else. Perhaps Markowitz worried his familial relationship with Uncle Dave Macon and Henry Thomas was speculative after all. Or maybe he wanted to merge with history in a way that was quantifiable, visceral even. With the Beatles, he knew he was with his people everywhere he went. On a bus once, he flicked on his transistor radio to "I Want to Hold Your Hand" and suddenly had thirty new friends.

But Markowitz being Markowitz, he could not tune in without his mind being turned on. Couldn't History, he asked himself, also mean the forgetting of History? Except perhaps for war and starvation, he could not think of a single event happening in the world that brought more people together simultaneously than a Beatles release. In the Beatles' army there were no soldiers and the Beatles themselves had no leader. JohnPaulGeorgeRingo was their name. A Beatles record didn't know the color of your skin or the country you were from. They are *post-racial*, he wrote in his notebook, becoming the first ever to employ that term. *Their titles say it all. Revolution. All You Need Is Love. Let It Be. The True Pop Moment is redemption without reflection.*

During the interim between *Rubber Soul* and *Revolver*, and for no longer than two weeks, Markowitz worried that beneath the Beatles' cultural wave lurked a nasty undertow. Once or twice he had a flash of Nazi soldiers goose stepping. These visions made him uneasy, to say the least. His doubts he tried to resolve in an essay entitled "The Beatles and Fascism: Hitler with a Human Face?" Fortunately, he didn't show it to anyone. The essay would have ruined his career before it began.

When *Revolver* came out he forgot his thesis. His mind became blown. There is no other way of putting it. It was as if he had plugged his brain into a socket until it was fried. Never quite able to just let things be, he set a trial for himself. He resolved to play no other record until *Revolver*'s secret was yielded to him. If from this test a critical maxim did not reveal itself, he would surrender himself to a lifetime of teaching political science. To hurry the vision, he swore to fast until it came. Somewhere during the thirty-third playing of "Tomorrow Never Knows" it arrived. He experienced an authentic transvaluation of values that was akin to Moses and the burning bush. To him was revealed the *Spirit of The Album*.

In light of *The Album* the genius listener became reprogrammed. What was "Barbara Allen" next to *Revolver*? Elvis, Little Richard, Little Eva now seemed to him fragments of a greater whole. Even the Beatles were suspect before this astonishing transformation of the medium. Before *Rubber Soul*, or maybe *Help!*, they had hardly more than a Detroit Girl Group, great, but essentially an awesome cover band who wrote catchy ditties. But…but…but…the guitar reverb on "Taxman" was amazing! It echoed throughout the whole record! This changed everything. *The Beatles were industrial workers changing the mechanism of pop music possibility.* To show his allegiance to the Pop Culture Transformation taking place, he vowed to kill his first love—not his wife, the 45. *The single is kid stuff, for teenage girls incapable of the kind of sustained reflection that the album demanded.* Even the Twerp, he said to himself between bites of a corned beef sandwich on rye his wife had given him because by then the vision had been glimpsed, was "merely astonishing" on "a song by song basis," this is how he was talking by then, but, whatever his talents, he did not make *Albums*. On the spot, he promised never to buy another Twerp record and thereby missed his famous "electric era," named by Markowitz a few years after it had happened.

Think about it, he said to himself, for at that point he was still his only audience, except for his wife. Masses of people lining up to buy a single song, over and over, is just a random weather pattern hitting your city. But multitudes coming together to buy *an Album*?! That was a world revolution in culture! *The Album* contained ten, twelve songs, though theoretically it could be less or more, wherein each song was more than a discrete entity because it was linked aesthetically to others surrounding it. The parts made the whole but the whole transcended its parts. *The Album*, properly conceived, expanded each song into a cycle as in opera, in Wagner, only better, since its story was more opaque and thus more subject to interpretation. Only the Germans had words for it. *Zeitgeist. Gestalt. Weltschemertz*—no, not that one. *The Album* was an insurrection in taste that was bringing the Invisible Republic to the world. Or at least begin his career.

We have entered the age of the album, he wrote in his notebook. *The album is a Philosophy unto itself. Kant would have made albums had he the technology. Hegel would have wanted to manage the Beatles, or at least write their liner notes. Their music enacts a mode of being.* He broke a pencil underlining the last three words.

The word *masterpiece* became very important to him. *Rubber Soul, Revolver,* and, most monumentally, *Sgt. Pepper's* were *masterpieces*, not lucky accidents like "Tutti Frutti" or "Hound Dog." Markowitz wanted to kiss himself, but he was too busy pursuing the implications of his own thought. *The Album* was a more potent aesthetic achievement and cultural statement than—than—than…novels, plays, films, *New Yorker* articles, everything. *The Album* formed an aesthetic and philosophical whole equal to the *Critique of Pure Reason* or the *Ordination* of Duns Scotus. And who knew it? A more or less anonymous graduate student named Markowitz.

In the freshman classes he was assigned to teach, he became the first academic in America to play Beatles records. John Lennon said the Beatles were bigger than Christ and with his students he subjected this claim to critical scrutiny. He played *Revolver* and read from The Sermon on the

Mount. Class response was encouraging. Students preferred the Beatles to the Son of G-d.

Into his notebooks he drafted essays that articulated his insights—one on *Rubber Soul*, one on *Revolver*, and then finally *Sgt. Pepper's*. Because I have access to his papers, which I am editing and plan to release under the title of *The Closet Markowitz*, I can tell you every word in each essay was identical and arranged in the same order but for the title of the album under consideration and the names of the songs discussed. Remarkably, though, Markowitz, despite the coincidence of the wording, revealed the unique essence of each recording. With precociousness unprecedented for someone unaffiliated with *The New Yorker*, he distinguishes between *the concept* of *The Album* and that jejune artifact, "the concept album," which he associates with Frank Sinatra. *In the Wee Small Hours, Come Fly with Me*, all that bullshit. *Sinatra*, his notebook reveals, *is a gangster solipsist, a prick with a voice.* Wonderful, isn't it? But there's more. *Where this "gangster" enacts the fantasy of becoming bourgeois,* Sgt. Pepper's *embodies the totality of culture as a permanent utopic ideal.* To read Markowitz is to know that the last notes of "A Day in the Life" render the entire history of Euro-American music beside the point and that the Sixties must forever be the last meaningful stage of human development. Unfortunately, no one read this essay until 1979 when he published it in a critical anthology of rock history. By then he was on to punk and the Beatles had been dead for ten years.

His "Beatles and the History of America" class was the most popular one in the department, but he felt empty. Only his students knew his thesis, since at that time no place existed to publish his thinking. The cultural magazines were immune to Higher Pop Thought. They were obsessed with trivia like Twiggy and the meaning of the Vietnam War.

One day while leafing through *The New York Times*, looking for the Style section and hoping to find something about the Beatles, he came upon a headline announcing the death of Martin Luther King, Jr. He skimmed the many reports vaguely expecting to see a picture of the Twerp. He hadn't thought of him since *Help!* No luck. Only more articles concerning the escalation of the war. What really galled him, though, was that he could find no mention of the Beatles anywhere in the paper. He began to worry that the Pop Moment was receding before its articulation had reached the masses—or at least the intellectual quarterlies.

Were the Beatles suddenly irrelevant? Their last record, *Magical Mystery Tour*, wasn't *an album* but a hodgepodge of songs they tried to disguise as a TV movie. They weren't even touring anymore. From this cloud of despair appeared a silver lining. Wait, he thought, doesn't their retreat from live performances prove that *The Album* was in fact everything? Right now, as the American cities rioted and the war escalated, the Beatles were hidden away somewhere, working on some unimaginable masterpiece that would unite an Entire Culture and bring it to Total Consciousness. Alone in his bunker, which was just an ordinary graduate student apartment, Markowitz waited patiently for the Next Revelation.

The Next Revelation arrived, exhilarating and terrifying all at once. Playing it for the first time, Markowitz wondered if he had contracted palsy just from touching it. He couldn't stop shaking, and his trembling continued even during the brief periods the record wasn't playing. The Beatles had tipped their hand to his thesis by naming it *The Album*. Technically, there was a third word in the middle but Markowitz wasn't fooled. *The White Album*, its "straight" title, was a code transmitted to the entire culture, and Markowitz was possibly the only listener among millions who could crack it. His responsibility awed him. He wanted to digest it like a feast and then shit it out in the gold bricks of his paragraphs. He would have eaten it like acid but no hippy was he. His mind didn't require chemicals to perceive the hidden dimensions music revealed. In his excitement, he tried to play all four sides simultaneously—but the technology for such listening did not exist then. Whichever part he played, he heard a buried message, a siren song such as Odysseus is said to have heard.

The Sixties are over, it said. *Run for your lives.*
HELTER SKELTER!
Markowitz tried to disbelieve his ears. He had thought
the Sixties were forever. But when the Manson family murders were announced, and pinned to a Beatles song from the
album, he felt a chill. He was not the record's only listener. It
wasn't that he and Charlie had heard the same voices issuing
from the *The White Album.* It was his recognition that within
a true pop culture critic might dwell a mass murderer. Some
records, perhaps especially certain hit records, demanded
execution. Chekhov, it is said, strove to squeeze from himself, drop by drop, the peasant hidden within. Markowitz understood within him a murderer possibly lurked. He feared
its escape.

As it happened, that very week, his old college roommate
decided to found a magazine to disseminate opinions devoted to "the Rock and Roll Moment" and explaining "the
Culture of Now." Markowitz felt equipped for this enterprise.
He decided to quit his graduate program and follow his ears.

As a condition of being invited to join the magazine as a
regular contributor, Markowitz was requested to address his
former roommate as the Founder. The foundling critic was
happy to comply. Next he showed the Founder his *Sgt. Pepper's* essay. He expected it to be published in the first issue.
"*Sgt. Pepper's?*" the Founder exclaimed. "Ancient history.
Write me something relevant." Markowitz was so stunned
by this answer he blacked out on his feet. Consequently, he
could not hear the Founder ask him what they should name
their venture. Nevertheless, from the heart of his unknowing,
the name of the Twerp's most famous song issued from his
lips. "That's perfect. You're a genius," the Founder said. At
that moment, Markowitz awakened from his brief trance.
Finally, someone had noticed.

He was given album reviews to write. His excitement
quickly diminished. He was used to listening only to music
that moved him. What could you say about a Blue Cheer
album? Silence. James Taylor? Mind boggling that the Beat-

les have sanctioned him with their label. The Grateful Dead? He'd kill them if they were alive. Reviewing records week after week caused him to rethink the implications of mass murder. Bad records he saw were deathless. Even criticism couldn't kill a terrible record. People bought them anyway.

He considered returning to his dissertation, tentatively entitled "The Turntable and American History." Before he could get back to work on his prospectus, though, the Founder suggested he review the Twerp's rumored new release. Markowitz searched his incomparable brain for recent evocations of the Twerp. On the radio there had been that single "Subterranean Homesick Something or Other." Chuck Berry on amphetamines with Jack Kerouac shot like heroin into his brain. Frankly, it had scared Markowitz. He had tried to read *On the Road* but couldn't identify with the lifestyle it portrayed. He dreamed of owning his own house one day.

To prepare himself for the review, he asked the Founder for an expense account. He wanted to investigate what the Twerp had been doing since the Beatles had effaced him from memory. Upon receiving his modest allowance, which would have been larger had he been plugging the records of the magazine's sponsors, he headed straight to his *favorite* record store and purchased the Twerp's last five records. The last release—with the Twerp's face smiling like he was a country bumpkin—he did not like so much. The others, from his "electric era," were astounding. The weird thing was he thought he had already heard some of these songs recast as Beatles songs.

Remember this was before everything went online. Information in those days was surprisingly hard to come by. He called up a friend to ask him what he knew of the Beatles and the Twerp. His friend had the scoop. "Didn't you know that Twerp turned the Beatles on to marijuana? That's where *Revolver, Pepper*, all that shit came from."

"No shit," Markowitz answered, dumbfounded.

"The drugs alone cannot account for what happened. The complexity of the Twerp's lyrics transformed the songcraft of Lennon and McCartney. Harrison was awakened too. The Beatles' songs achieved a new, unprecedented depth that was enhanced by their sonic experimentation. For his part, the Twerp was inspired to add electric textures to his incomparable words, something he always wanted to do. His music provoked their music, and vice versa, until they were playing this phenomenal game of hide and seek where what was found was, for lack of a better phrase, the Sixties." Markowitz was stupefied but not so stupefied that he did not write into his notebook every word his friend said.

He was stupefied because he realized it was the Twerp who had provoked the Beatles to create *the Album*. He pulled out *Sgt. Pepper's* to stare at its cover. The hair on the back of his neck stood up. Why hadn't he noticed it before? In the top right hand corner sat the Twerp looking like he was between puffs. He looked like he did the day he had met him in the park. He would not have been surprised had the Twerp just started talking to him from the picture. Markowitz couldn't explain his feeling but he knew it anyhow. The Beatles' great period had sprung from the Twerp's head. The little shit was everywhere. How naïve he had been to think he could escape him! He felt like Columbus meeting Leif Erickson. Wherever Markowitz went, there was the Twerp. Only death could divide them. And even then… Markowitz put down the Beatles record and turned to the mirror ready for combat. If his career was to get off the ground, he needed to nip this Twerp phenomenon in the bud. No more surprise sightings. Somehow he had to nail him to the mast of his own critical perception so that he never appeared except when Markowitz wanted him to appear. He'd bought his records. There was no reason why he could not own the bastard.

What I am about to relate surprises me as much as it will you. For the first and only time in his life, Markowitz resolved to become epic. He donned his best armor, given to him by

the Creator in which he did not believe, through the inter-
vention of his mother. Initially wanting to rid himself of all
vestiges of culture, he stripped to his essence and strode to
the mirror for the ultimate showdown. He carried before him
his best weapon—no, not that!—his mind. Frankly, his body
unclothed was not terribly inspiring. The only person in the
world who cared about it was his wife.

He did not like what he saw. He felt unarmed. Quickly,
he retrieved the *Sgt. Pepper's* album cover to use as a shield.
More confident now, he returned to the field of battle, closed
his eyes, and endeavored to call forth the image of the Twerp.
Self-conscious mysticism did not come naturally to Markowitz
but at this moment, his belief that the Twerp was everywhere
was total. No stranger to the deep questions of philosophy, not
to mention dialectical materialism, he considered whether the
Twerp was his own projection or perhaps a manifestation of
some hidden force that bound everything together. And then
a playful, somewhat hoarse voice came into his head—it was in
fact the same one that Eve heard when she first saw her image
in the water. Markowitz had not read *Paradise Lost*, though,
so he could not recognize it.

Whatever its provenance, upon hearing the voice, he felt
nausea unknown since that day at the concert. Then, to his
intense embarrassment, he experienced a stirring in his loins
like he was kid again about to wake up from a wet dream. Only
he wasn't dreaming. He opened his eyes and saw incontrovert-
ible evidence of this mounting sensation. He positioned his
shield to cover himself.

Ignoring the voice rising in his head, he decided to speak.
Three times he uttered the Twerp's birth name but the word
Zimmerman carried no magic. Behind his own face, he suspected another but closer scrutiny revealed JohnPaulGeo-
geRingo looking out from his loins. Their uniforms looked
ridiculous down there. He looked up. In place of the Twerp's
blue ice gaze, he saw just himself. Another wandering Jew.
His ancestors probably raped by the same Cossacks who had
raped the Twerp's ancestors and given him those blue eyes.

The waves of history seem infinite, but they fall in the same direction. You can't tell them apart. They had floated the two of them, Zimmerman and Markowitz, to America where they had invented themselves from songs. The real Barbara Allen would have had either one of them tried for assault if they had so much as looked at her. The thought made him want to laugh, which came out as singing.

Strange to relate, and stranger for Markowitz to experience, the Twerp's voice issued from his body. From his mouth and before his eyes out came every verse to "Like a Rolling Stone." When his body stopped singing, he felt empty. He did not understand what had just happened. For once, he saw no reason to theorize his personal experience. From his shield he removed the Beatles record and put it on the turntable. He tried to let its sonic effects, its music-hall atmosphere so meticulously fabricated from its studio technology, wash away what had just happened. During "She's Leaving Home" where the background singer hums "lift me up to Paradise," he fell asleep. An hour later his wife found him, curled up, cold. She covered him with a poncho she had purchased at a Grateful Dead concert once when Markowitz was out of town.

A vision of the coming decades came to him as he slept. Everything the Sixties promised would be destroyed. He saw Nixon resigning. He watched the Reagan Revolution and was appalled. He saw war after war being waged in the Middle East and then the Twin Towers falling into Manhattan, burning like the tower of Ilium had burned. And a shitstorm of terrible music. He understood the Invisible Republic was a utopia that lived while the record spun and he was its guardian. And then he saw—everywhere!!— what looked like aliens from other planets sporting strange pods in their ears. One of them looked like his wife! These creatures were nodding their heads to some tune he could not quite hear. The last thing he saw was Obama sitting at the feet of the Twerp, wizened and aged, singing about changing times before a crowd of people wearing tuxedoes. Had the Invisible Republic come true? And there he is too, watching it on television, a computer screen, actually, but his dream did not know that.

And through it all, Markowitz sensed his own stubborn persistence, listening to and writing down History, however exalted or awful, as it appeared in rock, pop, soul, disco, punk, hip-hop, Indie Rock, and Americana. He even saw himself as an old man reading from his collected works—his dream had access to YouTube.

The next day, he woke up feeling refreshed having forgotten the day before. He called the Founder to pitch a new idea for an essay, which he referred to as a think piece because he knew the term would impress him. He mentioned the Kennedy assassination and the CIA. He spoke of the Vietnam War and the dissolution of the Beatles. He discussed futures splintered and the need to shore fragments now against ruins to come. In short, he said the Sixties were ending and we could not let that happen. "Of course the Sixties are ending," the Founder replied. "It's 1970."

"The Sixties were supposed to be forever," Markowitz replied.

"Oh, you mean a marketing concept? Great idea. It'll be a few years before that pays off for the magazine, though. We may have to talk about the seventies a lot before we revive the Sixties. But then," the Founder's eyes became starry, "we can talk about the Sixties until we die rich, fat, and famous. We'll fucking copyright the decade."

"You don't understand what I am saying. The Sixties is an ideal. It's a form of cultural knowledge. It's History on the edge of becoming Paradise and then diverging at the moment of transcendence and leaving us all broken up to contemplate what might have been. We must recreate it wherever we are."

The Founder rarely understood anything Markowitz said but as he was having trouble filling each issue of the magazine, he decided to encourage him. "Write that up, Gabe, and send it to me. I don't know about a long essay yet. I am still trying to build advertising here. But that new album I mentioned is due any day now. Supposed to be a double album. It's called *Self Portrait*. I'll send it over once we get a copy."

Without even hearing the record, his review was leaping to mind. He recalled one of the axioms from his notebooks. *The critic shall create the taste where none exists.* Writing, albeit in his head, was so easy he felt that he was just copying from some prior text already written for him. His essay posed a question and then he made up the answer. He left parts of it blank so he could fill in the song titles later. He had just gotten to the halfway point when he cursed his bad luck that this magazine had not been up and running when *Sgt. Pepper's* was released. *The New Yorker* would have reprinted his essay in an expanded version. He would be the John Updike of rock criticism by now.

A week passed and the album had not arrived. He became antsy. The future was now and he couldn't wait. He grabbed a blank notebook and wrote on its cover, "for later." He started furiously scribbling. Lists, pages and pages of them, many entries annotated. The Ten Best Albums of the Sixties. The Ten Greatest Songs of the Sixties. Rock and Roll and for the Desert Island. For that one he included entries from the fifties so as to diminish the number of times the Twerp appeared. No one knew it, but he had just copyrighted the Sixties. From this notebook would come four award-winning books, with multiple reprints. My bookcase is filled with them.

Restless and filled with the joy of creation, he experienced his gathering power. He could hardly contain himself. He considered sending his review to the Founder but he did not want his methods questioned. He had to wait for the album to be delivered. What was the delay?

On a hunch he called the same friend who told him about the Twerp and the Beatles. Criticism requires perception but connections help too. His friend worked for the publishing company that copyrighted the Twerp's songs. He said the Twerp's file had been very active for the past three years. From the basement of a secluded house in the upstate

New York woods, he had been making records, demos they were called. Everybody in the office was abuzz. The Twerp's manager was ecstatic. Viable product, he kept repeating. Better than the Beatles. "Have you heard any?" Markowitz asked, breathless.

"No, I'm not that important. But listen. Just the titles are terrific! Too Much of Nothing, Lo and Behold, I'm Not There, I Shall Be Released, Sign on the Cross." Markowitz did not like the sound of that last one but otherwise he was near hyperventilation. "When is he going to release them?"

"He's not. He thinks they are shit. He's working on something much better he's going to release instead." That must be the record I am supposed to review, Markowitz thought. He became deflated. He didn't want to hear the official record. He didn't care how good his review was. The review of the secret record would be better—especially if he was the only one to hear it. No one could dispute his point of view.

His friend thought the phone had gone dead when Markowitz's voice was suddenly screaming in his ear. "Can you get me a copy?! I have to hear these songs!!"

"I could get fired for that."

"Please!" the critic screamed. "Pretty pretty pretty please!"

His friend hung up.

Five days later, Markowitz found in his mailbox an unmarked package. The US Postal Service had not delivered it. He assumed the Founder had dropped by the promised review copy of the new album. He was wrong. Inside the brown wrapping was indeed a double album but what it was, and who made it, was a mystery. The cover was simply a beat up white cardboard sleeve with the words "Great White Wonder" stamped in the corner. Inside were two records with blank labels. Out of the sleeve fell a handwritten note. "From a friend. Good luck." He didn't recognize the writing.

Something higher than me is playing with me, he thought. He was tingling. Destiny was tickling his balls. Suddenly, he knew what it was. The secret recordings! Imagine the White Album was yours alone to describe! He reached for a pen. He

crossed out "Great White Wonder." He tried to think of something catchy and subversive and that would wear well. Once
he gave them a name, they would be his. His pen wrote before
he knew what it was writing "The Basement Tapes"! Perfect!
His pulse was racing. To calm himself, he decided to wait until
sundown before he played them. History is easier to discern
when the light is crepuscular. The anxiety was unbearable and
sweet. He felt like Lenin arriving at the Finland Station.
The sun's light hardly lingered in the air when the needle touched the disc. The first sound he heard was noise.
Static. The records were poorly pressed. The music, such
as he could pick up, was undeniably potent, like drinking
moonshine whiskey during prohibition. A nervous laughter erupted from him. He realized he was enjoying his first
bootleg recording. He was its distiller. He'd be sipping this
shit for years. He has just signed on as its distiller. He hoped
the Twerp never released it. And then he started hiccupping.

An hour later he had regained his breath and could con-
centrate on what was playing. Beneath the hiss and pop of the
sound ran a murmur, sometimes it sounded like a carnival
and other times a dirge, and at one point he thought he heard
someone shout million-dollar bash. He heard Judgment Day
and the Resurrection too. For an atheist, he was surprisingly
undisconcerted. During "Sign on the Cross," he thought he
saw the Creator who some say made this world and then
abandoned us to it. The Creator was in flight, running and
making, as he ran, a sound that was the same as that which
Markowitz's record player was making. As the Creator fled,
the fallen world left behind seemed to rise up on the strains
of the music and and…and…Markowitz could not say. He
lacked the conceptual frame to articulate his thoughts. The
brilliance of *Sgt. Pepper's* had not prepared him for what he
was experiencing.

His pen lay heavy in his hand and his notebook pages
looked vaster, whiter than a blizzard on the plains of Kansas.
Like Sisyphus climbing the hill, he wrote anyway. *Awake as
in dreams.* He had never felt so percipient. *This music is the*

underside of this world. History's inverse seam. From dreams a Higher Reality is stitched. Forms fall away to reveal the binding. This music turned the terrors of the Sixties inside out and revealed history as it should have been and perhaps was since you could hear it here. The songs evaded time and death, which were always present, and no more terrifying than a star's light. The critic doesn't know it but he's having a religious experience. Hiding this knowledge from himself, he adopts the vatic mode. *History is content, music its counter-form, and I am its auteur!!!*

Once, words about a "dream" or maybe it was "all you have to do is dream" came into him and he thought for a second the Twerp was singing Johnny Mercer or, worse, Sinatra. He didn't care. He became a pipe open at both ends mumbling to himself in tongues only he could decipher.

The words to the songs were an obstacle, like the Smith records, but harder to make out. Half of the time, but only half, he couldn't hear what the Twerp was saying. *The sound's capacity to be reproduced is irrelevant and antithetical to its expression. The music transcends the technology that transmits it.* Ten years later, these very words would appear in an essay he wrote about punk music and its destruction of existing forms. *Christ, what I could write if only I could make out the words!*

He found his phone and started dialing.

"Hey, I received the package you sent me."

"I don't know what you are talking about."

"Those secret records you told me about."

"Really, I don't know what you are talking about. I never sent them."

"I just want to ask one more favor." The silence on the line sounded like an invitation. "If he's copyrighting the songs, can you at least send me the lyrics? They're kind of hard to hear."

Markowitz never received a lyric sheet. He had a thought not even Aristotle had contemplated. Lyrics were irrelevant, useful to understand but not essential. After all, sung words were just sounds. Until the critic said what they meant—

put his words to the song—it didn't matter what they were. Music was the voices in his head produced by the sound of the sound. He was a sound clairvoyant like those early guys, Pythagoras and Aristoxenus of Tarentum. He was Markowitz of Berkeley. Some had second sight. He has second hearing. He was no mystic, though. That was hippy bullshit.

Knowing that the music of the spheres had been revealed to him caused him to evaluate his place in Creation. Jesus, he said in appreciation, though not in prayer, you really would have to be G-d to discern every nuance this stuff possessed. For moments too fleeting to be called seconds he considered what it would be like to be G-d and to have your own sound system. He was an atheist, though, and if he were G-d, he would have to disbelieve in himself.

Waves of sounds were washing over him until all songs became one. Something he thought might be called "I'm Not There" played over and over even though the needle was at rest. His head had a repeat function before machines did. Like the singer, he was where he wasn't. The false boundaries that divide the present from the past and from the future had disappeared. In Markowitz the signals of Creation had found transmission, and he called them the Sixties.

His trancelike state did not prevent him from writing. In his notebook he reproduced the words to "I'm Not There" exactly as the Twerp sung them, a miraculous feat, since the Twerp was so drunk at the time of the recording even he didn't know what he was saying. Unfortunately, those pages have been torn out, so I cannot reproduce them here. I checked the Twerp's website for the official version, but they are incomplete. Perhaps they never existed. Who can catch the wind in the leaves when all is still? All that remains are these cryptic statements, *Waterfall...rising up...the air crumbling into sound...listening is breathing...a pleasuredome of sound...Gan Eden...like an amphitheater...a curtain patterned like a setting sun rising... androgynous something with a harp peeking out...too bright... the rolling sun...Where am I?*

His closet is pitch-black. The candles are blobs of wax. He doesn't know where he is and no one else does either, not even his wife. Let's just say he is no longer in the present but he's not exactly in the past either.

Wherever he is, there's a buzzing between his ears—it's been sounding for hours. His thoughts persist. Thinking apparently generates its own energy—if you are a great enough critic. The buzzing he confuses with the bell he heard *that long-ago day*, not this one. He had been listening to the Basement Tapes and dreaming a damsel with dulcimer looking oddly like the Twerp when his doorbell ringing had interrupted his blissful reverie. It was the Founder bringing him the record to review. At the time, he was angry to have been interrupted because he had been in the midst of a once-in-a-lifetime critical insight. But Markowitz was always experiencing such feelings. A professional hazard. After the Founder departed, he played the new record. It was nothing like what he had been hearing. The Twerp had hidden the good stuff! This shit corresponded precisely with the review he had begun in his head a few days earlier, which was to be expected. He was always having that experience too. He finished his review and then the rest of his life happened, some of it now available online for video review.

At this point, it is difficult to say precisely what he did or did not remember. Could he have recalled the dream I saw in his eyes that day at the bookstore? Whatever the inspiration, that record with the ridiculous cover came into his mind. He wondered if it was as bad as he said it was.

A light or something like it came into his eyes. Why not play it again? Maybe this time he would like it. He was a critic! It was never too late to be right. Then the light in his eyes became brighter, almost like the sun had rolled into his closet. Why not listen to every record he ever made, especially the ones I panned or outright ignored! I'll re-review the Twerp's career. There's no point to just listening to every record from 1970. I'd have to review *Atilla*, the first Billy Joel album, and that would kill me. I could start by reviewing the Sinatra album and then

write a new review for every album. If I listened to them in reverse order, I could trace the Twerp's evolution without being
prejudiced by my perception of his earlier work. I'll destroy
time and hear each one as if I have never heard it before!

And so Markowitz began a journey possibly not attempted
since King Cheops rode in his great Khufu ship. The record
of that journey remains undocumented, but fortunately, I
have been able to piece together from the blank pages of
Markowitz's last Listening Notebook the outline of his miraculous voyage.

The Sinatra album established a pattern that was repli-
cated with each record. Everything he knew was wrong. The
album being played, whichever one it was, was and always
would be the Twerp's greatest record. From genius to genius
they veered. Each album was a revelation, so astonishing he
did not bother to review them. The next one, which was the
last one, was better than the last one, which was the next one.
There is no need for me to recount the titles. You can look
them up yourself.

He grew younger as he listened. By the time he came to the
Jesus records, he was ready to convert. Fortunately, strict ad-
herence to his methodology prevented him. He could not stop
until he had reached the end, which was the beginning. With
Herculean strength he compelled himself to keep going back
through the Rolling Thunder Revue of '75, then the Comeback
Tour of '74 until finally he came to the epicenter, the 1970 piece
of shit, which, to his amazement, was, when he heard it, the
GREATEST RECORD HE HAD EVER HEARD IN HIS LIFE. He was
devastated, bereft, and exalted all at once. He stretched himself
out on the floor of his closet, glowing, feeling as Mary might
have after G-d had knocked her up.

His quest might have ended in 1970 but the critic's will was
inexhaustible. The desire to have the last word—to be right—
had not yet left him. Yes, he had missed some things these
last decades, but didn't the heart of the Sixties remain to be
recaptured? When he gets to '68-67, the Basement Tapes, he
wants to pause forever in their aura. It's as if he's in the after-

life now. They are perfect, everything he dreamed of music being, and everything he had always said they were. They were more, actually, and this realization provokes in him a feeling resembling humility. Still, something pulls him on, something beyond his knowing, the buzz of the sound, call it, and now he's come again to the music of '66-65. It's like being reborn—not that he knows. Heard now, after hearing everything else, they seem less like a peak than part of an endless chain of mountains in which any one of them is worth the climb. Nothing about them is not what he thought they were. I was right, I was wrong, I was right, I was wrong, he mumbles as if in prayer.

At this point, he alters his methodology. To justify his decision, he has recourse to Zeno's paradox wherein if you move toward your object in jumps, and each jump accomplishes half the distance remaining between you and your object, you will never arrive at your destination. His idea is that he doesn't want to come to the end of the mountain chain. He wants this feeling of exaltation to continue forever. It occurs to him that since records obligate the listener to play them a half at a time, he should already be in a position where he never arrives at the end of his quest. Yet, something about Zeno's theorem must be flawed because despite playing each album one side, or a half, at a time, he seems to be running out of them. He can determine no way to play only half of the second side, and then half of half of the second side, and so on, so he chooses a more conventional route to delay the inevitable. He decides to add material and thereby trick time by altering the manner of it duration.

Into his rigid program of reverse chronological ordering, he inserts his massive bootleg collection, most of which he had not yet heard. Typical for a listener of Markowitz's pitiless ethics, the prospect raised for him a moral dilemma. He could restrict himself to bootlegs that preceded 1965. *Everything I need is already in my closet!* But why stop there?

Shouldn't he hear everything? Virtually every show the Twerp had ever given, from 1961 to last week in Hamburg, existed online, doubtless in the cloud. Should he go there? And if he did, would he disappear? But there was a practical concern. He had no idea how to access this cloud. As if by magic, his wife appeared bringing a laptop that she somehow ran through his record player speaker so he could imagine he was playing records he had misplaced and not digital files.

Before rebooting his listening orgy, he pulled from the lowest shelf one of his Elvis calendars. At the top of the calendar he crossed out 1965 and wrote 2014. Lucky for Markowitz, each day fell on the same day of the week as it did in the year of his intended listening. He estimated the Twerp had played in the range of 3,164 shows, averaging two hours each, for a total of 263 consecutive twenty-four-hour days. He calculated how many days, including brief naps, remained until he finished his project. He wanted his wife to know when he would be finished.

These recordings introduced a mini-eternity into Markowitz's otherwise ruthless countdown. There were so many of them! In a year, he couldn't hear them all. Markowitz heard them in a single night.

The bootlegs floored him even more than the albums had. At some point, the years became mixed and he surrendered to their randomness. 1974 Boston, 1979 San Francisco, and 2011 Beijing seemed like the same show to him. And it was great! Eons of listening history he had missed were being restored to him, but finding each show on the laptop, then running it through the record player wearied him. He wanted to shuffle the shows together and remembered reading somewhere that the iPod let you do that. Instantly, his wife materialized with an iPod classic and set him up with his own iTunes account. Then she transferred the sound files to his new toy, and in the twinkling of an eye, Markowitz's was reliving the Twerp's entire bootlegged career on Genius Shuffle.

From his Elvis calendar he never crossed off a day. Markowitz was but the strumming of his guitar or the intake of breath that caused a line of verse to pause. He could not know it, but he was ascending into the cloud.

At one point, suspense overwhelmed him. He realized at some point that show when he had spoken to the Twerp for the first and only time would come into his ears. Finally, he would hear the song about the changing times as the Twerp had sung it that day. But when the song came on, the Twerp slipped his mind. The song returned to him the beauty of his wife's youth, which in truth had never left his eye.

He saw her above him, holding a package. "I have mail for you." He recognized its shape.

"Not another album to review?"

"It's a record but not a review copy."

"What is it?"

"Play it and see. On the package, someone has written 'B-B D----'s First Recording.'" "Who sent it?" "I don't know. The doorbell rang and this was all I found."

He waited as she seemed to put the record on the spindle. It's so dark in here, he thought, how can she see. He wondered where the Sinatra record had gone.

But stop! Relax in brief respite. Biographers who understand the task at hand take the same as easily as possible. From time to time we like to lay our pens aside awhile. Uninterrupted writing fatigues, like digging. I borrow these words from another writer to introduce a feeling of stillness into my narrative at this crucial point.

Markowitz is quiet. He couldn't move a pen if he wanted to. He feels himself spinning round and round like a record. His mind and body are no longer in relation to each other.

There's a bumping in his brain. For a long time he can't hear anything except the needle hitting the disc's edge and circling as if the groove can't be found.

Then a crackling and a hiss. The distinct sounds of a piano being pounded.

A voice shouting words he can't quite make out. Non-sense syllables. The Twerp could not have been older than sixteen. He tries to hear beneath the roar of the disc, which was actually the sound of the past, this world, interfering with the next one. The sound of the sound becomes clearer. Markowitz's brain surrenders as his ears vibrate. The voices of every record he has ever heard merge into a shout. Awopmopabulopawambamboom. And underneath, a beautiful rising chorus that sounds like doo-wop.

"Markowitz is dead—woooooo. Markowitz is dead—woooooo yeah."

Whereupon, his soul, which he did not know he had, chased the demon out.

The next morning, his wife found his body, a blank note-book pressed to his chest. She closed his eyes and turned off "That Lucky Old Sun."

It had played all night, into the Invisible Republic, where Markowitz lives on among the sounds he tried to write.

Girl of Few Seasons

RACHEL KONDO

The night before he left for basic training, Ebo had one last pigeon to kill—a cream barred homer from the old line of Stichelbaut. The bird was from a long strain of impressive racers, a gift from his mother when he was nine years old. Ebo had put off killing this bird, his favorite, by killing all the others first: one, sometimes two, a day. It had to be done. The birds would not stay away from their coop and his leaving home meant there would be no one to care for them. Not his mother, not Daddy, who wasn't his father, and especially not his younger sister Momoyo, who was a ward of the State. Momo would have if she could.

Ebo lay awake on his futon with his ankles crossed and one arm crooked behind his head, so still he could see the moonlight shifting about him. Even the water stain on the ceiling felt like something new to see, as if the old blight was now a bloom. In a matter of hours, Ebo would be a soldier, though he hadn't much considered it. He was thinking of Momo, her absence his constant companion.

As children, on a night like this, they'd creep through the house and out the door. The Buddhist temple wasn't far, just down the street. There, a half circle of taiko drummers practiced their beats. They were bare-chested men with strips of braided cloth tied around their heads. They struck the drum skins with such force sweat leaped from their bodies in an upward rain. Momo's delight always found expression. She would throw her arms wide and bend her knees, the rhythm moving through her like a small-lipped wave. Her eyes would close, her mouth round to a little plum seed. Her face would cant to the moon as if its meager light was warm like the sun—something Ebo could see, but not feel himself.

Now, what he could feel, he could not see—these memories of his sister, each a smooth river stone set to his naked chest. Ebo shifted on his futon and tried to bring his hand to the heaviness, but the arm behind his head was numb. He waited for life to return to it as the darkness began to lift. It was no longer late, but early.

*

For some, the Vietnam War was about moral duty. For others, it was a son grown too fast and gone. But for Ebo, the war was not about anything, not even killing or dying. He thought Vietnam might be like Maui, a place too quiet for fear. He thought the war might be a nameless river flowing strong after a heavy rain. If he let it, the war would take him away from Happy Valley to places he'd never been.

The United States Army had deemed him Private E-1, a ranking so low it didn't even warrant insignia. Those people who knew Ebo thought his graduating from high school a minor miracle; that he'd languished for ten months without a job was no surprise. When word of his enlistment got around, they figured the Army would give him a haircut, a uniform, something decent to do.

But Ebo had his plans. He understood enlisting meant a free trip to the induction center at Fort DeRussy on O'ahu, an island over. From there, he would travel to basic training on the mainland to a place he'd never even seen on a map. But that didn't matter. It was enough to first be sent to O'ahu, to where he could see Momo at the Waimano Home for the Feeble Minded. He'd waited nine years to visit; there hadn't been money for it sooner. What happened to Ebo afterward in Vietnam, he did not have the time to consider. Momo would be fourteen by now.

*

The newly hatched squabs were the easiest to practice on. Ebo had taken a hammer to the yellow fuzz on their heads. The first squab, he'd struck too hard; the second, not hard enough. With a few other birds, Ebo had tried a sharp knife, but couldn't get the pressure right, nearly cut them in two. In the end, with the older birds that had been with him some time, Ebo took each one tenderly in his hands, lifted them high above his head, and drove their skulls to pieces against the cement.

This was the way Ebo would kill his last bird too. Better to do it now in the dull gray light of early morning than the less forgiving blare of later. He moved soundlessly through the bedroom and into the darkened hallway. He sidled past his mother's room, timing each footstep with the click of the Westinghouse fan. In the living room, he saw Daddy sleeping on the couch with an arm draped over his head and one leg bent to the carpeted floor. Though he didn't need to—Daddy was hard of hearing—Ebo eased the screen door against its latch.

The low-slung moon was a chalky thumbprint in the sky. Ebo crossed his arms against the cool and turned by degrees to all that its sheer light touched around him. Happy Valley, he knew, was nothing more than the skin between the knuckled ridges of the West Maui Mountains. Only a smattering of houses crawled up its slopes, none of them much to look at. His feet found those few patches of grass to step on as he moved through the backyard. He dipped his head beneath the boughs of plumeria, heavy with flower, and knew where crab spiders predictably spun their webs. He could guess the size and heft of the gecko that clicked its tongue into the darkness. *Big buggah*, he thought.

The coop was a mishmash of materials, built piecemeal with tin and scrap metal, spare plywood and chicken wire. It sat at the back of the yard on cinder blocks two feet off the ground with mounds of pigeon kaka beneath it. The landing jutted out from the roof to make the coop appear as if it leaned. The door itself was just two pieces of discarded mesh screen that Ebo had sewn together by hand.

Next to the coop was a shallow sandbox that had been Momo's playpen. Now, it was where fifteen dead pigeons were buried. To ward off critters and stench, Ebo had placed a plank of plywood over its opening with a hollow tile brick on top for good measure. There was just the business of the final bird and then it would be a grave.

He sat on his heels and plugged his fingers through the chicken wire of the coop, looking for that bird now. In earlier years, it had roosted on a high post with its head tucked into its plumped body, its eyes slivered in half sleep. But recently, with age, the bird had lost the battle for a perch and lived with the weakest as puffed dots about the wire floor. And there the bird was now, still responding to pecking order, though the others were long dead.

Ebo unlatched the eyehook and dipped through the door, startling the bird into winging itself backwards, making little wafts of wind. Ebo called to it softly—*pssssh, pssssh, pssssh*—before swiping at it with trained hands, as was routine. He held the bird to his midsection, felt its heart like a tiny machine. He fanned the bird's wings, one after the other, to check its feathers for lice. He then held the bird up to one side and peered into its ball bearing eye flitting in its stitch of a socket, remembering only then that his purpose was to extinguish its tiny light.

Exiting the coop, the screen door slapped against its frame as if to call Ebo awake to the yard, already flushed with sunshine. His dawdling had cost him the gray curtain of early morning that, now lifted, revealed a world vivid with color. The killing of his bird would need to be done in clear view, without ceremony or sentiment.

Ebo stationed himself at the slab of concrete between the house and carport, widening his stance to be sure of his footing. He knew from practice to not hold back, to put his whole body into the effort. Allowing himself any fear or pity would result in pain for the bird, a dragging out of its death. The bird was just a steady heartbeat in his hands, bred for calmness, known for being trusting. With both hands, Ebo raised it high above him. He tightened his grip, working his fingers into the bird's soft give, and still, it did not struggle. He then raised himself to his toes and hesitated by telling himself not to hesitate. He reached higher, the highest he could go, and one by one, loosened his fingers as if to release the bird to the immense sky it belonged to, the sky it now climbed.

*

Long before any birds, it was just Ebo and his mother on their own. People had clucked their tongues in disapproval, but Ebo never minded. He had no father, but he had everything in a mother. Her hips were fuller then, more inviting, and little Ebo, wanting to be close, always had a fistful of her dress. He had seen how others watched her mouth as she spoke, her lipstick perfectly applied. He had seen this in the man his mother brought home when he was five, the man who flicked a Primo beer bottle cap at him and he happened to catch it. The man had winked, smiling so big his cheeks rounded into two mountain apples. By the time Ebo learned to call this man Daddy, there was another child, a girl they called Momo, and buckets full of bottle caps.

All these years, they lived quietly across the street from Tasty Crust, the diner Ebo had been frequenting since small-kid time. This morning, he would go for his usual breakfast. But unlike most mornings, he would need to say goodbye. He breathed in the cool morning air with the heat just beneath it. Seeing no cars, he still skipped to a jog when crossing Mill Street, his rubber slippers slap-slapping like fat rain against the pavement. When he got to the other side, he turned to look at his house against the West Maui Mountains, the mountains against the blue gray morning. It was unremarkable, his house. Walls of thin plywood held up a corrugated tin roof that had rust in the dips of its divots. The carport sheltered a dead Ford on cinder blocks. Clothes hung on a sagging line and brushed against the Ford's dusty hood so that the hems of Daddy's work shirts were never entirely clean. This is what Ebo would leave behind and what he would take with him like a picture in his pocket.

He walked into the sticky warmth of Tasty Crust where the old-timers were at their usual stools, living out the best part of their day, the part that was spent in the company of others. They'd each brought their copy of *The Maui News,* though they'd read it through at home. This morning, they wore Aloha shirts and their veteran caps and pins. They'd done this, marked their calendars even, for Ebo, who had enlisted as they did for their wars.

"Howzit, young man!" said Flora, the waitress who spoke for everyone.

Ebo smiled, sat on a stool at the counter. Flora set down a mug of coffee, pivoted her body like a sprinkler as she wiped the counter. Her hair, a manapua bun sitting plump on the curve of her head, had never been let down, the coif of her fringe sprayed stiff for years. She had never been anything else, which was a comfort.

"Big day today," she said, as much to the counter as to Ebo. "We is proud of you, young man, I can tell you dat. You go get'm and say you is born and raised Happy Valley. We make'm *good* in Happy Valley."

An old-timer slapped a hand to a thigh. "I remembah when you was one small buggah, legs danglin from duh chair," he said. "*Hooooo-eeee!* You was one *cute* buggah. But some rascal, you!"

Small laughter then; the others remembered young Ebo too. To this, Ebo dipped his head low, nodding, shielding himself from the gleam of attention.

"Time fo kau kau!" said Flora, setting before Ebo a plate of hot cakes with an ice cream scoop's worth of butter on top. It had been some time since Ebo's mother had been there to stab at the butter with her fork and paint circles on his stack, then her own. Back then, she'd drizzle syrup too, when Ebo would say, at whatever age, "Ma, I get'm." After Momo came along, his mother didn't have time for Tasty Crust, for their early-morning breakfasts. After Momo, she stopped being just his.

But Ebo understood. Even as a baby, Momo had been generous, smiling wide when spoken to, as if she had been born to give. Neighbors would wiggle a finger at her and she'd take it holding their gaze. So smaht, they'd say, noting her dark irises, how they shone especially large and nearly covered the whites of her eyes. Her fine blue-black hair swirled into a single giri giri atop her head, a sign she would never be cause for trouble. But mostly she was a mirror for their mother, who looked at her baby girl to see her joy.

No one noticed young Ebo alone. By the time he was nine and Momo nearly five, he preferred the mountains of 'Iao Valley to the tedium of school, passing his days by the river skipping rocks, catching guppies, doing nothing. He quickly learned the word truancy. His mother's rice paddle had no effect and Daddy had said, not my kid. When Ebo was held back a year, people just shook their heads thinking him a good-for-nothing kolohe. But he'd proved himself good for enlisting—something to do, a way to be gone.

After clearing his plate, Ebo dipped his hand into his shorts pocket to pay. Flora, ever watchful, said, "Dis one on me, soljah boy." Her inflections and movements were a conductor's wand to a stand, orchestrating the old-timers so they knew to rise with Ebo and to salute him. To this, Ebo extended his hand to each of them as the other diners watched in silence. The cooks turned down the radio in the kitchen and peered through their cutout window fringed with open tickets. All the while, Flora kept to her work, wiping the counter where Ebo had just been.

*

Happy Valley by then was pulsing with moderate activity. The morning sun had risen to a low perch in a cloudless sky, emanating its white light as a softness on Ebo's skin. He stood at the edge of Mill Street again, scanning the blue brightness for his bird beneath the visor of his hands.

A Buick sounded its horn in two successive beeps, sending Ebo back a step. As the Buick coasted by, the driver threw Ebo a left-handed shaka out the window. "A hui hou!" said the driver, to say *until we meet again*. Ebo's head tilted back with a smile to acknowledge the driver, a smile that was gone by the time he crossed the street. Soon Ebo would not be so known, something he had wanted for years.

Back at the house, his mother stood at the stove working a pan. Egg shells were halved, two Vienna Sausage cans curled open, everything crackling to oil and heat. Daddy was still on the couch with a pillow pressed to his face. Ebo stood there watching the house as it would be without him in it.

One hand to hip, his mother was in her usual meal-making stance: her weight shifted left and her right foot touching down to the linoleum by just a toe. Her National Dollar dress hung on her too-thin frame like drapery, as if there might not be anything behind it. To Ebo, she was the size of a child, but she was not new like a child. Her hair had lost its luster and could no longer hold color, had given in to a blank and lifeless gray. Her gaze avoided most living things and was too often fixed to the floor. She was a woman afraid of loss so that she was first afraid of life.

Even when they were a family of four, and then three, there were only ever two chairs. Plunking down to one now, his mother's movements quickened. Not a minute passed before she turned to Ebo with a plate of food in hand and set it before him at the two-person table.

"You hungry?" she asked.

"Nah," said Ebo, "I pau eat."

"No, you–eat."

She darted back and forth, bringing him a pair of chopsticks, a glass of milk, as though he was just a boy and not a young man of nineteen, all lean muscle and strength. But because he was her son, he was a boy still. And because he was leaving home that day, she stopped fussing about the kitchen and sat down opposite him. The only other time he could remember his mother sitting like this was the day she made that call about his first pigeon.

That afternoon, she'd sat Ebo down and told him to sit still, which made him squirm. He had wanted to go play, but she shushed him, said to listen. She picked up the receiver of the rotary phone, as gleaming black as her hair was then. The dial turned and stuttered, turned and stuttered, and by the time she spoke, two warm hands had suctioned to Ebo's eyes. He loosed himself free to face Momo, whose smile was shy one tooth. He flicked her forehead and called her *puka mout* to make fun, but she only smiled wider, which made them both laugh. Snapping her fingers to quiet them, their mother spoke a final few words into the phone. "Yes. Can." She hung up smiling, something she didn't hide then. She said, "What you tink, Ebo, you like birds?" Ebo had never been asked what he thought and looked to Momo for how he should feel. Momo beamed as if giving to Ebo was giving to her. She flitted across the kitchen floor on her toes and flapped her arms like wings. Over and over she said, "Happy Ebo! Happy Ebo!" and he knew then he'd been given a gift.

*

Ebo washed the dishes for his mother, the only thing he could think to do for her. At the sink, he watched his coop through the screen window, waiting for his bird, always the last to finish circling. When it finally descended, Ebo turned off the water to see it skitter back and forth along the length of the landing. He knew the bird needed food—it was long past the hour when it was usually fed. But Ebo knew he shouldn't feed what he would soon kill, something he'd allowed himself to be distracted from doing.

He reasoned with himself. Better to give the bird a little more time in the sun while he packed, was his thinking. He calculated the hours he had left before his ride to the airport arrived and went about gathering his few toiletries in the bathroom. There really wasn't much he needed where he was going, all of it amounting to the knapsack he'd had since grade school, the one with the busted zipper. He went to retrieve it from his bedroom closet and found it laid out on his futon instead. Even more startling was a shirt folded neatly and, next to it, a pair of shoes. Ebo kneeled down to these things, astonished they were there and that they were his. He pressed a finger to one milky white button in a long line of them. He lifted a shoe to his nose to breathe in the leather, put the tip of his tongue to the heel. He'd never had anything new before, let alone anything with buttons or laces. How his mother had fixed the zipper on his knapsack, he didn't know. How she'd found the money for these things was even more of a mystery. All he knew was that this was his mother's way: to give all she could, and when there was nothing left, to give her very will.

Once she had secured Ebo's first pigeon with the breeder, the bird soon posed another problem for his mother—it needed a loft. For two weeks, she had pressed Daddy to build one, but he'd only shaken his head at the expense, though it was the effort he wouldn't give. When she made up her mind to build one herself, she made her way on foot to the junkyard, with Ebo and Momo trailing. There she selected wood panels either discarded as excess or abandoned as trash. Ebo found a large piece of chicken wire curled around a tire, which he had worked hard to unfurl. All the while, Momo picked through the dirt for nails, examining each one closely, speaking aloud what she discovered. "You good for Ebo," or, "You no good. Not for my Ebo." The usable few she clenched in one hand, as if Ebo's happiness was something she could hold and keep safe.

That his mother and sister did this on his behalf was almost enough for Ebo. All of the fuss was just for him—he didn't need more. The small makeshift coop they built, however shoddy, was entirely his. With the little coop, he started to believe. He believed in the promise of this pigeon and he believed Daddy might be pleased, maybe even impressed, with their handiwork.

When Daddy's ride dropped him home from work that evening, Ebo and Momo hurried to the jalousie window in the bathroom to watch him discover what they'd built. He nearly missed it, but then he didn't. Setting down his lunch pail and water jug, he crouched low to examine the structure. When he began to circle it, sizing it up, Momo pressed her head to Ebo's shoulder. Ebo felt her flinch when Daddy kicked the heel of his foot into the coop so that the sorry thing folded into itself and fell. Daddy used both his feet to further trample what they'd built, until there was no trace of their efforts in the tangle that remained.

Chest heaving, Daddy snapped open a folded lawn chair and set it down facing the pile of wood and wire. Ebo stared hard at Daddy sitting there, one knee bouncing wildly. By that evening hour, with everything on its way to darkness, Daddy appeared a darker shadow. But then movement caught Ebo's eye. Momo was no longer next to him—she was in the carport. She walked toward Daddy so slowly her dress barely moved at her knees. Her hands were cupped protectively in front of her, as if in prayer. When she stood before Daddy, she splayed open her hands from prayer to sacrifice. Daddy glanced at her offering, which Ebo knew was a Lucky Strike. Daddy looked at his child, who was every inch his, and scooped her onto his lap. They stayed that way awhile, long enough for Ebo's mother to flick on the overhead light and see what had happened, long enough for Momo to begin picking through the dirt again for nails and for Daddy to help.

*

Now, whenever Ebo looked for Daddy, Ebo knew to look there, in the carport, where Daddy smoked on the bench seat of the dead Ford. Daddy had had the bench seat removed from the car years ago, after Momo was sent away, after he'd injured his back at work and could no longer sit down to a lawn chair.

Ebo elbowed the screen door open to its usual high-pitched wheeze. At the bottom of the steps, he plugged his feet into rubber slippers and shuffled over to Daddy, who was exactly where Ebo knew he'd be. With his new pair of shoes waiting for him, Ebo now needed socks, something only Daddy owned. Ebo sat down on the bench seat next to Daddy, but Daddy stood, though there was room enough for two. Daddy relaxed against the frame of the Ford and lit another Lucky Strike. Speaking through pinched lips, he said, "You ready to go?"

Digging a knuckle into his eye, Ebo said, "I bettah be."

Daddy pulled on his cigarette and nodded. Two steady streams of smoke issued from his nostrils. He used to work for Maui County in road maintenance, but it had been some time since he'd paved a pothole or disposed of a dead mongoose. It had been even longer since Daddy served with the 442nd in the Second World War, making Daddy the closest person to Ebo who had not only left the island, but returned. In the silence, the two men were careful to avoid each other's eye, an intimacy they did not know how to share. Any other day and

one of them would've walked away by now. But the moment
for that had passed and Ebo was still there, needing socks.

"Gotta ask you someting," said Ebo as he stood to ask
Daddy squarely. Daddy pivoted back down onto the bench
seat, set his elbows to his knees, and hung his head between
his shoulders. Ebo, in turn, leaned against the Ford so that
like two reluctant dance partners, they'd traded places.

"I know what you like ask," said Daddy. "Some kine ad-
vice. I know. Soljah to soljah. But only get one ting fo say..."
Daddy looked up and settled his gaze seriously into the middle distance. Ebo hadn't anticipated this. He gently pushed
off from the Ford, stood tall and waited.

"Duh ting you gotta do," said Daddy, "is...no die."

A brief moment passed with Ebo thinking Daddy sincere.
It stretched long enough for Ebo to open his dry mouth and
try to match the sentiment. But Daddy threw up his arms in
amazement of his own humor, amazed Ebo hadn't yet agreed.
"You see? Das it! Jus *no die*. Easy." Daddy spun out laughing so
hard he began to cough until he choked. Ebo could only look
out at the pavement of the driveway, staring into the sunlight
until his eyes began to water. Once recovered, Daddy flicked
the butt of his cigarette and it rolled, still burning, into Ebo's
line of sight. "Ay," muttered Daddy, groaning as he stood, as if
standing would be the hardest task of his day. Before disappearing into the house, Daddy called out to Ebo, "Eh, maybe
go Paukukalo. One last time. Jus fo Daddy, eh?"

Ebo slunk into the sun and faithfully toed the butt dead.
He pinched its mess between two fingers and dropped it into
a gallon bucket filled with sand, figuring the bucket had another week or so to go. Since he was a boy, it had been his
job to empty the ashy filth into Tasty Crust's dumpster when
no one was looking and to go to Paukukalo Beach for a clean
bucket of sand.

Mindlessly, Ebo tapped his toe against the heft of the
bucket, as if he couldn't muster the will to kick. But the will
existed and manifested itself in sudden movement. Ebo tore

down the driveway and hung a right onto Mill Street, jogging a ways until turning to face oncoming cars in a backwards shuffle. Everything siphoned to the power of his hitchhiker's thumb, now asking for someone, anyone, to stop. He didn't have the time to walk the two miles, but he had his thumb and his suddenly supreme need to go to Paukukalo—not for sand or for Daddy, but for his own sake.

A truck slowed mercifully and Ebo swung himself into its bed, rode the distance as if it was something to endure and not a necessary means to his end. The truck puttered along the back roads down toward the ocean, which, from Ebo's position, could not be seen until he was there. Then, the ocean was everywhere, something he couldn't *not* see if he tried. Two pats against the truck's side and the truck rolled to a stop. Ebo alighted, gave another grateful tap to the truck as it drove away, and waited. He waited until he needed breath, so that when he breathed, he did so as deeply as he could.

Without anyone there, the beach before him was a lonely stretch of beige with an unfurling wave for company. In a trancelike state, Ebo trudged through the sand toward the water. In a tremor of heightened awareness, he understood this place as it might've been uninhabited, before the insistent road lined its coast, before anything so much as a human foot dimpled its surface. Like the sea-salted wind in his hair, the dimensions of time could be felt, tasted, moved through. Whatever it was that every person through all of history might've felt as they looked upon what he was seeing now, all of this Ebo experienced as a tiny pinprick in his chest.

He sat down cross-legged. The grainy warmth beneath his legs brought him back into his own skin, his own memory. As they had for so many years, his hands routinely combed the sand for opihi shells, which Momo had loved for the purple swirl of their underside. He would do this while Momo chased waves as they pulled away, the same waves that would, in turn, push back toward her and send her squealing. She was happiest here, Ebo knew. Though she would never learn

to swim, the sun and water and sand were enough to ani-
mate her, like music does dancing. Remembering her now,
an opihi shell appeared in Ebo's fingers like a tiny sand-swept
miracle. He brushed off its back and belly, blew on it for good
measure. He studied its purple swirl and the thought came to
him that it wasn't just its color Momo had loved, but the fact
that he, Ebo, had searched for her, would not stop searching
for her, until he found one.

*

Momo wasn't dead, which might've been easier. She was nine
years gone. She had been taken from life as Ebo knew it,
meaning life as Ebo lived it was arranged around what had
been and what should have been—two points on an axis that
would never curve toward what actually was. Staring into
this regret was for Ebo the same thing as having his eyes
open at all.

In the end, it had taken Daddy three full weekends to
build Ebo his loft. By that time, Ebo's mother had decided
on a second pigeon, a common blue bar, which she didn't
say, but Ebo knew, was for Momo. What Ebo didn't say was
that he resented this.

The first week they had their birds, the birds did not readily
know their new home and flew back to their previous coop.
Through their mother, the breeder had instructed Ebo and
Momo to gather twigs and leaves and place their findings in
the corner of the loft. A morning or two later, a nest was built.
Three days more and Momo's blue bar sat in her nest, pressing herself into her first egg. Another speckled egg followed.
It took a few more weeks for the squabs to hatch themselves
through perfect circles carved at the tops of the eggs, another
few for their yellow fuzz to be replaced by feathers.

With their squabs in the loft, Ebo became convinced the
birds would no longer stray. He decided to test his bird, the
cream barred homer, by taking it into Iao Valley, a mile or so

up the mountain. He'd wanted to do this alone, but Momo had followed. Even though she'd had a sinus infection that week, she would not be left behind.

The basin was dark, dank, teeming with life both seen and unseen. Banyan trees laced their fingers overhead and the fragrance of white ginger was silk on their skin. Ebo carried his wicker basket in hand as his bird stamped its feet for balance. He walked at a steady pace knowing he couldn't exactly lose Momo, but he'd wanted her to struggle in some way. And she did—she struggled to keep up when everything in her wanted to take her time. When too much distance stretched between them, Ebo turned angrily to Momo, only to see her head back, mouth open, as if the immense lushness of sight and sound might tip her over. In seeing this, Ebo saw what was beautiful. But because he had wanted it all to be his to see, and not Momo to see it through, he became mean.

"You! Some stupid, you! Hurry up!" he snapped.

Between two peaks was a riverbed of boulders rounded smooth by icy water that flowed from the mountains. Ebo's mother's mother had washed clothes there, singing her songs from home. It was where families picnicked, babies were baptized, kids passed their summers atop the rocks— every good and perfect thing.

The boulder on the other side of the river was large and flat, like a platter tipped to a lean. Because it was the only space exposed to the widest spread of open sky, it was where Ebo determined he would release his bird. But the way to it was through a thick part of the river, heavy with deep waters gone stagnant from stillness. Cresting the glassy surface was a line of rocks, like beading on a necklace laid out. Having told Momo to watch from the edge, Ebo toed his way across, alternating hands with his basket. But she followed him, put her feet wherever his had been.

On the other side, she couldn't keep still for her excitement and it angered Ebo further. He lifted the lid to his basket but when the bird didn't move, he kicked a toe into the wicker. The

bird still did not move, as if it didn't know to look up, so Ebo
pulled it from the basket and tossed it upward like a handful of
confetti. The bird teetered and lifted, teetered and lifted higher.
It made its way up and out of sight, all of it over without ever
having been what Ebo imagined the afternoon would be.

For a boy of nine, his disappointment registered as in-
justice—what Ebo should have had, he'd been denied. And
on that day, it was Momo who had denied him his freedom
to be something other than what he felt he was: second in
everything. Because of this, Ebo quickly maneuvered his
way back over the rocks and disappeared behind a tree. He'd
wanted Momo to feel abandoned and scared, just for a little
while. She called after him, confused. Even when she cried,
Ebo stayed hidden.

The sun, it seemed, would set on his bitterness. It was darkest first in nature. As the daylight dimmed, Ebo saw his hand
become a featureless shadow and knew his game was over.
But he revealed himself just as Momo was halfway across the
river. When he called to her, she looked for him and slipped.
He heard her go under and bob right up, pulling for air. By
the time he'd crawled over the rocks to her, water had already
aspirated through her nose, flowed past her already swollen
sinuses, and settled its bacterial filth wherever it could.

They were late and Momo was soaking wet, a double offense. Ebo tried to hurry her along. But Momo's bare feet
pinched with pain and she moved slowly, made heavy by her
wet clothing. Gone was her wonder of the place.

By the time they neared home, it was dark. Their mother
scoured the street with frantic eyes. When she finally saw
them, she started running. Ebo put his arms up, but his
mother peeled them down to slap him upside the head.

"What's duh mattah wit you? You make me sick!"

Momo was ushered straight into the bathroom. Ebo flung
himself down to the kitchen table where Daddy was sitting.
Daddy said, "Look at me, boy." Ebo slowly raised his eyes to
Daddy, who chose this one moment to look Ebo unflinch-

ingly in the eye. Ebo hung his head low until the tears came and he could take no more shaming. He scurried from the kitchen to his bedroom, pausing at the bathroom door to see his mother pouring hot water over Momo's bowed head. It would be his last opportunity to see Momo as he knew her, but her hair obscured her face.

Without dinner and with the trouble he was in, it was difficult for Ebo to sleep. At some distance, he heard the taiko drumming pulsating like a gigantic heart fearful of stopping. In his mind, the drummers were slick with sweat, moving in synchronicity like streamers of light. He could see their spectral dance, arms flailing faster, harder, just short of breaking. In his dream state, Ebo believed he was the drum and the wooden sticks that pelted his body painful, but necessary.

By morning, he woke up spent. He turned over on the futon to see Momo with her back to him, as she often was. But this morning she was arched in an unnatural way, as if she, too, was in pain. Ebo poked a finger into her, then again. When she didn't respond, he pulled on her shoulder and lost his grip on her too-hot and slippery skin. He tugged harder, with two hands. When her body finally tipped toward him, it came heavily and without grace. He saw then what he would never unsee. Momo's face had rearranged itself in the night. Her eyes fluttered with fever to a new spiritual rhythm and where there had been so much life, there was only white.

*

To excise the beach and his memories, Ebo ran all the way home, as if what he felt he could sweat out of his system. In the backyard, he peeled off his T-shirt and stood beneath the hose for longer than he needed to. The initial thrust of warm hose water soon ran cool over his face. His bird was now on the brick steps of the coop, waiting beneath the shade of the awning. Without the sound of feed clanking against the metal troughs, the bird hadn't been called through the one-way trap door that funneled into the loft.

Ebo knew he couldn't kill it, had somehow always known. He turned off the hose and shook the water out of his hair. Determined to put a brick at the opening of the fly pen to keep the bird out, he would teach it the cruel lesson of having no home. Then it would be like the strays nobody wanted, or even liked. Just a rat with wings.

He shooed the bird into the plumeria trees and went about loosening the brick. The brick had been there for years and was embedded in grooves of hard earth, so it took some effort. When at last it came free, Ebo stood with it in hand only to find his mother behind him, peering into the coop at an unnecessary distance. He set the brick down, unsure of what she wanted.

"Show me yo bird," she said.

Ebo thought that maybe she wanted to kill the bird herself, which made him hesitate protectively. She'd probably wanted it dead all these years. But his mother rarely asked anything of Ebo and he dutifully went about trying to locate it anyway.

His mother hadn't so much as glanced at the coop after Momo's illness, with some part of her needing to blame the bird to keep from blaming Ebo. He understood her reasoning. If the business of pigeons had never happened, that day wouldn't have happened. There wouldn't have been the river, the bacteria, the fever, all of which reduced their atmosphere to the thin air of the aftermath. There wouldn't have been the attempts to explain, to name, to apply medical sense to what had happened.

Momo had had a cold, yes? *Yes.* The virus had weakened her immune system and allowed a secondary infection to take hold. *OK.* The circuitry of her brain could not withstand a fever that high. *OK. OK.* Words like *bacterial meningitis* were spoken. Words like *hyperpyrexia* and *apneic attack.* And when those words didn't register, there were apologies for the one thing that everyone understood: that Momo was not dead, but gone.

Ebo only knew that a stranger had come home to him from the hospital. Like an oversize infant, she went between a playpen in the living room and that sandbox Daddy had built for her in the yard. Ebo would sit with her, listening to her new language come out as guttural moans that would stretch and deepen into a sort of song. When she was given a blue and yellow helmet to wear for when she seized, her face was pinched beyond what little recognition Ebo had been holding to.

In time, doctors spoke of Waimano Home. Though it was located on another island, a world away, they insisted Momo would receive attention specific to her condition. They said Momo wouldn't know the difference between her home and Waimano, that she would in fact be happier. But the day she was taken away was the day Momo's song grew to its utmost, growing louder as the distance between her and her mother stretched wider. That distance now spanned two islands, with miles of ocean and nine years of time in between. It was a distance Ebo would travel in just under an hour.

He launched another rock at his bird in the plumeria tree. He didn't mean to hit it directly, but to scare it back to the loft. Like the first rock, this one hit the bird's branch and fell to the brittle leaves below, two thuds that sent the bird higher. With his mother waiting, Ebo grabbed a handful of smaller rocks with which to cover more area, but she called him back to the side of the loft, to where she stood next to the can of feed.

"Show me how," she said, knowing the feed was the way to the bird. Ebo ran a hand through his hair, frustrated that his mother had witnessed him not thinking straight. He hurried in and out of the coop with those things that fed and watered the birds—a foot-long metal trough and a milk carton gutted at the center. By using his thumb at the spout, Ebo showed his mother how to hose everything off.

"Gotta be clean," he said and she nodded. At the feed can, he removed the lid and filled the scoop with the right amount. "Gotta keep birds little bit hungry. Dat way dey come back." She nodded again.

Though the entry was plenty high for her to walk through, Ebo saw his mother dip her head into the loft after him. She

made circles with her eyes, pulled in all there was to see.
"Long time," she said. "Look good." Ebo guided the scoop
along the trough's opening so that the feed fell against the
metal in a clatter. It wasn't long before they heard the clank
of the fly pen drop back into place and the bird was pecking
at the feed with its feathered tail raised behind it.

As they watched, Ebo felt the dusty air constrict, making
the confines of the coop feel even smaller. He wasn't used to
a second body being in there with him. He also wasn't used to
having his mother close like this, in an enclosure, where they
might say those things they couldn't say elsewhere. He knew
if there was ever a time to tell his mother exactly what had
happened that afternoon with Momo, specifically his part in
abandoning her, that time was now.

"You know I goin see Momo," he said as a means of
bringing up the subject. He'd told both his mother and
Daddy that seeing Momo was possible. But he'd kept from
them that seeing her was the very reason he'd enlisted. He
knew it was an impulsive and outsized decision that war-
ranted, even deserved, criticism. They would have said to
get a job, wait for money, then go to her. But he'd tried for
a job; ten months he tried. He couldn't wait anymore and
yet he couldn't explain his impatience. Because how could
they know what he hadn't confessed? How could they understand the guilt within him, located somewhere beneath
the ribs like a dark hunger he fed with secrecy? This guilt
that defied reason, that kept its own time, made its own
sense—how could he tell his mother about it here, like this?

She stood staring down at the bird with her arms crossed
at her midsection. Had she heard him? Ebo wondered. Perhaps she had something she wanted to say to Momo, or for
him to give her? Ebo thought maybe this might be the thing
to ask his mother, was about to ask when she spoke first.

"Dis bird. Still plenny strong. Good fo my baby girl. You
take dis bird to Momo."

*

When just a half hour remained, Ebo slipped into his new shirt as if he was putting on another skin. He buttoned the bottom button first, then undid it, thinking that way was wrong, the top button was right. He hadn't even needed to ask Daddy for socks, because his mother had either found two pairs for him or made Daddy give them over. He wore a pair now in his new shoes, which made his feet feel awkward with bulk. He wished he had pants to wear rather than shorts.

Ebo's mother appeared in the doorway. He thought she might be pleased with his new look, all of it owing to her sacrifice, but she was distracted, barely noticed. She muttered something Ebo couldn't hear. When he asked her to repeat it, she shook her head looking at the ground as if she'd dropped the words she had wanted to speak.

"Ma—jus talk. Say what you gonna say."

She looked up at him, emboldened: "You and me. We go O'oka."

"O'oka? Why O'oka? I gotta go airport."

"Jus come. Fas kine. Real fas."

It was the last thing Ebo expected, his mother suggesting they go to the grocery store down the street. Still in his new shirt and shoes, he trailed her from the house as reluctantly as he had when he was a boy. Grocery shopping bored Ebo both then and now, but especially then, when it was his job to keep Momo from touching everything on the shelves. Back then, Ebo would put his feet at the center of the tiles and avoid stepping on the lines, encouraging Momo to try and copy him—a little game. Now he had to focus on keeping up with his mother. In the midday heat, her cotton dress stuck to the skin of her back. She didn't break pace, nor did she speak. Ebo worried he'd ruin his new shirt with sweat and billowed it for breeze.

Once in the air conditioning of O'oka, he relaxed. But his mother was still intent on something. She took Ebo by the elbow, stood slightly behind and urged him forward. They moved up and down the aisles in this way. If he had still been a boy, she would've had him by the scruff of his neck.

Of course he knew this fierce focus in his mother. He
glanced back at her as she scanned the faces of other patrons,
moving on the moment they were not what she wanted. But
what she was after was not in the store. When they moved
past the entrance again, she happened to look out the door
and finally see. Ebo felt a tug at his shirt and lowered his face
to his mother's. He breathed in her sweet and sour as she
outstretched her arm and pointed toward the parking lot.

"You see dat man?" she said. "Quick. You see him?" She
did not look at Ebo, but he looked to her when she said, "Dat
man, he yo real daddy."

Ebo stood perfectly still to take in everything that moved.
What he had seen was an old man in an orange vest gathering shopping carts, wearily pushing them forward and out
of view. The old man had been all there was, so Ebo waited
for someone else to see. He waited as people continued to
shuffle past, as a voice spoke over the intercom, as registers
pinged open and groceries were rung up. Ebo waited until
the sounds became for him a sort of silence.

*

It wasn't until he'd arrived at the airport, checked in, and sat
down in the terminal that Ebo looked into the brown paper
bag his mother had given him. In it were mochi balls she'd
made, as well as Spam musubi that was still warm to the touch.
He turned one musubi over in his hand and saw how the
rice was stained brown with shoyu, how the dark green nori
wrapped around the sliver of Spam and held it in place. This
food he had taken for granted he now studied like a keepsake.

Airport time felt different from the experience of time
elsewhere, and Ebo, who had never flown before, worried
he would somehow miss his flight. But no one around him
seemed bothered the way he was, all these people whose
travel purposes were so different from his. None of them
noticed Ebo, who was going to war on their behalf. No one

noticed him until his bird began to stir in the silver carrier at his feet. The woman seated next to him located the source of the fluttering, leaned over to peer through the bars. "What's dat stuffs…?" she asked, putting her fingers to her nose to ask after the clumping at the pigeon's beak. "Called *cere*," said Ebo quietly. "Like nostrils." The woman nodded and looked away. Soon she was among the many who were standing in a hurried response to boarding call.

Everywhere Ebo looked, the words PAN AM could be seen scrawled across the body of the plane, printed on a little white bag in the seat back pocket, embroidered into the edge of the hats the stewardesses wore tilted to a lean on their heads. Though he tried to be casual about it, Ebo watched closely as a stewardess demonstrated safety procedures. He pulled the tail of the strap too tightly across his abdomen and gripped the armrests during takeoff. He was amazed at the feeling of suspension and closed his eyes to feel it fully. When he opened them again, the plane was airborne. Ebo looked through the window to witness his whole island come into view and simultaneously shrink in size.

The flight to Honolulu took thirty-two minutes, gate to gate. Just as Ebo was finishing the last of his passion guava juice they'd served, the plane started its descent. Deplaning gave Ebo a slight headache, how everyone crowded him, how all of a sudden there was only one way out. In no time, he had followed the flow of passengers to baggage claim and found himself presenting his case to a taxi driver. He needed to go to Waimano Home and he only had eight dollars—would this be enough? The taxi driver shook his head, but opened his door to Ebo just the same.

As they drove along the H-1 freeway in the frenetic pace of pau hana traffic, Ebo rolled down his window and put his face to the wind. He was unsure of how he'd manage a ride to Fort DeRussy by day's end, but figured he'd deal with things as they came. Before long, the taxi exited the freeway and the glut of cars simply fell away. They drove switchbacks up the mountain along a narrow road skirted by tall pili grass and monkeypod trees. After a time, Ebo worried the driver had misunderstood him, but then he saw it off in the distance: a building, austere and feather-white. Closer still and Ebo could make out the steel bars along the top floor windows. The taxi dropped him off at the front of the building, but Ebo walked away from it at first to see it against the mountain. Off in the distance was a pool drained of water, sloping from shallow to deep, where a number of stray cats had gathered. The kittens played amid dead leaves and trash while the older creatures sat there, watching Ebo. As he made his way back toward the entrance, he noticed the building's exterior paint was chipped and peeling so badly it made a pattern. State-owned and operated, the building suffered from decay—not from negligence, but from lack. Ebo stepped through the doors and into the powerful smell of Pine-Sol that came at him like a wall.

After signing into the nurses' station, a middle-aged woman in pink scrubs said she'd walk Ebo to where he needed to go. She eyed his carrier and asked Ebo what he'd brought, saying, "We don't like to upset the residents, you understand."

"Jus an old bird," said Ebo. "Won't be here long."

He breathed through his mouth as they made their way, deciding there was at least a sterile sort of cleanliness to the place that he could appreciate. Along the walls were chicken-scratch drawings in crayon and chalk. Within the corridor were disabled patients, some whose eyes followed Ebo. Others sat in their crumpled bodies, waiting. "Dis place," Ebo asked of the nurse, "what is it exactly?"

The woman flicked her long braided ponytail over her shoulder. "At first, it was an asylum," she said. "Fifty years ago they called the residents 'spiritual morons' if you can believe it." She kept moving, skittishly on alert. "On good days, we think of it as a sanitarium. On the best days, a home." The nurse then pivoted on her thick-soled shoes to face Ebo briefly. "You must have memories of Miss Momoyo before her mental status change. How old was she again?"

"Momo was five," said Ebo.

"Well, what amazes me—and what you'll see too—is how intact her nature is. In all her sweetness, she is perfect. Isn't she, Billy?" The nurse said this as she patted the shoulder of a man with bulging eyes and a jaw that went in opposite directions. She then pointed up a set of stairs, and left Ebo to go it alone.

He took his time to the third floor. At the last step, he leaned forward and looked to his right. Momo was where the nurse said she'd be, at the end of the hallway with a mop in hand. Mopping, he'd been told, gave her a sense of duty, and of home. But even without the mop, Ebo knew it was her in the helmet, now red and black. He approached slowly, soundlessly, and sat on a bench along the wall with his elbows tacked to his knees. Ebo saw that Momo, at fourteen, was taller than their mother. He saw that her hospital gown fell to her calves where fine downy hairs grew undisturbed. From her full lips hung a short thread of spittle, and as she mopped the tiles, Ebo saw she did so within the lines.

"Momo," he said and she stopped her work to slowly look up. He said her name again to bring her gaze to him. When she at last settled on Ebo, it took her some time to register a presence, then more time still to register it as familiar. All of this Ebo mistook for blankness and he looked away feeling foolish for having hoped she would recognize him. But when the mop handle fell to the concrete floor, he looked again at Momo, whose delight he'd forgotten had always found expression. The shaking of her hands, the stamping of her feet, the insistent whimper, everything lacked articulation that Ebo made up for by standing and reaching for her, by using his feet to dance around her, by shaping his voice into words—"Ebo here, Momo! Ebo here!"

*

He'd been told they could sit outside for a short time. Ebo led Momo by the hand with the other gripping the carrier. When they came to a bench beneath a bottlebrush tree, he swept off the tiny red needles from the surface. Before them was a view of Pearl Harbor, the inciting place of the previous war, the one before Ebo's.

In the thin-aired silence, the bird cooed to be let free. Momo heard it and again took her time locating its source. Ebo lifted the lid to the carrier, and the bird, sensing the distance from home, the long journey ahead, struggled against his grip. He held the bird in front of Momo and she raised a curious hand. Ebo waited for her finger to reach the bird's body and when it did, he made it so that it was Momo who tapped the bird free.

Ebo knew the bird was too old to make it home, knew that it would die a watery death trying. But as it circled them now, climbing higher and higher, he let go of everything he knew. He craned his neck to track the bird as it became just a curl of calligraphy against a cloudless sky. All the while, Momo looked across the ocean in the direction of home, waiting for the bird to dip into view.

Kaat

EDWARD HAMLIN

The call about Stone comes just as Kaat is removing her soufflé from the oven, the snug apartment amurmur with meandering piano music. The soufflé's rise is perfect, its russet crown flawless; through a dozen attempts in as many weeks she's nearly mastered the form. Even Stone's noticed. "Merde!" she says as the phone jangles, the heat of the porcelain dish seeping through her red oven mitts. "*Godverdomme.*"

Kaat cradles the soufflé like an infant thrust into her hands by a stranger, uncertain what to do with it. Above the skylight a cloud shifts; the late sun of the rue de la Clef filters in to spark against the hanging copper pans. For a long moment it seems as if the caller has given up. As she crouches before the oven, the scent of toasted Gruyère fills the kitchen like a divine annunciation. The unseen pianist delivers up an airy chord. But then another ring drills through the air, cruel and urgent.

The chef wavers; the phone insists; the soufflé quivers.

What she needs is for Stone to bang through the door and kick off her motorcycle boots and sit down to dinner. But Stone is late; this will be her on the phone with some poor excuse. When she'd called forty minutes ago to say she was on her way, Kaat waited exactly ten minutes and put in the soufflé, calculating the time carefully, wanting to have dinner on the table the moment she walked in. She imagined Stone trudging up the narrow stairs, talking on her mobile and expecting nothing special in the way of dinner, only to discover the elegant table and realize how fortunate she was to have Kaat Mertens in her life. She imagined Stone melting, just a little; Stone taking her in her leather-jacketed arms that smelled faintly of exhaust; Stone kissing her unprompted. She pictured the smile that would come—the smile that could be so hard to earn. All this Kaat had allowed herself to imagine while beating egg whites and grating cheese and cranking out the bottle cork. Yet now here she is, alone with her fragile offering and a phone whose harsh trill only makes the flat seem emptier.

Kaat decides that Stone will get exactly the soufflé she deserves. Avoiding the hallway mirror, she ferries the porcelain dish to the table—the salad already dressed, the ivory roses trimmed and arranged, the Sémillon poured—and drapes it with a paper napkin, all the love in it gone flat and cold.

*

Collapsing into the deep armchair after nearly two hours on her feet, Kaat takes up the phone.

"Madame Mertens?" says a strict voice she doesn't recognize. The woman inflates the *r* in *Mertens* as if to make a point: you are a foreigner, you will never be French. Not that it's so different back home; with her Flemish name she's as much a stranger in Charleroi or the Ardennes as she is here in France.

"Oui," Kaat replies, taking care to make it a Parisian *Ouais.*
"This is Doctor Brodeur," the woman says in English—
another dry slight. "I am here at l'Hôpital Cochin with a
Madame Stone Brewer. She gives you as her wife."

"Wife?" says Kaat, the word thrilling for an instant—
arresting—until she realizes that a *hospital* is calling about
Stone. "What's happened? Qu'est-ce qui se passe?"

"Your wife will recover."

"Recover!"

"Madame Brewer has a motorcycle accident. In la rue
Gay-Lussac. She is in the intersection with la rue des Ursulines when she should not be."

"She passed a red light?" Kaat asks, but already knows.

"This is what the police say."

"Can I speak with her, please?"

"Madame Brewer is sedated. It is necessary."

Kaat grips the pillowy arm of the chair. "Necessary why?
What's wrong with her? Qu'est-ce qu'elle a exactement?"

"Her right femur is broken. And some of the small bones
of her right foot."

Femur, Kaat whispers, trying to recall the meaning of the
English word. *Female* echoes irrelevantly in her mind. But
then the Dutch word comes: *dijbeen. Haar rechter dijbeen is
gebroken.*

"And numbers of *other* problems, Madame Mertens—
contusions, road abrasions. Problems in various parts," the
doctor adds, a hint of rebuke in her tone. Kaat imagines her
shaking her head at the untidiness of Stone's injuries. "We
needed to sedate her in order to correct these problems.
Later there are surgeries on the foot and ankle, of course."

"Of course," Kaat says, as if she knows. There is something subtly wrong with the surefooted doctor's English. Kaat
senses it but can't pin it down, her own English inadequate
to the task.

The doctor's voice drifts from the mouthpiece; she answers a question over her shoulder. More important matters

await her, injuries more dire. She's needed elsewhere. Kaat pictures a self-important Parisienne with all the advantages, auburn hair twisted in a tight bun, nails perfect, eyeliner applied with surgical precision. The way Frenchwomen always dress as if for a photographer. But in a simpler tone the doctor confides: "She is very lucky, Madame. Your wife. It could be much worse, you know. If you want to see her she must be waking up after the next few hours. You know where is l'Hôpital Cochin? We are in Montparnasse, rue du Faubourg Saint-Jacques. In case you are new to Paris."

As if it were her plan all along, Kaat clicks the phone off and takes the soufflé and turns it out into the garbage, leaving the rest of the meal intact on the table, untouched as a museum display. The golden wine still catches the light. The ivory roses fling their blossoms up in frozen exaltation. A few moments later she's in a taxi, speeding along the rue Linné past the botanical gardens and the mosque and crying into her sleeve, not caring what the African driver might think. When she opens the door and steps onto the hospital's curb, he waves away her euros and says: "Désolé, Mademoiselle. I'm sorry, miss." And is gone.

*

When Stone awakes, her first concern is what's happened to her motorcycle.

Kaat has been sitting with her for more than an hour, the patient mostly unconscious but restless all the same, the broken leg propped on a foam bolster. Stone's always been an agitated sleeper, and under drugs it is no different. The room smells of tired linoleum and some solvent that hasn't quite succeeded in sanitizing it. In the other bed an old woman chatters at the television in Arabic. On a metal pole a cluster of machines tinks and flashes and compares notes on Stone's slow progress toward wakefulness, the data incessant, compulsive, precise. For a long while Kaat sits transfixed by the

fluctuating red numbers, the digital chatter, until an orderly
brings her a plastic demitasse of bitter coffee.

Traces of the accident lie like stigmata on Stone's body.
Patches of her coarse, straw-blond hair have been shaved so
that wounds can be dressed. Her hard cheek is black and blue
as though from a punch gone astray. A wound at her elbow has
been crudely stapled. The broken leg, braced in a rigid white
plastic collar, rises from its bolster like a ceremonial cannon.

Along the patient's hand snakes a rivulet of dried blood.
Kaat traces it with a moistened fingertip, touches it to her
tongue, her lover's essence faintly metallic, as if something of
the crashed motorcycle has entered her bloodstream.

She tries to imagine the skid, the fall, the blaring horns.
The twisted bike, the debris in the street. It must have been
terrifying for the driver too.

At some point Stone snorts abruptly and tries to speak.
"Wha—" she mumbles. A scowl drops over her angular face.
"The *fuck.*" On the metal pole the instruments react, the elec-
tronic beat quickening, the red digits counting up.

Kaat leans forward to take her hand, careful not to jar the
bandaged fingers. Her American's hazel eyes open suddenly,
sharply, confused but on high alert.

Kaat does her best to smile. "Salut," she says, and lays a
palm on Stone's good cheek. The eyes search the spartan hospital room, scrutinize the machines beside the bed, turn back
to Kaat's.

"Where's my bike?" Stone says thickly.

Kaat has no idea—it hasn't occurred to her to ask. "Don't
worry about that right now," she says, stroking the damp forehead. She tries another smile, a kiss on the brow, but Stone
only turns away.

"It better not be stolen. Plenty of dykes would kill for that
ride."

"Chérie—"

Stone closes her eyes. Kaat sees them roll beneath their lids,
perhaps replaying the accident: she has the impression that if

she tracks their movements, she might be able to experience the collision as Stone did. At a certain point, the eyes jerk suddenly to the left and Stone winces. The moment of impact? Kaat feels sure of it. Quite suddenly Stone is very afraid. The skittish machines beside the bed tell the whole story. Kaat squeezes her lover's hand lightly. To her surprise the hand squeezes back.

*

All Stone's roughness, all her aggression toward the world, comes from fear—this much Kaat has understood for some time now. On occasion the fear breaks through the bluster nakedly and shows its face like the honest fear of a child. In these moments Stone is irresistible to her. For a time—sometimes for days at a stretch—Kaat will hold her lover's soul in her hands. For a time Kaat is powerful beyond measure. To stroke her American's flushed and tearful face, to cradle the big head in her lap, is everything. She wishes it didn't take a crisis for her lover to drop her mask, but she understands now why Stone's developed such thick skin, why she finds it so frightening to let go.

Once these moments pass they never speak of them. The times of collapse and exposure are a secret they carefully guard, through a kind of unspoken pact. These cloudy eyes that ask for help are reserved for Kaat. Their secret pleading is intensely private. She and Stone speak to no one of it, least of all to each other. Sometimes it takes Stone days to find her way back, to reassemble the Stone the world knows, Kaat unfailingly kind to her as she goes about it, the two of them mingling like confluent waters. They can make love for hours at a time while Stone is in limbo—Kaat in the lead, Stone pliant and grateful beneath her, the sounds of Paris creeping under the door and singing through the thin rippled windows, the day passing.

*

The first of Stone's breakdowns came during a trip to Chicago, where they'd gone to meet what remained of the Brewer
family. Back there they still called her lover Sally. In the
kitchen of a dilapidated bungalow her girlfriend's mother
had sat and picked chicken from her teeth and cursed her
husband, Hank, who, it seemed, had moved to a trailer in a
rough part of East Chicago soon after receiving a diagnosis
of lung cancer. He'd left nothing but gambling debts behind;
his wife still got calls at all hours of the night from strangers
demanding money. She was convinced he was trying to hide
behind his illness. He'd disavowed his former life, left her to
clean it up. All this Stone's mother had related bitterly, as if
the cancer were some kind of greedy mistress he'd run off
with. How bad must the marriage have been, Kaat wondered,
for him to flee it with death staring him in the face?

When they'd first arrived at the bungalow's salmon-pink
door, Stone had introduced Kaat as her girlfriend. At the
time, Kaat thought this a kind of aggression, just Stone
brawling with the world again—the world represented in this
case by her own decrepit mother, whose bony shoulders were
locked in a painful-looking hunch. But it didn't matter to the
woman that Stone was gay, for the simple reason that Stone
herself didn't matter to her. Kaat saw it plainly. As they said
their drab goodbyes, she slipped a warm furtive hand under
Stone's flannel shirt and laid it softly against her lower back,
a hand of tender comfort, her own heart breaking. They left
with no promise to see her mother again, without even the
smallest of social courtesies, and turned the car toward East
Chicago, whose rancid air and shattered glass and stark poverty were beyond anything Kaat had ever witnessed.

They found the trailer park in the back lot of an abandoned steel mill with shot-out windows, more gypsy camp
than anything, a forlorn gathering of metal shanties propped
up on cinderblocks and rusted wheel rims. Forty minutes
alone with Stone's ravaged and drunken father had been
nearly enough to reduce both of them, Kaat and Stone, to
tears. "That won't be me," her lover insisted when the old man

stepped outside to piss against a tire. "That will *never* be me, baby." When they left, Stone lay on the back seat of the rental car and clutched herself like a woman freezing to death, legs jackknifed to her chest, inconsolable, untouchable, while Kaat tried to find her way out of town. In the rearview mirror her lover cried convulsively and finally fell asleep from sheer exhaustion. They made rough love that night in a truck stop hotel, eighteen-wheelers maneuvering in the lot with backup alarms squawking, Stone childlike afterward, curled up against her Käätche for simple protection. The unbearable day had opened something new between them, had washed away a rampart that had always kept Stone apart.

In the morning, over breakfast at the hotel waffle bar, sitting ten feet away from a black family who held hands and prayed over their food before eating, Stone said: "Marry me."

Speechless, Kaat said *yes* with her eyes, a television prattling over her beautiful lover's shoulder, a blond news reader with stupendous breasts their witness.

Now, in a too-bright hospital room in Montparnasse, Stone's hazel eyes open again.

"Sorry, sweets," she says. With her bruised cheek it causes her some pain to smile, but she manages it. "How fucked up is it that the bike's the first thing I think of, right? Stone cold."

The battered hand finds Kaat's and squeezes it. It's always like this: the selfishness, then the unexpected grace. The saving words. The humble shame, however passing. Yet never once has Kaat felt such moments to be insincere. She's seen her lover hit bottom enough times to understand that they are all too real. In her moments of humility Stone is genuine, and this, more than anything, has held Kaat's respect. She's never known anyone as emotionally honest as Stone Brewer.

Now Stone raises herself to her elbows to examine her broken leg, trying to roll it, to test the heavy brace. The effort exhausts her. Collapsing back onto the hard mattress, she searches Kaat's eyes and says, "What happened to me, baby?"

Kaat stays through the dreadful hospital dinner—a Styro- 295
foam tray of oily pâté and bland chicken and limp haricots
verts—Stone's attitude improved somewhat by the absurdity
of the food. Shoving the grayish pâté to the side, she gives a
bark of a laugh and says: "Fucking dog food. Or *dog*. They're
trying to kill us. Who's in the kitchen, Al-Qaeda?" In a flat near
Place Monge, meanwhile, an elegant table sits empty; a perfect
soufflé lies broken in the bin under the sink. But Kaat would
rather be here; it hardly matters what's on the menu.

As the orderly clears the remains of the meal a knock comes
at the open door. They look up to find a fiftyish, spike-haired
woman in a white doctor's coat asking to come in. With a quick
glance, Kaat and Stone agree that she's gay.

"Doctor Brodeur," she says, offering her hand to Kaat. Kaat
feels the wedding ring, the hard little band. "I'm glad you came
by. I see the patient is awake? We get her home to you tomorrow, I think." After examining Stone with a sure touch, she says
goodnight and begins to pull the door shut. "A little privacy,
no?" She smiles, and disappears. For a long moment, Kaat can't
reconcile the brusque voice on the telephone with the warmth
of the woman who's just stepped away. She'd imagined a smug
young doctor, not yet forty, utterly straight and impossibly dull.
Still the French can baffle her.

"Did you see what she was wearing?" Kaat says.

Stone inclines her head.

"A ring, Stone. A wedding ring."

Stone's eyes widen slightly. "Good for her."

Kaat lets the comment hang in the air, hoping for more, for a
smile at least. But Stone occupies herself with trying to slip two
fingers under her leg brace to ease the pressure on her skin. She
has no problem with awkward silences. She never has.

"I should get home," says Kaat. It's neither the time nor the
place to press the marriage idea. For now, for tonight, she tells
herself, she should be grateful that Stone is alive. "And you
should get some rest," she adds for good measure.

Stone's face falls. "Stay, Kitty."

"I'll be back first thing in the morning, *mijn schat.*"

Stone looks past her as if addressing someone else in the room, then consults an imaginary watch. "Princess needs her beauty sleep."

"You're the one who needs sleep."

"I just woke up."

"But that was the drugs. It's not the same. It's not rest."

Stone peers out the dreary window. There is a funeral parlor just across the street, sandwiched between two brasseries.

"Go. I get it. It's been a rough day for you." But when Stone turns back with her battered face there is a familiar pleading in her eyes.

Kaat takes both her hands. "You'll be coming home tomorrow. I will take such good care of you, Stony."

Something falls out of Stone's gaze. Some connection wavers, a signal lost. "Kaat?" she says. "A favor?"

"Anything."

"You can say no."

"Anything."

"Call the police about my bike, OK? Tonight? They're always there. Obviously."

*

Kaat decides to walk home. As she makes her way past the flower shops and red awnings and graffitied Métro entrance, her relief slowly gives way to annoyance. Petty as it seems, she can't excuse Stone for bringing up the motorcycle again. Nor can she excuse her for missing dinner, for the recklessness that has landed her in the hospital rather than at her own beautiful table.

Kaat knows this much: Stone didn't run the red light in the rue Gay-Lussac just to get home faster. She didn't risk her life to hurry back to her lover. No; she ran the light out of bravado, convinced she could beat the Fiat rolling toward her from the rue des Ursulines. Kaat has seen her take such

chances a hundred times, while clinging to her back on the
Ducati or following behind on her own little Suzuki, Stone's
unwelcome birthday gift to her the year before. As she walks home through the old streets, the whole business leaves her irritable and exhausted. It is time for Stone Brewer to graduate from her anger—to release both of them from the past. To settle down and make good on her word. To marry her.

*

In the privacy of her heart Kaat sometimes goes even further. It's time for her lover not just to marry her but to have a child with her, a family. This is what will finally tame Stone Brewer, vault her beyond the past, heal her. To be a parent will change everything. Over the past few weeks, while walking home from the Sorbonne through the humid summer afternoons, her academic obligations reduced to weekly meetings with a few graduate students, Kaat has sometimes imagined that she's returning home to Stone and their daughter—a red-cheeked Flemish-looking girl, puckish and bright and tender. As parents they'll complement each other perfectly, Stone stern but affectionate, Kaat doting but firm. Stone will teach her English; she'll teach her Dutch. She can imagine it perfectly on some days, though not at all on others. By fits and starts the scene has slowly come into focus.

Only two weeks ago did she finally find the courage to raise the idea with Stone. It was on a Saturday evening; they'd retreated to the sofa after gorging on moules and frites and lager, two bottles of Stella Artois making her bold. She lay with her head in Stone's blue-jeaned lap, gazing up at the spadelike jaw, and after several false starts said, "Stony?"

Stone's gaze drifted downward, drawn by the shift in her voice. "Hey Kitty, Kitty," she smiled, kneading Kaat's earlobe gently between her fingers. "Is somebody a bit toasted?"

"Not at all…not much. But I need to ask you a serious question."

"Oh boy. Here we go."

"Stony…what if we had a child?"

To her relief Stone did not look away, or frown, or stiffen. Kaat had prepared herself for the worst of reactions. Instead, the hazel eyes held hers without wavering. The thumb and forefinger fondled Kaat's earlobe sweetly. For a long while they drifted in perfect innocence, water running in the neighbor's pipes, eyes settled lightly into one another's. When Stone tried to speak at last, her voice was gone, which made both of them laugh. She was not supposed to be the timid one. In her muteness a future seemed to open its arms.

"Don't you think you ought to make me an honest woman first?" she said when she found her voice again. "Before we go and get us a gaybie?"

"You know I want to marry you. You've known that since Chicago."

Stone's fingertips moved to Kaat's face, stroked it absently. "Sometimes I still can't believe Hollande signed it. Like, it can't be real." Stone paused. "You know what? I don't think anyone at the Ligue really thought we'd win." But they *had* won: thanks in no small part to the relentless lobbying of the Ligue des droits, the gay advocacy group Stone had latched on to soon after her arrival in France, the same-sex marriage law had finally passed.

"So," Kaat said, feeling the moment begin to slip away, "will you really have a baby with me, Stony? After we marry?"

Stone touched a finger to Kaat's lips and frowned. "I said so, didn't I? Why isn't that good enough for you?"

"It is! I just needed to hear it again."

But Stone was already shifting Kaat's head from her lap. "That Stella goes right through you," she said, and left Kaat to wonder at the sudden change in weather. From the hallway came the sound of the bathroom door creaking shut, then the surprising click of the latch. Never had Stone cared about her privacy in the bathroom. It was Kaat who'd taught her to shut the door when guests were in. To Kaat's ears the

little click might as well have been a pistol shot. After a long
while Stone reappeared only to say she was going to bed.

Kaat lay awake most of the night, convinced that her lover
would soon change her mind, that the marriage idea would
unravel. There would be no little family. There would be no
Flemish girl. But in the morning, Stone awoke in a buoyant mood and proposed a civil ceremony, something small,
in the autumn perhaps, a simple gathering of friends. Her
colleagues from the Ligue would be there; some of Kaat's
colleagues too, her Sorbonne left-wingers, the twentieth-cen-
tury art faculty, even Directeur Lévy if he'd deign to come.
Over breakfast the idea progressed from notion to project,
Stone bringing the calendar to the table and penciling an
arrow across the last two weeks of September.

When she burst from the shower an hour later, her color
was high. "You know what? We may be the first ones to do
this," she said, toweling off vigorously. "At the Ligue, I mean.
Thierry and Yves are dragging their feet, and Agnès has to
divorce her old man before she and Lise can get married. It's
you and me, babe. You and me. Pioneers!"

The pace of it all, the way Stone had suddenly seized the
wheel, left Kaat nearly speechless. She caught her heart racing, but it felt more like anxiety than joy. After Stone left to
meet a friend, she puttered around the apartment, tidying,
dusting, touching every surface and book and keepsake as if
delivering the good news to the things that populated the life
they shared.

*

There hasn't been time to discuss the logistics of becoming
parents, but privately Kaat's given it a good deal of thought.
She knows she wants to carry their child, and Stone's said in
the past she'd never want to give birth, so the basic division
of labor seems clear enough. But whom can they ask to be
the father? They have no close male friends, really—certainly
none close enough to ask for such an intimate favor. And

perhaps it's better not to mingle friendship with procreation. On the other hand, there are no sperm banks in France. Even straight couples can't conceive through a donor. Most drive to Spain or Italy and come back with their precious cargo hidden away like contraband. She and Stone could make it a holiday—take a week on the Amalfi coast, maybe, some Italian man's seed tucked in her womb...or drive to Spain, drinking a last bottle of wine before visiting some clean white fertility clinic in Seville, its refrigerator full of proud Andalusian DNA.

It can all be worked through somehow. The important thing is that Stone has agreed to the plan. They will have a child...Kaat will push for a Flemish name, Adrie or Margreet, perhaps, Mieke or Lieve...

And so, with summer recess dwindling, Kaat has focused more on the wedding than on what would follow. Only this morning, in fact, she passed a happy hour working on the guest list and seating plan, jotting notes and diagrams in a student notebook labeled M A R I A G E —in the course of which, gradually, she'd decided to cook Stone an elegant dinner, to greet her with a perfect soufflé. She hummed as she worked away in the sunny kitchen, cycling through an old Kate Ryan number they'd danced to at Chez Moune and then putting on the thoughtful Satie, her thoughts turning expansive. Down on the street children thumped away at the last humid burst of summer. The whole day had been building toward an affirmation—until Stone Brewer, in a moment of bad judgment, shattered it to pieces.

Kaat walks on through the close evening, trying to understand why Stone still takes such stupid risks, why she allows the old anger to control her. Her American has landed well, after all: a good life in Paris, a circle of friends, meaningful work, a woman devoted to her happiness. What began as a rebellious road trip across Europe has ended in this. But they'll have no future together if Stone dies on a motorcycle first. As the narrow lane angles left, Kaat realizes that she's been walking faster and faster.

In front of an Italian restaurant, a half dozen motorcycles stand like centurions at attention, arrayed in a gleaming phalanx. The first is a bold red Ducati identical to the one Stone rode from Calabria up through Italy and Switzerland and into a new life in France, the same one she crashed just a few hours ago. The sight jars her badly—could it be Stone's? But no, it's impossible. Stone's bike must be as banged up as she is. This Ducati, pristine and proud, stands apart from its fellow soldiers, plainly in command. As Kaat passes she gives it a wide berth, stepping down onto the gray pavers and moving quickly on.

Outside a Caribbean restaurant, the smell of grilled meat fattens the air. "Goat," she says aloud, and realizes in the same moment that she's hungry, though not for goat. At a sidewalk stand she buys a crêpe and eats it in a doorway without tasting a thing, the proprietor in a hurry to close up and be gone.

Night has fallen, setting all the lights of Paris ablaze. In Place Monge the market stalls stand empty, blue awnings rolled and stowed atop their metal frames, doves cooing in the trees. At home a ghost meal awaits her, wilted salad and tepid wine and a ruined soufflé. What made her think she could count on Stone? Kaat pictures her soufflé and feels tears coming, relieved when the sudden blue flash of a police car brushes them away.

*

Back at the apartment, slumped on the sofa with a glass of the neglected Sémillon in her hand and her feet up on the green leather ottoman, Kaat tries once more to picture her wedding day. At the moment, she can't imagine marrying Stone. The accident has thrown it all out of focus. She can't recall the last time they made love—it must have been early summer—and this too seems to cast the marriage into doubt. Taking up the MARIAGE notebook, she begins to skim through her lists of caterers and hors d'oeuvres and wedding outfits, the Sémillon tart under her tongue, the window tipped open for air, a brief chaos of scooter horns breaking out in a nearby street. How sure the plan had seemed this morning. Stone, she'd decided, would wear a vintage morning jacket and brocade vest, she an ivory dress with an art deco headpiece...

With a turn of the page, she comes to the guest list, each name recorded in her careful hand. This last, more than anything, makes the wedding seem real again, because behind each name is the face of someone she knows. But even here there are choices yet to be made: next to two of the names, in a more tentative hand, Kaat has inscribed a question mark.

First there is the matter of her mother back in the Antwerp suburbs, who seems not to have divined that her daughter is gay. (Mercifully for all, her right-wing father, an old Vlaams Blok fascist who hated gays as much as he hated Jews and immigrants, is long dead.) It is hard to imagine Anke Mertens sitting quietly while her daughter marries another woman. She can be counted on to dress elegantly, in her understated bourgeois fashion, but not necessarily to hold her tongue.

Yet perhaps the possibility shouldn't be dismissed so quickly. Freed at last of her late husband's sarcastic anger, perhaps she's softened and come into her own. One door has closed; perhaps another's opened.

What little Kaat knows of her mother's current life comes mainly from photos Anke sends of her burgeoning garden. The email messages that accompany them are bogged down with the scientific names of shrubs and plant viruses and organic insecticides, as if Kaat were a botanist who'd find such details intriguing. But beneath these dry bulletins Kaat sometimes senses a silent outreach, as if by scrupulously avoiding news of her private life Anke Mertens were inviting her daughter to begin a deeper conversation.

Kaat has never found it within herself to accept the invitation. The conversation, once started, could lead anywhere. But now would be the moment to reconsider. Perhaps Anke would take her daughter's outstretched hand warmly. Since deciding to marry Stone, it's begun to seem worth a try,

though she will have to go to Antwerp and ask in person, to
come out to her properly before breaking the news that she's
getting married.

*

The other guest in doubt is Lucie Prudhomme. Perhaps it's
ridiculous or unfeeling to think that the first woman she fell
in love with should be present at her wedding, but Kaat can't
just write Lucie out of her story. Lucie was the centerpiece of
her life for six years, all through graduate school and a string
of confusing breakups and reunions, through bouts of flu
and departmental politics and student dinners scrounged on
the cheap, through Kaat's dissertation defense and the thrill
of Lucie's one-woman show at Xippas. A beautiful painting of
Lucie's—a large ochre abstraction vaguely suggestive of two
intertwined hands—hangs above her right now, with Stone's
blessing. "What do I care?" Stone had said after moving in.
"You think it should bother me just because she stole your
cherry? I don't give a good goddamn about that, Kitty Kaat.
And I kind of like that brown."

In a locked file drawer in her office Kaat still has every letter Lucie ever sent her, a precious archive on stippled paper
that Lucie made herself. Kaat's fingertips know the texture
and softness of the paper as intimately as she once knew her
lover's skin. For as long as they were together Lucie never
stopped writing her love notes, even in the dullest stretches
of domestic life. Unlike Stone she's a true romantic, a French-
woman through and through, with high cheeks that flush at
the faintest endearment or slight.

Somewhere in Lucie Prudhomme's delicate head there also
lurks a vocation for melancholy. Medication might help, but
she's always worried that it will deplete her art; suffering, she
says, is part of the alchemy. To Kaat's practical Flemish soul
this is romanticism carried much too far. Twice in the course
of their years together, after coming home day after day to

find her lover sleeping on the sofa with her back turned on the world, pale and sour and unwilling to seek help, she'd asked Lucie to move out—wrenching decisions, fraught with a guilt that drove its nail into her with killing headaches. It wasn't Lucie's depression she found unforgiveable; it was her lover's attachment to it. Though they'd come back together after each breakup, in truces brokered by confessional talks and searching kisses, nothing had been truly resolved between them.

There were happier times, of course, many of them. Whenever Kaat walks past their old apartment in the rue Descartes—the apartment where she first learned to make love with a woman—she thinks of the summer morning, nearly a decade ago now, when they threw the windows wide and ate brioche and melon after their first night together. She cherishes the memory of a particular evening nestled together on the bed with books in hand and linden flower tea in a pot Lucie had thrown, Paris stilled by a December snow. The delicacy of Lucie's nape will always be with her, and the scent of her scalp in summer. Though it ended, finally, with Lucie's departure for a post as a painting instructor at an art school in Dijon, in some ways it has never ended at all. Lucie lies as deep in her as a mother tongue.

The rumor that she is back in Paris for summer recess, living somewhere in the Marais, has murmured under Kaat's skin for weeks, but so far she's resisted the urge to reach out. The past is the past, or should be. Only when she pictures Lucie sleeping with one of their old friends—perhaps Marie Beauvais or Raquel Simon, who've always wanted her—does the urge to see her become nearly unmanageable. Thankfully, Stone's daily presence in her life has stopped her from acting on it, though it's true she's twice taken the Métro to the Marais and walked aimlessly through the galleries, hoping to run into her and at the same time praying not to.

She hasn't said a word to Stone about Lucie's return. But the fact is that Stone might have heard about it from any number of people. Such news travels fast in their tight-knit

world. When Kaat thinks of her old lover driving back to
Dijon for the fall term, it's with a pang of relief and a pang of
longing that can't be disentangled. Has Lucie heard that she
and Stone are to be married? Has she felt a pang of her own?
When Kaat tries to picture her at the wedding, it's a pale
Lucie she sees, a Lucie lightheaded with sorrow but unable, as
always, to ask for what she needs. It won't bother Stone to have
her there, of course; Stone, after all, will have gotten the girl.
The question is whether Kaat can ask such a thing of Lucie.
She'd surely feel obliged to attend if invited, regardless of the
violence it might do to her heart. This puzzle Kaat cannot at
present solve. And so a question mark stands next to the name
Lucie Prudhomme, like a splinter that refuses to yield.

In the morning, as she tosses away the coffee grounds and
prepares to go see Stone at the hospital, the telephone rings.
It is a woman from the police department with an accent
she can barely follow. Gradually, she makes out that Stone's
motorcycle is being held at a pound in Évry. After three days
the city will charge thirty-seven euros a day to keep it; after
six weeks it will be auctioned off or destroyed. Kaat wants
to ask whether the bike is still in condition to be ridden, but
the woman hangs up before she can formulate the question.

Évry, it turns out, is a good ways south of the city, down
near a dangerous banlieue full of desperately poor immigrants. There were deadly riots there soon after her arrival in
France, smashed windows and burning police cars and some
kind of notorious murder. Besides the question of safety,
there is a practical problem: how will she get the broken
bike back, if it can't be ridden? Certainly not on the train.
On the way to the hospital, hunched under an umbrella in
a warm rain, she considers her options. As she comes to the
Boulevard de Port-Royal it occurs to her that the department's newest faculty member, a Spanish El Greco scholar
named Miguel Ruiz de Soto, owns an old white Fiat truck.

Surely he'll be happy to help. There is no more polite, good-natured man in her world—gay, plainly, with elegant manners he wears with admirable ease. She's always meant to have him for dinner so that Stone can meet him. Perhaps helping her retrieve Stone's motorcycle will open the door to a friendship outside the department. Satisfied with her plan, Kaat crosses the road and passes the funeral parlor, the rain letting up a bit just as she ducks inside the hospital.

*

"Wrecked!" says Stone when Kaat kisses her and asks how she's feeling. "Like I been rode hard and put up wet."

"What does that mean, exactly?" Kaat smiles.

"Beat upside the head. Shit-kicked. Fucked up."

The hard sounds of English can sound even harder in Stone's mouth. Stone seems in a good mood despite her rough language. Kaat lets it go.

"Hey," she says, squeezing Stone's good hand, "great news. I found your bike."

"No shit. What kind of shape is she in?"

"I don't know yet. I haven't seen it. The police have it."

"What?" Stone says, sitting up with difficulty. "It wasn't my fucking fault, you know. The guy ran the light. He was totally off sides. They've got no right to hold it."

"I don't think it's like that. They just cleared it out of the street, and—"

"And now they're going to keep her in hock till I pay up. I get it. Just like Chicago. Motherfuckers."

The pointless conversation is cut short by the arrival of the orthopedic surgeon, a harried black doctor with a bright pink scar on his neck, the kind of scar that raises questions. Stone stares at it openly. After holding X-rays up to the fluorescent lights, the doctor announces that he'll be operating on Stone's foot in the morning.

"No way!" Stone exclaims. "Brodeur said I'm going home."

The surgeon shakes his head. "Non, non, ce n'est pas possible.
ble. Docteur Brodeur est du même avis que moi." Stone regards
the man with a blank look. He turns to Kaat in exasperation.
"Vous pouvez traduire pour votre amie américaine?"
"Elle comprend parfaitement le français, Docteur."
"Bien. Á demain, Mademoiselle," the doctor says coldly to
Stone, and sweeps from the room.
"Shit," Stone says. "I'm not sure I want that guy going at
me with a knife in his hand." She slumps back in the bed, eyes
glazed. "But whatever." At a stroke the doctor has crushed
her buoyant mood. It occurs to Kaat that her lover must still
be on painkillers: something isn't quite right about her. She's
passed from cheerful to combative to deflated too quickly.

Kaat takes her hand. "Maybe it's better to get the surgery
over with? So you don't have to come back."

Stone only sighs. Outside, the rain is stiffening into a
downpour. From the hallway, oddly, comes the sound of
bagpipe music, some television show blaring in another
room. Quite suddenly Stone seems as depressed as Lucie
Prudhomme ever was, and Kaat feels a rebellion welling up
inside her, an urge to flee the room.

In the draining silence that follows, she comes to a decision. When the nurse arrives with a paper cup of blue pills
for Stone she excuses herself, saying she has to run by the
department office to sign a form and promising to stop by
later. This time Stone barely reacts.

*

The arrangements are quickly made. With a telephone call
from the taxi Kaat sets her plan in motion, and by noon she's
sitting next to Miguel Ruiz de Soto in his battered little truck,
her phone directing them out of the city on the A6 as her
companion asks tactful questions about Stone. The rain has
passed, and as they put Paris behind them the sky breaks
open on a brash August sun.

"Miguel," she says as they trundle past Orly, "Stone is more than just a friend to me, you know. But you probably guessed that." She smiles over at her colleague, who smiles in return—a lovely, considered smile.

"I didn't have to guess. I knew. It's obvious from the way you speak of her." Again the elegant smile. Despite his decrepit vehicle there is something very refined about him. Kaat wonders if he comes from money. "I understand these things, Kaat. And I think you know why."

In the crisp sun, his Spanish features strike Kaat as exquisite, somehow painterly. There is something of Lucie's delicacy about the man—a touch of her elegant bone structure, a certain sweep of high forehead, a politesse—but unlike Lucie he always seems to be in good spirits. In the months since he's joined the department, Kaat has never seen him out of sorts. If they were both straight, she thinks, there might be something between them—who could say? As it is, she feels entirely comfortable in his presence. It's as if they've known one other for years.

The police pound, in a battered district near the roadway, is surrounded by a tall fence topped with barbed wire. Public housing buildings with torched windows stare down from all sides, drawing a bead on passersby. It's as bleak as East Chicago, Kaat thinks; Stone's cancerous father might appear at any moment.

In the tiny office, Kaat produces the motorcycle's registration card and signs the necessary papers while Miguel stoops to converse with a mangy poodle lazing in the sun. A few minutes later, they locate Stone's bike marooned in the vast yard, laid down in the dirt like a fallen soldier. Together they inspect it, finding less damage than Kaat expected: a crushed fender, a gashed tire with twisted spokes, some clawlike scrapes across the gas tank. The Ducati is neither more nor less damaged than its rider. With care they hoist it upright and wheel it up a plywood sheet into the back of Miguel's truck.

At the Moto-Clinique off the rue Saint-Jacques, Stone's mechanic, Denis, inspects the Ducati with care, shaking his head, prodding at hoses, wiping away smears of oil, and finally sitting astride it and turning the key. With a fierce buck the machine roars to life. Miguel takes a nervous step backward.

"Elle marche encore!" says Denis, pleased with what he's hearing. "She will be OK." He can have the work finished in a week. "Et Mademoiselle Stone?" he asks.

"She will be OK too," Kaat replies, nodding at the Ducati, "when she sees her baby again."

*

They haven't eaten, so Kaat insists on taking Miguel to lunch. At a bistro, they share steak-frites and pizza and talk of the plunging Spanish economy and the latest defections from the art history department. Finally, after a second glass of wine, the talk turns to her companion's boyfriend, an art restorer in Chicago.

"An American?" she says, leaning closer across the small table. "From *Chicago*? Stone is from Chicago. What a small world."

"Look at us!" says Miguel with an easy laugh. "Both pussy-whipped by Yanks."

She's never heard the term, but its meaning is clear enough.

As her companion describes his boyfriend Randall—they met while Miguel was doing an internship at the Art Institute—Kaat finds that she very much likes the way he speaks of him. They've been together almost exactly as long as she's been with Stone, the relationship moving toward the two-year mark. "Which is when everyone breaks up," Miguel laments. "Two years is as long as American men can stay together. He says he wants to marry me, but with me here and him there—I don't quite believe him, you know?" Her companion shakes his head. For the first time she sees unhappiness flit through his brown eyes. How well she understands it.

"The gay life over there, it's not about settling down with any one man, Kaat. It's all clubbing, tricks, one night stands. With guys my age, anyway. The ones who lived through the '80s and '90s are different. Some of them are really settled, really married. I envy those guys. Not the fact that they lost so many friends, of course, but for who they are now. You know? It's like people who survive a war—all they want is a quiet life afterward. It's what I want too, but I don't know if Randy's ready for that."

"And what about your family? Are they ready for their son to marry another man?"

Miguel laughs. "If you knew my family you wouldn't need to ask that. When it comes to scandal I'm the least of their worries."

"How so?"

"My Aunt Rafaela, for example—a year ago, she nearly married a bisexual Turk half her age. Does that give you some idea? We've been fighting over the same men for years."

All this Kaat hears with a racing heart. "Miguel," she says as he pulls up before her building, "come for dinner soon. Will you?"

*

Perhaps it's reckless to entertain Miguel Ruiz de Soto only a week after Stone's discharge, but as the day approaches, it begins to seem the best of plans.

All but trapped on the third floor by the unhappy combination of crutches and a steep, narrow stairway, Stone Brewer has slid into an ill-tempered gloom that repels Kaat's every attempt at cheering her. Never a reader, the patient passes her shapeless days watching World Cup reruns and French cartoons she barely understands, the hours muddled and slow. Kaat's American is withdrawing into herself deeper by the day; she speaks more to the television than to her fiancée. At

night she sleeps with her broad back turned, in bitter collo-
quy with the Matisse gypsy who glares from a framed print
on the wall. For her part, Kaat finds excuses to leave the apartment as
soon as Stone is fed and settled, needing the freedom of the
streets and shops to clear her head. It was the same with Lucie's depressions: she had to escape. She tells herself that Stone
is suffering—that she'd rebuff anyone's efforts at kindness,
not just hers—but this is not at all how she'd pictured her
lover's convalescence. She'd planned to spoil Stone, to dote on
her, but Stone will have none of it. When Kaat scoured Paris
one afternoon to locate a particular brand of American ice
cream Stone adored, Stone said she wasn't hungry; when she
sat next to Stone sewing up the gashes in the jeans from the
night of the accident, Stone didn't look her way once. None
of Kaat's kindnesses seem to get through.

At times Kaat feels a panic rising, an old dread of melancholy lovers. If Stone doesn't come through it soon, if she
doesn't pick herself up and take charge of her own happiness, Kaat's not sure what she'll do. But then she reminds
herself that her battered American is a tiger in a cage; she's
no Lucie. When she feels well enough to pick her way downstairs again, her mood will surely improve…

In the meantime, Kaat will bring a Spaniard's easy smile
home with her and see what it can do. Dinner is set for eight;
Miguel will bring something Moroccan, perhaps a lamb tag-
ine, and Spanish wine. Kaat will make a soufflé and épinards
with fennel, perhaps a radish salad. The ad hoc menu pleases
her. With Miguel she feels she can improvise.

As she's browsing the outdoor market for ingredients, a
baguette poking from her knapsack, the telephone in her
pocket rings. It's Denis, Stone's mechanic: the Ducati is ready.
He'll stay another half hour if she wants it tonight. Without a
moment's thought she knows she does. If anything can shake
Stone from her foul mood, it will be her beloved bike. For the
Ducati she might even find her way downstairs. And surely
its return will cast a warm glow over her first encounter with

Miguel. She tells Denis she'll be there in fifteen minutes, pays for two bunches of épinards and hails a taxi.

The bike stands gleaming on the sidewalk outside the Moto-Clinique, cherry red and newly waxed. It might as well be a fighter plane waiting on the tarmac, sleek and coiled and ready for battle. At the sight of it, Kaat's heart lifts: this will be balm to Stone's soul. After paying the startling bill, she distributes her groceries between the two fringed saddlebags, mounts the bike and with Denis' help adjusts the mirrors and pedals. When it roars to life under her she rises from the seat in alarm, having forgotten the raw power of the engine. The petite Suzuki that Stone's given her can hardly compare. "Can you manage it?" Denis asks. She doesn't know, but it isn't far to get home, and if she can't handle the bike she'll just park it and walk the rest of the way.

She keeps to side streets, creeping up the rue des Cordelières past the gated lycée and into the rue Pascal, letting everyone pass her by, idling at every intersection until the way is completely clear. The sun has slipped behind the mansard roofs and Paris is gradually cooling around her, drifting toward night. The side trip to collect the Ducati has made her late; there is a good chance her guest will arrive before she does. His American boyfriend, he's said, has taught him Yankee punctuality. Thankfully, she's prepared most of the soufflé ahead, leaving only the egg whites till last. The table is already set beautifully. There will be time for a leisurely glass of wine, time for Stone and Miguel to get acquainted as she sautés the épinards and heats the oven, the chef keeping in the background by design. She imagines the two of them talking about Chicago as she goes about her business; she imagines Stone's eyes lighting up, Stone raising a toast to her old town. She imagines the Stone she loves most, relaxed and witty and warm, the Stone who'll watch her from the corner of her eye and then kiss her openly in front of their guest. Surely Stone still has it in her, this capacity for spontaneous affection; she must. No accident could take that away.

Kaat picks up her pace as she passes her favorite boulange-rie, the bike thrumming under her, and turns into the rue Monge. If Miguel's arrived before her, Stone's resurrection might already be underway. It will all go well, she tells herself. Miguel's good breeding almost guarantees it. With his charm and his command of American English, her Spanish friend will make an excellent first impression.

*

It's as she idles at a red light, watching tourists stream into a mediocre fondue place, that it strikes her—finally—why it is so important to her that Stone and Miguel get along. Really, there's no mystery in it at all: for a week now, without it ever rising to her conscious awareness, she's been wondering if Miguel Ruiz de Soto is meant to be the father of their child.

Kaat laughs out loud at the realization and revs the bike into a low growl. The hungry tourists look up in surprise, see a lean ginger-haired woman on a red motorcycle and look away, drawing their own conclusions. *Of course* she'd think of Miguel as the donor—how naïve she's been not to realize it! If it were someone else's life, she'd have seen it ages ago. Yet only now has it occurred to her. As she eases across the intersection the elements of the plan slip together frictionlessly.

She likes everything about Miguel Ruiz de Soto, after all: his looks, his refinement, his kindness, his youth. Not to mention his passion for El Greco, whom she loves. And his pedigree: apparently his family goes back generations in Toledo, the old master's adopted town. Centuries ago, the Greek genius was painting his peculiar masterpieces around the corner from Miguel's ancestral home while Bruegel labored away in her very own Antwerp. The symmetry of it seems somehow fated. What more could she and Stone ask for? She imagines his sperm nestled in her womb and finds the idea comforting rather than strange, sensible in a way that pleases her practical Flemish heart. A problem neatly solved.

The more she considers the idea, the more the evening takes on a special savor. She'll be watching the two of them through different eyes now. When she rounds the final corner and sees Miguel's white truck parked a block from her building she feels a lightness in her chest she hasn't felt in a long while. It's just how she felt, years ago, when coming home to find Lucie Prudhomme's yellow Vespa parked at her door. The Vespa meant that her new lover's scent, her special blend of *J'adore* and Swedish shampoo, would be lingering in the narrow stairway, drawing her upstairs where a soft kiss waited.

Tonight it is Miguel Ruiz de Soto upstairs—not her lover, exactly, but perhaps the future father of her child. They will be lifelong friends now. Perhaps he's already with Stone, asking her questions in his keen way, neither of them understanding the evening's significance, because only Kaat knows what this first meeting means. With care she tucks the Ducati behind the white truck and dismounts and slips the key in her pocket. She lays a hand on the hood of the truck: still warm. Three floors up, Stone might just now be hobbling into the living room, bidding Miguel to sit anywhere he likes.

In her excitement Kaat is almost to the building before she remembers the groceries in the Ducati's saddlebags. "Et merde!" she says under her breath, smiling at her own forgetfulness, and turns back up the narrow street. Tonight she's no better than a distracted teenager. She must be careful not to let it show.

Part of her is tempted to ask Miguel tonight, with all parties present, to father their child. But it would be a mistake: the friendship should be allowed to ripen first, and she must broach it properly with Stone. As she unbuckles the flaps of the saddlebags she tells herself to keep a level head, to keep her emotions from running away with her.

The épinards, wine, and fennel are quickly transferred from the left saddlebag to her knapsack. In the other saddlebag sit the baguette and a precious box of macarons from Pierre

Hermé, a little extravagance she's chosen for the evening. As she empties the bag, a bit of piano music ripples down from above; Debussy, she thinks. This will be Mademoiselle Snyder, the English piano teacher who lives on the second floor. They'd talked of Debussy and Matisse in the vestibule one day, a passing conversation that sent Kaat off to listen to all the Debussy she could find. The painter and the composer had tilled parallel fields, it seemed, but somehow her scholarship on Matisse had neglected this angle. Soon enough she'd fallen in love with Debussy, whose delicacy spoke to her heart. Now the arpeggios drift down like a flutter of tiny wings, a perfect accompaniment to the evening's encounter.

Smiling, Kaat moves the baguette and the box of macarons to her knapsack. To be certain she hasn't overlooked anything, she sweeps her fingers through the inside of the Ducati's saddlebag, expecting to find nothing—and there, to her surprise, discovers a slender envelope half crushed by the macaron box.

Her mind goes blank, the Debussy taking a sharp minor turn. An ambiguous chord hangs in the air like a medusa in a wave. Kaat's fingertips probe the envelope, stroke it, take it gently between thumb and forefinger. Almost immediately she recognizes the smoothly woven paper, soft as a woman's cheek, and the rough wax seal, as yet unbroken. Hidden away in a locked drawer of her life she has two hundred envelopes just like it, each addressed to her in Lucie Prudhomme's elegant hand, their own seals broken with anticipation or zeal or worry, the precious archive of a long affair.

As she stands in her deserted Paris street with Debussy swirling down, Kaat tries to think where she might have left one of Lucie's love notes for Stone to stumble upon. They are all hidden away in her office; she's certain of it. Since the breakup, she's treated them with curatorial rigor, holding them apart from her domestic life. When Stone moved in she purged the apartment of all traces of Lucie save the painting over the sofa. And yet the texture of the paper under her fingers is unmistakable. It is Lucie's paper, made in the corner of her studio as a mental break from the harder work of painting. Kaat knows well the workbench with its tubs and deckles and bunches of violets waiting to be pressed into the wet pulp, the little jars of saffron threads and lavender leaves and flecks of gold leaf that make each sheet a work of art. Every detail is thought through, yet there is a spontaneous beauty about the paper that is all Lucie's. The exquisite envelopes her lover makes from it might as well be origami, being assembled somehow entirely without glue. And the seal—Lucie's designed that too, her every letter stamped in violet wax impressed with a hummingbird. How many of these works of art did Kaat find waiting on her pillow, or tucked in her briefcase, or hidden in the mailbox amid bills and flyers?

Kaat clutches the envelope inside the saddlebag as if to keep it from escaping into the world. She needs to understand what it means. Did Lucie slip it into the mail slot in the days before the accident, knowing full well that Stone might discover it before Kaat did? Why take such a risk? She might as well have planted a bomb under their bed. With a twist of excitement, Kaat pictures Lucie over in the Marais, so close by, jealously penning the kind of note she'd write when they were still together. *Chérie*, it might say, *I've been thinking so much about you. I know we said it was over, but since I've been away…and now with this news about you marrying Stone…*

If Stone were to read it first…but Kaat can barely imagine her reaction. Perhaps her foul mood has nothing to do with the accident and everything to do with the letter in Kaat's hand. But Stone hasn't even opened it. Kaat's fingers tell her the seal is intact. Could it be that Stone Brewer is afraid to read the note inside? The envelope alone must have shaken her—even her—as Lucie would have understood perfectly well.

The implications fly through Kaat's mind like a pulse through a wire. For a single disorienting moment Kaat imagines herself moving to Dijon, leaving Stone and the rest of her Paris life behind, taking up with Lucie again, with her

first love, the rightness of it obvious now, her dalliance with
Stone Brewer only a necessary phase, something she's gotten
through only to find her way back to the love of her life…

Kaat closes her eyes, takes a deep breath and draws the
envelope from the saddlebag. In the close air she weighs it
in her hands. Off in the distance, behind the Sorbonne, the
bells of Saint-Séverin toll the hour. For the moment, she is
alone in the narrow street, hemmed in by narrow cheerless
buildings that have been there since Pascal's time, the heavy
scent of the city's history settling upon her. The Debussy has
faded away, unable to compete with the church bells clanging
against the bare façades.

When she opens her eyes she sees that the envelope is
indeed one of Lucie's—not that she's doubted it—and then
sees something that takes her breath away. Inscribed in gold
ink, in Lucie Prudhomme's perfect hand, is the name STONE.

Kaat sways on her feet, her eyes widening, the street closing in suddenly.

With her thumbnail she begins to pry up the flap of the
envelope—the wax seal resisting, the well-made paper resisting, her heart resisting, all of her fighting the urge to read
what is inside. With the smallest of gestures the fabric of life
can be torn. Kaat's nail slides toward the wax; her legs waver
under her. From above, the Debussy begins again, skitter-
ing among the parked cars. Miguel's white truck sends her a
doubtful look.

When Kaat looks over toward her building and traces the
brick wall up to the third floor—on instinct, really—she sees
Miguel and Stone standing on the little truncated balcony,
Stone's hand on her guest's shoulder, a glass of wine cradled
in his delicate hand.

At a stroke Kaat tears the envelope down the middle, sev-
ering the name STONE cleanly in two, and lets it drop into
the dirty street.

*

She crosses into Belgium at Paradijs, the A22 effortlessly turning into the E17, the old border station abandoned. It's past ten; traffic is light even on the main artery. In Harelbeke she crosses the first of the canals, all the signs in Dutch now, the constant warmth of the Ducati helping with the cool night air. She hasn't prepared for this trip: she has no proper jacket, no helmet, nothing a rider needs except a hunger for the road. It's only herself, flung from Paris like a fugitive on the run.

She wonders what Stone is thinking, whether she and Miguel are inching the white truck through the streets of Paris, looking for her, alarmed by her disappearance—but no, Stone would give it more time, would let the situation ripen before taking action. She'd tell her guest not to worry, would minimize it all and propose another glass of wine, then another. Not knowing Kaat's habits, Miguel would find it hard to contradict her, the two of them never guessing that she's already hours out of Paris, in another country in fact, and that she has no intention of coming back. Not tonight. Not ever.

Chilled, Kaat exits outside Ghent and takes a turn through the countryside, coasting down a farm road alongside a disused-looking railroad track, the bike throttled down, the fields packed with tall corn. Bruegel country: the old man must have lingered on the edges of a peasant wedding in a place like this, sketching, then ridden back to Antwerp to paint it. But soon enough the fieldstone farmhouses give way to suburbs marked out with characterless brick tract homes. She might as well be coming into some bleak American town. Following her instincts, she finds her way back to the highway and merges in among the long-haul trucks and pushes the Ducati harder, the engine glad to open up again. It won't be long now. From Ghent to Antwerp it's less than an hour, then a short sprint across the Scheldt and down to Kontich on the E19. She'll be there well before midnight.

Except that she allows herself another detour, another diversion into the countryside that periodically beckons from the side of the road. Somewhere before Waasmunster she spots a packed dirt trail just beyond a loose fence that runs

along the highway, the outer limit of some farmer's field;
pulling abruptly onto the shoulder she picks her way down
the gentle embankment and veers off into open country
again, quickly finding herself surrounded by green cropland.
The Ducati plays along, gripping at the trail and then at the
blistered pavement that follows, a willing accomplice in her
flight. Once again the houses turn modest and old, almost
primitive; there is a stone cottage at a crossroads that could
have been borrowed intact from a Rembrandt. A blanket of
vermilion roses clings to its rough wall with Flemish tenacity.
In the side yard, a stone trough awaits the morning swill.
Kaat motors on through a tiny town, idling the engine to
quiet it down, the sound of the bike raucous nonetheless in
the narrow lanes.

On the outskirts of the next town, she spots a gas station
and pulls in to refuel. She's realized she's very hungry and
wishes she hadn't left her knapsack with its baguette and macarons in a Paris street. In the attached shop, she asks directions
to Kontich and the teenager behind the counter's never heard
of it. Together they break open a map and study it in under
flickering lights, picking out a route that avoids the highway,
weaving through Zele and Dendermonde and Willebroek and
Boom and entering Kontich from below, avoiding Antwerp
proper. After buying a Piraat Ale jacket for warmth and a stale
shrimp croquette for her hunger, she's back on the road, the
map in her empty saddlebag, the road going dark the moment
she puts the little town behind her. The Ducati's headlamp cuts
through the Belgian night like a cry.

She thinks of Paris as she rides. A few hundred kilometers
to the southwest, in a third-floor apartment on the Left Bank,
her life is slowly letting go of her: she can feel it all the way
from here. The batter for a soufflé stiffens in the refrigerator;
her clothes hang motionless in the closet. She wonders if Stone
is with Lucie Prudhomme. Has Stone fled to her French girl—
their French girl—in Kaat's absence, taking advantage of her
disappearance? As the kilometers clock by, Kaat pictures Stone
hobbling down to the street and hailing a taxi and speeding

over to the Marais, Lucie meeting her at the door in the silk kimono Kaat gave her years ago. Perhaps Stone fears Kaat will be there, that the secret of the letter is out—her gentle Belgian girl furious now, beside herself with rage, righteously demanding that Stone and Lucie account for themselves, reason firmly and frighteningly on her side. Perhaps Stone would like to save their love—to marry her after all—the letter forcing a needed crisis. Perhaps Kaat was a fool not to storm upstairs with the letter in her hand and tear it open in front of her American, to demand an explanation, to have it out...

But there is no way to know what Stone is doing or thinking. Nor, for that matter, Lucie. It could be that Stone and Miguel Ruiz de Soto are on their phones right now, calling the police and calling hospitals to track her down, panicked by an absence that is so unlike her, an unsuspecting Lucie meanwhile asleep in her bed. But as the Ducati plies through villages and open fields, Kaat finds that she no longer cares. Whatever is happening back in Paris is not her concern now. On a stretch of open country road she lets the Ducati take off, opening the throttle wide, the cool night air of Flanders rubbing at her face, her mind clear and calm for the first time in weeks.

Once she crosses the Rupel it all begins to look familiar. Quite suddenly she is oriented, as if she's never left. On the outskirts of Kontich she passes a bank whose digital clock says it's just after midnight; her mother will have been asleep for hours now. Kaat moves through the slumbering neighborhoods of her old town as quietly as the Ducati will permit, gliding past the tile-roofed bourgeois houses, the orderly hedgerows, the soccer fields and schools and shadowy bosques, an ease settling over her, the hours elongated now, the endless day having drifted noiselessly into the next.

Decades ago, in a park near the family home on a night just like this, she'd made love to a boy and known it wasn't right, but hadn't known why. The Mertens family had only just moved down to Kontich from Antwerp, her father's law office having relocated from the city. She'd known Mattheus Timmermans for less than a month when she followed him

into the boxwoods behind the park's tennis courts, carried off
by his self-confidence and the BMW motorcycle his parents
had given him for his seventeenth birthday. They'd lain down
in the damp grass, a damp moon dangling from the branches
above. She'd not resisted when he slipped off her soft blue
T-shirt and touched her small breasts, but at the same time,
she had no desire to lay his body bare, to explore him, to touch
his surprising penis or take it in her mouth as her friend Griet
had dared her to do. She lay under him like a doll as he went
to work, silent except at the moment of penetration when a cry
escaped her. Hardly more than a boy, he'd assumed it was a cry
of pleasure and thrust deeper, chafing at her insides, a groan
welling somewhere in his pumping lungs and escaping into
the bushes only when he came, the condom dry and painful
within her, his lips dry when he kissed her. He'd managed to
avoid her eyes the whole time. Within a few minutes he was
gone, making some excuse and speeding nervously from the
park on his BMW while she lay in the grass with her knees
clutched to her chest and wondered why she'd done what she'd
done. Not a moment of it had brought her pleasure.

Later she'd wonder if it was young Mattheus Timmermans
who'd soured her on sex with men, but in time it became
clear that it was more than this. It would take Paris to explain
it to her, and Lucie Prudhomme. Now she possesses the truth
of it intimately, she carries it within her and will carry it always, lover or no lover, wherever her road takes her.

Her mother's staid house lies only a few blocks from the
old park with its mossy trees and mirror-still lagoon. There is
a loose chain slung across the park's access road; she steers the
bike easily through the wet grass to skirt it. The lane that winds
through the oaks and catalpas is deserted but for a Persian cat
who startles and flees as she approaches. Kaat guides the heavy
bike down past the tennis courts, past the roller-skating rink,
past the boathouse and the benches scattered among willows
that reach out over the dark waters. When she kills the Ducati's engine, the stillness of the suburbs closes in like a woolen
blanket. In Paris there is no real darkness; here the darkness

invades everything, seeps under every bush and infiltrates every flower bed like a soaking rain.

Kaat dismounts at the top of a grassy hummock that leads down to the boat launch and walks Stone's motorcycle to the top of the ramp, the dead weight of the machine straining forward, gravity groping at its smooth flanks. *Dank je*, she says, and releases her hold on it gently. With a certain elegance the Ducati glides down the ramp, managing to keep an even keel on its fat tires, and disappears into the black water with barely a sound. Kaat watches the red fender sink out of sight, then the side mirrors, and finally the tip of the windshield. A trio of geese bursts suddenly from the bank, startled into flight, and it's done.

As she leaves the empty park and turns down the lane that leads to her mother's house, Kaat pictures Anke Mertens fast asleep, alone in her bed and perhaps grateful to be so, her ill-tempered husband long gone, no one but a snoring dachshund to break the stillness of her life. In the years since her husband's death she's cultivated a stupendous garden, periodically sending her distant daughter photos of prizewinning tea roses, of lichened walls bursting with wisteria, of her pond with its imported Japanese lava rocks and showcase koi. Never once has she sent a photo of herself. Not a single image contains a trace of the gardener, a hint of how she looks, of how she carries herself in the world as she nears eighty. Only the garden speaks. The garden has become her language. As Kaat turns the final corner and runs her fingertips along the stone wall, the Flemish air is all at once full of honeysuckle, the lane full of mute shadows, the night full of grace.

Contributors'
Notes

HUGH COYLE

Hugh Coyle's publications include *The Boston Review, New England Review, Green Mountains Review, Scribner's American Writers Series, The Café Review,* and *Christopher Street,* among others. His work has received a Pushcart Prize, a Bertha Morton scholarship, a Heekin Award, and a grant from the Vermont Arts Council. A graduate of the University of Iowa Writers' Workshop, he served for many years on the admissions board of the Bread Loaf Writers' Conference. He was previously the Administrative Director of the Bread Loaf School of English, where he also produced the program's humorous daily newsletter, *The Crumb.* His latest project, the historical novel *Peace at Last,* explores the relationship between the explosives manufacturer Alfred Nobel and the writer Bertha von Suttner, the first woman to win the Nobel Peace Prize and one of the major inspirations for its inception. The novel-in-progress was named a semifinalist for the James Jones First Novel Fellowship in 2014. Building upon his international research, Hugh presented a master class on Bertha von Suttner's reliance on empathy at the Peace Palace in The Hague in June 2015. He has also presented an annual, hour-long historical slideshow, "Behind the Prize," to coincide with the announcements of the Nobel prizes each October.

CAROLYN FERRELL

Carolyn Ferrell graduated from Sarah Lawrence College and has an MA from the City College of New York. She has one book, *Don't Erase Me: Stories* (Houghton Mifflin, 1997), and her work can be found in *The Literary Review, Callaloo, Fiction,* and *Sojourner: The Women's Forum.*

EDWARD HAMLIN

E dward Hamlin's *Night in Erg Chebbi and Other Stories* was selected by Pulitzer Prize finalist Karen Russell as winner of the
2015 Iowa Short Fiction Award and went on to win the Colorado
Book Award. Over the past few years Edward's stories have won
the Nelligan Prize, the NCW Short Story Prize, and a Top of the
Mountain Book Award, and have been finalists or runners-up for
the Flannery O'Connor Award for Short Fiction, the Narrative
Story Prize, the Bridport Prize, Missouri Review's Jeffrey E. Smith
Prize, Sarabande Books' Mary McCarthy Prize in Short Fiction,
the Nelson Algren Award, the Mary C. Mohr Editor's Award, the
David Nathan Meyerson Fiction Prize, the Press 53 Award for
Short Fiction, and other competitions. His work has appeared
or is forthcoming in *Colorado Review, Bellevue Literary Review,
Missouri Review, American Fiction, Chariton Review, Printers Row
Journal, Tiferet, InDigest, Cobalt* and elsewhere. A New York native,
Edward Hamlin spent his formative years in Chicago and now lives
in Colorado. www.edwardhamlin.com

LISA HORIUCHI

Lisa Horiuchi is a September 2016 graduate of the UC Irvine Program in Writing, where she wrote "Bones"—one of a collection of stories exploring the triumphs and delusions of the American white-collar worker. She is a former marketing and business strategist with an MBA from the USC Marshall School, and has served in a wide variety of industries including toy manufacturing, health and beauty, software, and clean technology. A practicing Mahayana Buddhist, Lisa lives in Los Angeles with her family and is currently working on a novel.

RACHEL KONDO

Rachel Kondo was born and raised on Maui. In 2014, she was a finalist for the Keene Prize for Literature, as well as the Austin Film Festival Script Competition. Her writing has also appeared in *Electric Literature.* She is currently at work on a short story collection spanning Maui's sugar history, as well as a novel set during the island's methamphetamine crisis of the 1990s. At present, she lives in Los Angeles, California, and is a recent graduate of the Michener Center for Writers.

MICHAEL LOWENTHAL

M ichael Lowenthal is the author of four novels: *The Same Embrace, Avoidance, Charity Girl,* and *The Paternity Test.* His short stories have appeared in *Tin House, The Southern Review,* and *The Kenyon Review,* and his nonfiction in *The New York Times, Boston* magazine, *The Washington Post, Out,* and many other publications. The recipient of fellowships from the Bread Loaf and Wesleyan writers' conferences, the MacDowell Colony, and the Massachusetts Cultural Council, Lowenthal has taught creative writing at Boston College and Hampshire College, and as the Picador Guest Professor for Literature at Leipzig University. Since 2003, he has been a core faculty member in the low-residency MFA program at Lesley University.

ELI PAYNE MANDEL

Eli Payne Mandel grew up in Brooklyn, NY and studied English at Yale College. His poems, essays, and translations have appeared in *Harvard Review, The Paris Review Daily, The Saint Ann's Review, Prodigal,* and elsewhere. In 2014–15, he held the Frederick M. Clapp Fellowship in Poetry from Yale. In the fall of 2017, he is beginning a PhD in English at Princeton University.

UCHE OKONKWO

Uche Okonkwo lives in Lagos, Nigeria, where she works as managing editor at one of Nigeria's leading independent publishers. She has an MA in Creative Writing from The University of Manchester, UK (2012-2013), and she won the inaugural Africa-wide Etisalat Flash Fiction Prize (2013). In 2016, she was selected to participate in a trans-Nigerian road trip project by Invisible Borders, with the aim of documenting Nigeria's history and diversity. Her essay, "What the Road Offers" (published by Invisible Borders in 2016 as a limited-edition chapbook), was the product of the project. Uche's work has appeared in *The Manchester Anthology, Ellipsis, Per Contra, Ember, AFREADA* and others, and is forthcoming in *Lagos Noir* by Akashic Books. She will be attending a writing residency at OMI International Arts Centre, Ledig House, New York, in March 2017. *Photo by Rohan Kamicheril.*

TIMOTHY PARRISH

Timothy Parrish is a professor in the Department of English at Virginia Tech. He has published work on authors including Ralph Ellison, Philip Roth, William Faulkner, Cormac McCarthy, and Willa Cather. The author of three books, Parrish has also appeared in *Raritan, American Literary History, Prospects, Modern Fiction Studies,* and other journals. Parrish received a Ph.D. from the University of Washington.

About
Ploughshares

ABOUT THE EDITOR

Ladette Randolph is Editor-in-chief of *Ploughshares* and the author of four books: three books of fiction—the novels *Haven's Wake* (University of Nebraska Press, 2013), the award-winning *A Sandhills Ballad* (University of New Mexico Press, 2009), and the short-story collection *This Is Not the Tropics* (University of Wisconsin Press, 2005)—and a memoir, *Leaving the Pink House* (University of Iowa Press, 2014). She is also the editor of two anthologies: *A Different Plain* and *The Big Empty* (University of Nebraska Press, 2004 and 2007). Randolph is on the faculty of the Department of Writing, Literature and Publishing at Emerson College in Boston. She is the recipient of a Pushcart Prize, a Rona Jaffe grant, the Virginia Faulkner Award, a Best New American Voices citation, and two Nebraska Book Awards. *Photo by Tamra Turnbull.*

ABOUT
PLOUGHSHARES SOLOS

Over the years, *Ploughshares* has sometimes received longer submissions that were difficult to publish due to space considerations in the print issue. Ploughshares Solos is a digital-first series for longer stories and essays, edited by *Ploughshares* Editor-in-chief Ladette Randolph.

New Solos are published regularly and are available for download on your Kindle or Nook. (If you do not have a Kindle or Nook device, you can download apps for smart phones, tablets, and computers.) The stories and essays are collected in the annual printed *Omnibus*.

Ploughshares is excited to be breaking ground as one of the first literary journals to explore a long-story, digital-first format.

SUBMISSION GUIDELINES

Are you interested in submitting to Ploughshares Solos? Submissions to Ploughshares Solos should be longer works of original prose, either fiction or nonfiction, and generally 7,500 to 20,000 words. Submissions should otherwise follow the same guidelines and restrictions as regular submissions, and can be sent either through our online submission manager or through the mail.

We generally take submissions summer through winter, and close for the spring. For full submission guidelines and exact dates, please visit:

www.pshares.org/submit

STAY CONNECTED
WITH PLOUGHSHARES

Did you know that we have a regularly updated blog, featuring posts on writing, reading, and publishing, as well as book reviews?

BLOG

blog.pshares.org

WEBSITE

www.pshares.org

TWITTER

@pshares

FACEBOOK

facebook.com/ploughshares

New and back issues, as well as Solos,
are available on www.pshares.org/shop for: